AMERICA'S HEALTH

AMERICA'S HEALTH

A Report to the Nation

by

THE NATIONAL
HEALTH ASSEMBLY

OFFICIAL REPORT

HARPER & BROTHERS · PUBLISHERS
New York

Barber & Taylor 4.50

CONTENTS

INTRODUCTION

IN JANUARY, 1948, I received a letter from President Truman asking me, as Federal Security Administrator, to submit a ten-year plan for expanding the health resources of this nation and raising the health standards of the entire population.

The request followed a number of talks he and I had, over a period of some months, in which we discussed thoroughly the problem of health in the United States. The President has an intense interest in the subject and an extraordinarily realistic grasp of its many problems. We were both agreed that piecemeal efforts would not in themselves go very far to solve these problems. What was needed was a sober appraisal of the whole health situation as it exists today—a far-reaching analysis of the gap between the nation's present health resources and its basic requirements, together with a concrete program for achieving the desired objectives.

In order to secure a firm basis for my report, I convened a National Health Assembly which met in Washington, D. C., for a four-day session during the first week in May, 1948. This Assembly was attended by some eight hundred representatives of professional organizations and public and private agencies concerned with matters of health throughout the United States. The delegates were all people who knew the problem not only in terms of charts and statistics but also in terms of sick and worried human beings for whom adequate medical care was only too often a luxury beyond their means.

This is the official report of that Assembly. The following pages present the results of the thoroughgoing examination into all factors involved in the problem, conducted through panel discussions by experts in the various fields, together with a series of specific recommendations of practical measures to be taken.

The Assembly itself was divided into fourteen sections, each of which discussed a key problem of health.[1] Much of the groundwork for these

[1] Chapters I to XIV each deal with a section. In addition to the sessions of the fourteen sections, a number of general meetings were held, open to all delegates. One meeting was devoted to international health and is reported in Chapter XV. The other general meetings have not been included in this book, since their subject matter either has been covered in the various chapters or pertained simply to Assembly arrangements.

discussions was laid in meetings of the section planning committees and sub-committees held prior to the four-day session of the Assembly. To a large extent it was these capably handled preliminary sessions which made possible the comprehensive synthesis in the complete report.

Each individual report herein has been approved in this final form by the chairman of the section presenting it, though section recommendations were, of course, released in preliminary form at the close of the meetings. Anyone who has worked with the problem of preparing from transcripts a compact yet satisfactorily inclusive final report will appreciate the task entailed in compiling the present volume.

The report is decidedly well worth reading in its entirety. Never before, so far as I know, has a group of public-spirited citizens attacked this problem of health in the United States with a more genuine understanding of its critical importance or greater determination to get to the root of the matter.

To most readers, both lay and professional, these pages will reveal many startling facts of our present national shortcomings and health deficiencies. More than that, these facts, together with other established data, are set forth in their proper relation, so that the picture which emerges takes on a form and dimension that is literally overpowering.

Certainly no one can go through this book without recognizing what a wealth of factual information and food for thought is provided. Practically every vital problem affecting the health of an individual or of the community is here explored in painstaking detail:

Our need for more doctors, dentists, nurses, and other medical personnel, and how we may make it easier for young men and women to qualify for these professions;

Our need for more hospitals, and what we must do to expand and coordinate present hospital facilities;

Our need to strengthen the pitifully understaffed health departments and to establish new units to serve the forty millions of our population who live in areas which now do not have any organized health services;

The problem of chronic disease and of the millions of people in this country who suffer from one form or another of chronic invalidism;

The problem of maternal and child health care and the need of bringing services of this nature within the reach of every mother throughout the nation;

The problem of rural health and of the vast areas in this country which have no hospital facilities of any description and only the minimum of effective medical care;

The problem of medical research and what must be done to achieve a fuller knowledge of the cause and possible cure of cancer, diseases of the heart, tuberculosis, venereal disease, mental illness, and other scourges of mankind;

The problem of the cost of medical care, so that its burden for the great bulk of our people may be lightened; and

Many other problems, including those connected with rehabilitation, dental health, nutrition, and environmental sanitation, together with a fruitful discussion of effective state and community planning.

On every major issue, except one, the members of the Assembly were in agreement. The one issue on which they differed was the matter of payment for medical care. But even here they agreed that "the principle of contributory health insurance should be the basic method of financing medical care for the large majority of the American people"; they differed only as to the form which the insurance should take. Some believed that it can be achieved through voluntary plans; others believed that a national health insurance plan is necessary.

My own report to the President, published in September, 1948,[2] draws heavily upon the findings of this Assembly and, in general, follows the substance of its recommendations. On the controversial matter of payment for medical care, however, I recommended, without reservation, a system of national health insurance which had had strong support within the Assembly and had already been publicly endorsed by the President.

One thing which the report of the Assembly has emphasized, and with which I am in entire agreement, is that no complete and rounded program for better health in this country can be accomplished merely by Congressional legislation. It is a project which must be planned and executed on a regional, state, and community level.

Since conferences similar to the Assembly but adapted to the area in which they are held should be an important first step to local action on health needs, readers may be interested in the procedures by which the National Health Assembly was formed and through which it operated. A brief summary of these follows.

The President, in his letter, outlined the philosophy which became

---

[2] *The Nation's Health; a Ten-Year Program* (Washington: Government Printing Office, September, 1948), $1.00.

fundamental to all our thinking and organizing. He wrote that national health goals and a program for attaining them could best be developed as a joint endeavor, requiring "the co-operation of state and local governments, voluntary organizations, the medical and health professions, as well as all of our citizens working together."

The first step was to select a group of outstanding men and women to serve as an Executive Committee. It was our decision that, in every phase of the Assembly, we should attempt to make sure that all interested groups, all divergent views, had the fullest opportunity to be represented.

We chose, first of all, from among the top people in each field. We tried to balance the distribution not only geographically but also as between professional and public members and between different viewpoints. We then left to the Executive Committee the framework of discussion, the organization, and the direction.

This Committee of thirty-eight was, I believe, as representative a group as could have been brought together. Their names and their affiliations, as listed below, evidence a cross section of American opinion.

Rev. John W. Barrett, Vice-President, Catholic Hospital Association

Edward L. Bortz, M.D., Former President, American Medical Association

Rev. Beverley M. Boyd, Federal Council of the Churches of Christ in America

Mrs. J. L. Blair Buck, President, General Federation of Women's Clubs

Earl Bunting, Managing Director, National Association of Manufacturers

Miss Elisabeth Christman, Secretary-Treasurer, National Women's Trade Union League

John W. Dargavel, Executive Secretary, National Association of Retail Druggists

Graham L. Davis, President, American Hospital Association

Miss Katherine Densford, President, American Nurses' Association

Louis I. Dublin, Vice-President, Metropolitan Life Insurance Company

Robert P. Fischelis, Secretary, American Pharmaceutical Association

Judge Jerome N. Frank, United States Circuit Court of Appeals

Vlado A. Getting, M.D., Commissioner, Massachusetts Department of Health

Albert S. Goss, President, National Grange

William Green, President, American Federation of Labor

Most Rev. Francis J. Haas, Bishop of Grand Rapids, Michigan

Paul R. Hawley, M. D., Associated Medical Care Plans

Miss Frieda Hennock

Harold Hillenbrand, M.D., General Secretary, American Dental Association

Mrs. L. W. Hughes, President, National Congress of Parents and Teachers

William Harding Jackson, Chairman, Hospital Council of Greater New York

Eric Johnston, President, Motion Picture Producers and Distributors of America

Mrs. Albert D. Lasker, President, Albert and Mary Lasker Foundation

Mrs. David M. Levy, Citizens' Committee on Children, New York City

George F. Lull, M.D., American Medical Association

Mrs. Eugene Meyer, Washington *Post*

James L. Morrill, President, University of Minnesota

Philip Murray, President, Congress of Industrial Organizations

James G. Patton, President, National Farmers Union

Mrs. Anna M. Rosenberg

R. L. Sensenich, M.D., President, American Medical Association

Earl O. Shreve, President, Chamber of Commerce of United States of America

Frank Stanton, President, Columbia Broadcasting System

M. W. Thatcher, President, National Federation of Grain Co-operatives

Jerry Voorhis, Secretary, Co-operative Health League of the United States of America

Walter White, Executive Secretary, National Association for the Advancement of Colored People

Charles F. Wilinsky, M.D., Trustee, American Hospital Association

Abel Wolman, Chairman, Executive Board, American Public Health Association

These Executive Committee members were consulted both individually and as a group on all basic decisions. Ultimately a tentative list of areas for discussion was drawn up; it was revised several times, in response to new suggestions, and out of this evolutionary process the fourteen discussion groups or sections of the National Health Assembly were organized.

The next major step was extremely important—the selection of the section chairmen. It was essential to have chairmen with whom all groups could work and who were widely known in their fields and impartial in the execution of their responsibility. Many personal and group consultations were behind every individual choice.

The sections finally determined upon and the chairmen selected were as follows:

What Is the Nation's Need for Health and Medical Personnel?
Chairman: Algo D. Henderson, Associate Commissioner, New York State Department of Education

What Is the Nation's Need for Hospital Facilities, Health Centers, and Diagnostic Clinics?
Chairman: Charles F. Wilinsky, M.D., Trustee, American Hospital Association

What Is the Nation's Need for Local Health Units?
Chairman: Haven Emerson, M.D., Columbia University School of Public Health

Chronic Disease and the Aging Process
Chairman: James R. Miller, M.D., Board of Trustees, American Medical Association

A National Program for Maternal and Child Health
Chairman: Leona Baumgartner, M.D., Director, Bureau of Child Hygiene, New York City Department of Health

A National Program for Rural Health
Chairman: Joseph Fichter, Master, Ohio State Grange

What Is the Nation's Need for Research in the Service of Health?
Chairman: Andrew C. Ivy, M.D., Vice-President, University of Illinois

What Is the Nation's Need for Medical Care?
Chairman: Hugh R. Leavell, M.D., Professor, Harvard School of Public Health

State and Community Planning for Health
Chairman: Florence R. Sabin, M.D., Chairman, Committee on Health, Governor's Postwar Planning Commission, Colorado

Physical Medicine and Rehabilitation
Chairman: Henry H. Kessler, M.D., New Jersey Rehabilitation Commission

What Can Be Done to Improve Dental Health?
Chairman: Ernest G. Sloman, D.D.S., Dean, School of Dentistry, College of Physicians and Surgeons, San Francisco

A National Program for Mental Health
Chairman: William C. Menninger, M.D., Medical Director, The Menninger Clinic, Topeka, Kansas
What Can Be Done to Improve Nutrition?
Chairman: Frank G. Boudreau, M.D., Executive Director, Milbank Memorial Fund
A National Program of Environmental Sanitation
Chairman: Arthur D. Weston, Chief Sanitary Engineer, Massachusetts Department of Public Health

The chairman of each section then participated in the selection of a small committee to assist in advance planning for that section. In the choice of these committees also, the effort was to assure wide representation of both professional and non-professional groups. To each such committee was attached a staff assistant from the Federal Security Agency, whose responsibility it was to assist in compiling factual material for the section discussion and to perform other secretarial functions as directed by the committee. These planning committees drew up tentative patterns for discussion, but their suggestions were subject to the approval of the section delegates themselves when they assembled.

The delegates were selected with the same care that had gone into the choice of the Executive Committee, the chairmen of the sections, and the planning committees, and without exception they were eminently well qualified. Here the choice was not easy. The groups had to be large enough to give full representation to all shades of opinion; at the same time, each had to be small enough for efficient work. Lists of potential delegates were conned again and again to assure that as far as possible the best in each field were included, that all geographical areas were represented, that women had a full voice, that minority groups sent delegates, and that the many professional and voluntary organizations would be heard.[3] As further assurance that the democratic processes would work freely, all Assembly meetings were open to representatives of the press.

I am firmly convinced that the success of the National Health Assembly was—and that of any other similar body will be—in direct proportion to the care that is taken in securing not only the professional eminence of the members but also full representation and democratic discussion. I sincerely hope that readers of this book will find in it a challenge to ensure that the creative forces which emerged in the Assem-

[3] Registrants and staff assistants in each section are listed in an appendix at the end of the respective chapter.

bly will continue, through co-operative, joint endeavors of laymen and professionals, in stimulating plans and activities to meet national, state, and community health needs.

On behalf of the President and the government, I am glad to have this opportunity of repeating the thanks we all feel to the delegates who attended the National Health Assembly at their own expense. They gave of their best to help assure a strong program for national health.

I am sure the delegates join with me in thanking the Assembly's secretariat. Primarily responsible for its technical and administrative success were Howard M. Kline, Executive Secretary; his assistant and successor as secretary, Cornelius A. Wood, Jr.; and Abe L. Savage, Director of Information. To these men fell the responsibility for the many day-to-day decisions upon which the success or failure of an enterprise so largely depends. They and their able assistants worked conscientiously. The intelligent and smooth-running Assembly sessions stand in themselves as tribute to their work.

Co-operating with them wholeheartedly were the officers and staff of the Federal Security Agency, the section staff assistants, and many others. Unfortunately space does not permit me to mention all of them by name, much as I would like to do so. But I cannot refrain from thanking Leonard A. Scheele, Surgeon General of the United States Public Health Service. To him and to the splendid corps of health workers which he directs I am particularly grateful.

Only the individual cities, towns, and counties can properly evaluate *their own* health needs. They alone can decide what can and should be done and how their plans can be geared into the plans of other communities and into the developing state plans.

No nation-wide health program can be better or stronger than the sum total of the community and state health plans, and the value of these must depend upon the enthusiasm and determination with which the people themselves translate them into effective action.

For, in the final analysis, health is everybody's business. And only if everybody makes it his business shall we, as a nation, be able to do the complete job that so desperately needs to be done.

OSCAR R. EWING
Federal Security Administrator
Chairman, National Health Assembly

March, 1949
Washington, D. C.

AMERICA'S HEALTH

《 I 》

What Is the Nation's Need for Health and Medical Personnel?[1]

MEETING as a section of the National Health Assembly during the Assembly's four-day session in May, 1948, fifty representatives of groups concerned with health problems earnestly considered the nation's supply of well-trained and qualified health personnel, the existing and estimated future need for their services, and the financial and other factors that bear on the problems of education and training for health services. The reports of the Personnel Section's three subcommittees responsible for evaluating the evidence and recommending action disclose strikingly parallel situations in the fields of medicine, dentistry, and nursing. In brief, the nation as a whole cannot count on having adequate numbers of trained health personnel in all geographic areas until some provision is made for (1) increasing the funds available to the institutions that provide education, (2) aiding qualified candidates who cannot meet the cost of professional education, and (3) assuring larger numbers of qualified persons opportunity for a career in the health professions.

The problems faced by the Section on the Nation's Need for Health and Medical Personnel are basic to the discussions in all other sections of the Assembly. The first essential for reaching the nation's health goals is personnel to staff hospitals and clinics, health departments, research laboratories, and teaching institutions and to administer special programs for maternal and child health, mental hygiene, and control of special diseases. The facts and viewpoints presented in the Section's discussions are summarized in the present chapter, which also includes reports from

[1] The data in this chapter are summarized from statements made in prepared addresses and discussion. Lack of space precludes publishing the entire proceedings of the Personnel Section or even identifying the various speakers who presented facts and opinions for discussion. In this alternative attempt to summarize the proceedings, statements are included that may not have represented the unanimous or even majority opinion of the group. The subcommittee reports that appear on pages 24-30 should therefore be consulted for the conclusions and recommendations formally adopted.

liaison representatives in other sections on questions pertinent to man-power needs. The recommendations for action and the conclusions pre-sented by the Section's chairman appear at the end of the chapter; they set the sights for further progress in medicine and the allied sciences through greater public and private support of education and wider op-portunity for service in the health professions.

PHYSICIANS

Adequacy of Present and Estimated Future Supply

The United States now has the largest number of physicians in rela-tion to the total population in its recent history. Its present position in the quality of medical care reflects the standards of medical education set and maintained by the medical profession through the Council on Medi-cal Education and Hospitals of the American Medical Association, the Association of American Medical Colleges, and the State Boards. These standards require adequate personal supervision by instructors and ade-quate space, equipment, and material per student in the two years of preclinical work in anatomy, physiology, chemistry, pharmacology, pathology, and bacteriology. In the subsequent two years of clinical in-struction, each student—working individually in the wards and out-patient departments of well-equipped teaching hospitals—must be re-sponsible for supervised observation and treatment of at least three new ward patients a week, selected for their teaching value, and in out-patient departments must have similar contact with three new patients a day.

Medicine is not a science that can be taught to large classes by didactic methods. Minimum standards—surpassed in the better medical schools—call for at least 1 instructor to each 25 students in preclinical courses and for 1 instructor to each 8 or 10 students in clinical classes. Substandard schools have practically disappeared from the American scene in the last forty years; their return would spell disaster. Any hastily conceived plan to establish new schools or greatly increase the enrollment in already overcrowded existing schools would threaten our major safeguards to the quality of instruction and competence of graduates.

The annual rate of production of physicians has increased materially during the past twenty-five years, partly because of the accelerated medical-school courses that prevailed during the war. With the return to peace-time schedules the production rate will probably reach 5,600 new graduates a year, and as students complete their four-year courses in six new medical schools,[2] and in others that will doubtless be established, the supply of physicians will continue to increase. According to estimates of the American Medical Association, we can predict a ratio of one physician for each 707 or 717 persons by 1960, depending on the population estimate used. Of these physicians, possibly about 4 to 6 per cent will be retired or not in active practice.

Some General Considerations

To avoid overproduction of physicians, as was apparently the case in the depression years in view of the limited demand for their services, long-range needs for additional physicians require careful study of possible fluctuations in the economic cycle and of many economic factors which affect the practice of medicine. Under the stress of war, 60 per cent of the nation's physicians were able to serve 91 per cent of the population. Indications which point to a more efficient use of physicians in the future are improved and expanded hospital facilities, additional health centers, easier transportation, extension of group practice, expanded public health programs, increased use of auxiliary personnel, and discovery of more highly effective therapeutic agents. On the other hand, the adequacy of the ratio of physicians to the future population must be determined in relation to the higher illness rates among an aging population, the wider use of personnel and facilities with the extension of prepayment plans for medical care and hospitalization, and the probable increased number of physicians in the Federal service, in hospitals and health centers, and in research and teaching positions. The present shortages of physicians in some places and fields of activity stem from social and economic conditions which the medical profession believes need correction on a local basis before any attempts are made to augment greatly the supply of physicians in the United States.

Special Problems of Supply

Though opinions differed on the need for definite and immediate steps to increase the annual number of medical-school graduates, many pleas were made for measures to avoid existing and future shortages of physicians in certain fields of work. Evidence of the lack of public health officers, psychiatrists, physicians for the armed forces and other Federal

[2] Medical College of Alabama, Bowman Gray School of Medicine, Southwestern Medical College, University of Utah School of Medicine, University of Washington School of Medicine, and University of California at Los Angeles.

agencies, and of shortages of physicians in rural areas and among Negroes was presented to the Section in its own discussions and in reports received from representatives of other sections of the Assembly.

Public health. In this and other fields of health we cannot safely assume a *status quo* in the demand for health services and personnel or argue that we should do nothing because it is hazardous and difficult to increase the output of doctors. The whole process of health education— professional and lay—has been building up a demand far in excess of what existing personnel can render. Great medical discoveries and preventive procedures in every area in which they have been provided have increased rather than diminished the demand for doctors. In public health we face the stark reality of having only 3 to 4 per cent of the population protected by adequately staffed public health facilities. The number one problem of public health is the need for the expansion of training facilities in and out of accredited institutions, for the 10 accredited schools with faculty and facilities for training in public health have been able to train only one-third of the present personnel. Pending legislation for local health units provides for doubling the present staff of 30,000 people in local health departments in fifteen years. The need for Federal and state public health personnel is urgent, to say nothing of similar requirements of voluntary agencies. It is hard to reconcile any optimism over the adequacy of present resources of physicians with the deficiencies in recruitment and training in public health.

Psychiatrists. Faced at the outset with the chronic problem of personnel shortages, the Section on a National Program for Mental Health sent a representative to the meetings of the Section on Personnel to stress the seriousness of the lack of trained psychiatrists. A conservative estimate of the number currently needed is 10,000 (some set the estimate as high as 20,000), whereas only a bare 4,500 are available. Present training facilities, supplying about 400 a year, will give a tenyear total of about 4,000—an increment that obviously would not raise the total to the 10,000 now needed even if there were no deaths or retirements. Special training for leadership and teaching to make psychiatry a basic medical science rather than a special course limited to fourthyear medical students is an essential if the medical profession as a whole is to acquire adequate knowledge and skill in dealing with the emotional maladjustments that accompany or precede illness. The training positions in Veterans Administration hospitals, together with the 150 fellowships provided by the United States Public Health Service and its limited aid to medical schools that have requested assistance, are now the major sources of stimulus to psychiatric training.

Federal services. The Federal government needs a total of 3,000 physicians for an Army and Air Force totaling about a half million. To maintain the same ratio for a force of approximately 1,339,000 for twenty years, assuming that the majority of the Army doctors serve only two years, replacements at a rate of about 3,000 a year will be necessary. A classification system has been developed to permit calculation of requirements in terms of specialties and qualifications within specialties. Continued attention is given also to the use of ancillary workers to the greatest possible extent. Plans for maximum economy in the use of physicians and other medical personnel in the event of mobilization for another war call for assignment of the medical group to a unit when, and not before, the unit is alerted for service. The allocation of medical personnel to the armed forces is as much a civilian as a military problem and should be the responsibility of an over-all board with broad representation and authority.

The present legal authorization allows the Navy 4,016 physicians, or 0.65 per cent of the active-duty personnel in the Navy and Marine Corps. Of the 2,851 physicians now on active duty, 1,448 are reserve officers—a number which will be reduced to about 1,000 by August 1, 1949, when the reserve group will have been depleted by resignations. The Navy provides medical care for about 1,800,000 people, including active-duty, fleet-reserve, and retired personnel, dependents, some civilian employees and veterans, and the populations of various islands and territories for which the United States is responsible.

The Veterans Administration now has about 6,300 physicians, including residents and ASTP and V-12 physicians on duty, and maintains about 103,000 hospital beds with 92,500 patients. As a result of the building program, which contemplates increasing the number of beds to 140,000 with 126,000 patients by 1952, some 2,400 more physicians will be required. The Veterans Administration furnishes medical care sufficiently extensive to provide a clue to the medical needs of the country as a whole. Experience with this program reveals that a tremendous increase has occurred in the past half century in the man-hours of care that must be furnished by physicians and other medical personnel; this has resulted in a shortage of personnel greater than that which ordinary statistical analysis would indicate. The situation is further complicated by a proportionately greater shortage of specialists, such as neuropsychiatrists and doctors skilled in tuberculosis.

Negro physicians. Only 2.2 per cent of the 180,000 physicians in active practice in the United States are Negroes, though Negroes represent about 12 per cent of the total population. For the country as a whole the ratio is one Negro physician to each 3,337 Negroes; the average for the South is one to 5,000. Economic and educational handicaps are serious obstacles that deter many Negroes from attempting a medical career or prevent them from gaining admission to medical schools. On the other hand, Howard University Medical School, with a capacity for only 70 new students a year, has to turn away two qualified applicants for every one admitted. Of 595 Negro medical students in the United States, Howard and Meharry have all but 93. Those 93 are in the 27 other medical schools that have any Negro students, with a maximum of 10 in any one institution. If Negroes are to bear their full share of the responsibilities of citizenship, they should have an opportunity to carry their share of the load in meeting the medical-care needs of the country.

Other problems of distribution and special training. Much of the difficulty of attracting physicians to the Federal service and to rural areas, it was argued on the one hand, can be ascribed—like the shortage of Negro physicians—more to professional, cultural, and economic conditions than to the insufficient numbers now being graduated from the medical schools; areas and agencies in genuine need of more physicians should therefore attempt to provide conditions—as the Federal service has lately tried to do—which will make practice more attractive. On the other hand, some members of this Section urged that strong statements be made to indicate that the Section on Personnel recognizes the need for (1) more and better training in preventive medicine, psychiatry, and pediatrics, (2) personnel of the highest caliber for teaching and research positions in schools and hospitals, (3) better undergraduate, hospital, and postgraduate training in maternal and child health, (4) opportunities for postgraduate training for rural physicians, (5) externships and residencies for medical students in rural hospitals, (6) formation of a joint committee of medical educators and rural people to improve the orientation of medical education toward the social and technical problems of the rural health services, (7) inclusion of osteopaths in the estimates of the number of physicians available, (8) having medical schools and hospitals recognize and assume a continuing responsibility for keeping their graduates abreast of new developments in medicine, and (9) representation of consumers in studies of the extent to which medical schools are meeting the demand for physicians.

The subcommittee on physicians, expressing an unwillingness to modify its report to include specific recommendations on these points, agreed that they were appropriate for inclusion in a separate supplementary report by the Section's chairman.[3] The subcommittee had considered its task within a set and limited frame of reference and, in recommending that medical educators take on a responsibility for studying the extent to which medical schools are meeting the demand for physicians, had not meant to imply that consumers and private and public agencies should be excluded from an opportunity to share that responsibility. A study of the type indicated is already definitely planned as a forthcoming survey of medical education, under the sponsorship of the professional associations.

Estimating the Future Demand for Services

In a profession like medicine, requiring as it does some five or six years before a student can complete his schooling and internship, preparation to meet any fixed goal of supply for any future year needs advance planning. That goal, moreover, must be carefully established in relation to the probable demand for physicians' services. Estimates of the extent to which people in the United States will seek and receive medical care will depend on the assumptions made concerning the number and distribution of active physicians in relation to the size of the population of the area, employment and purchasing power, health habits, existing health programs and facilities, and the number of physicians serving special groups such as servicemen and veterans. Estimates of future demand therefore require setting some year like 1940 as a base line and some future year like 1960 as an end point, assuming from past experience the probable future rates of graduation, retirement, and death of physicians to derive a reasonable estimate of the available supply, and similarly making certain assumptions from recent trends in fertility, immigration, and mortality to figure the probable size of the population. These assumptions, furthermore, must be revised from time to time to take account of newer and better information.

The past offers far less guidance to the future demand for medical care than it does for estimates of the supply of physicians. Three bases

[3] See subcommittee report on p. 24 and chairman's conclusions and supplementary statement on p. 30.

of estimating the number of physicians needed in 1960 are therefore presented, reflecting three different assumptions. Basis I assumes as a minimal, foreseeable, effective demand for the services of physicians (a) that Federal agencies will be staffed to meet their estimated requirements, (b) that an adequate number of physicians will be serving in state and local health departments and hospitals for tuberculosis and mental disorders, (c) that the hospital construction program will call for additional physicians, but (d) that, except for these increases, the number of active non-Federal physicians will bear the same ratio to the population that it did in 1940—one physician to each 820 people. Bases II and III show what the requirements might be if the medical care furnished to the 1960 population were to meet two different standards of adequacy in relation to the need for medical care. One such standard is reflected in the physician-population ratio in 1940 in the twelve states that had the highest ratio of non-Federal physicians to population (Basis II).[4] The other is the standard estimated by the Committee on the Costs of Medical Care as the volume of physicians' services needed for a population unit if existing diseases and disorders were to receive all the care considered necessary (Basis III).[5]

As against an estimated total of some 212,400 active physicians in 1960 (Table 1), the estimates vary from 233,210 to 254,100 physicians for a population of 157,609,000, depending on the assumptions set forth in Bases I, II, and III (Table 2). Using different population estimates (Table 3), the number of physicians required to meet the potential demand might range from 227,500 to 260,700. If 1940 is an adequate

Table 1

EXPECTED SUPPLY OF PHYSICIANS IN 1960[6]

1. Total in 1940 175,146
2. Estimated graduates and other additions to the profession, 1940-59 132,104

                                                                        307,250
3. Estimated deaths, 1940-59 83,980
4. Total in 1960 223,270
5. Total active in 1960 212,356

[4] That ratio was one physician to each 667 persons; in contrast, the ratio in the twelve lowest states in 1940 was one to 1,372.

[5] Derived by multiplying the amount of physicians' time which medical experts considered necessary for the treatment of specific types of illness and defects by the volume of those conditions found per 100,000 population. Roger I. Lee and Louis Webster Jones, *The Fundamentals of Good Medical Care,* Publication No. 22, Committee on the Costs of Medical Care (Chicago: University of Chicago Press, 1933).

[6] Estimates prepared by the U. S. Public Health Service; see Appendix A for bases of figures and methods of computation.

Table 2

ESTIMATED NUMBER OF PHYSICIANS REQUIRED IN 1960[7]
(based on 157,609,000 population[8])

I. To maintain national 1940 physician-population ratio and staff the services specified.
II. To attain 1940 physician-population ratio of twelve best states and to staff the services specified.
III. To provide adequate (Lee-Jones) medical care and to staff the services specified.

Physicians for:	I	II	III
1. Care of individuals	185,269	234,105	210,354
2. Federal services	20,000	20,000	20,000
3. Public health services and tuberculosis and mental hospitals	11,623	[9]	11,623
4. New hospitals and health centers under Hill-Burton Act	16,318	[9]	[9]
5. Total active physicians needed	233,210	254,105	241,977

Table 3

ESTIMATED NUMBER OF PHYSICIANS REQUIRED IN 1960[10]
(under various population assumptions)

Estimated population[11]	I	II	III
153,375,000	227,500	247,800	236,000
155,075,000	229,800	250,300	238,400
157,609,000	233,200	254,100	242,000
162,011,000	239,100	260,700	248,200

base line for forecasts, if it is safe to assume continuation of present trends in high fertility, low mortality, high employment, and high per capita income, and if past progress is a guide to future advances in medical knowledge and skill and the extent to which the population can and will benefit from those advances, the estimated demand for physicians would be at least 15,000 more physicians than estimated current rates of supply will make available in 1960.

Financing Medical Education

The need for increased financial support of medical schools in the United States has on many occasions been described as critical. Without

[7] Estimates prepared by the U. S. Public Health Service; see Appendix A for bases of figures and methods of computation.
[8] Includes an estimated 1,456,000 persons in the armed forces.
[9] Included in line 1 of the table.
[10] Estimates prepared by the U. S. Public Health Service; see Appendix A for bases of figures and methods of computation.
[11] Includes an estimated 1,456,000 persons in the armed forces.

prompt and generous aid, few medical schools can maintain for long the high standards of education and research which safeguard and improve the health of Americans, the American position in medicine will decline, and only students from high-income families will be able to enter the ranks of the profession. A high point of medical advance was reached in the 1920's and 1930's, when most of the large medical endowments were established and when the state medical schools were greatly strengthened. As dividends of the investments of those decades we can point to the astonishingly low mortality from disease during the Second World War and the Army's report that out of every 1,000 whose injuries required hospitalization during the war 955 soldiers recovered.

Revenues of medical schools. In the past, the development and support of the medical schools has been far from uniform. Because of inadequate revenues the less-favored schools—about half the total number—have been unable to meet their full responsibilities for conducting modern programs of undergraduate training, to say nothing of graduate work and research. Although the 1947-48 budgets of the medical schools total about $43,000,000,[12] or nearly twice the sum on which they could count ten years ago, the increase has not kept pace with operating costs. Furthermore, much of the increase was derived from private funds which now seem far less readily available than in the past. There are now twenty-three schools—fifteen privately supported and eight state-supported—with annual budgets of less than $400,000. The continued existence of many of these schools is threatened unless additional funds are available to improve physical plants and to maintain educational and research programs.

Among important questions that university presidents, medical educators, government officials, and the lay public should earnestly consider are:

(1) Would modification of tax laws result in larger gifts and bequests to educational institutions?

(2) With proper education of the public, would an annual, conjoint fund-raising campaign furnish the support needed?

(3) Should Federal grants be made available, and if so how can the best interests and freedom of medical education be safeguarded

[12] More recent information from the *Journal of the American Medical Association,* 137: 39 (Sept. 4, 1948), indicates that the budgets for the academic year 1948-49 total about $51,000,000, excluding an additional $19,830,000 which the schools have estimated they will receive, from Federal and other sources, for research and special teaching projects.

by adequate assurance that (a) Federal support will be continued, (b) local support from both private and public funds will thereby be increased rather than diminished, (c) control and allocation of Federal funds will rest with a non-political group competent to evaluate the problems of medical education, and (d) schools receiving Federal support will be free from any form of political control?

As a result of increases in the costs of goods and services and the twenty-year trend toward a lower interest rate on invested funds, the value of the endowments of privately supported medical schools has declined markedly. Forty-three schools that receive no support from tax funds find their financial resources reduced by nearly one-half. Economies are perforce being adopted, and special services and special training programs are being cut. Research funds can be adequately used only by curtailing the regular programs of instruction. Among these private schools, constituting 60 per cent of the total number of medical schools in the country, are the pacemakers in standards of teaching and research. To abandon them or let them decline would be a tremendous social waste, for their laboratories, operating rooms, and equipment would have to be replaced elsewhere at higher expense. Proposals to increase tuition fees (now exceeding $700 a year in some schools) to cover the entire cost of education, currently ranging from $735 to over $5,000 per year per student, would virtually prohibit medical careers for all but a small proportion of the qualified young men and women. Suggestions that the medical schools should practice medicine for profit offer hazards, since the schools might find it hard to preserve an unbiased judgment if they have a financial stake in certain procedures and methods of practice.

Perhaps what is needed to solve the financial problems of the medical schools is not a new plan but rather the co-ordination of the various forces already concerned with the problems of health. A first resource might be to have units of local government carry—as many cities and towns now do—the major costs of medical care of indigent patients, since at present few medical schools can finance this philanthropic service. As a second step, the medical schools—perhaps with the co-operation of the large foundations—might re-examine their methods and procedures in view of the enormous increase in their activities. The third resource, the Federal government, cannot avoid facing its need to relieve the plight of the endowed medical schools. The government is spending millions annually for medical research and health improvement. Although many private schools, fearing Federal control, are hesitant to accept such aid, the difficulties envisaged can surely be resolved by sensible people with mature political and social consciousness. The British government, like the great philanthropic foundations of the United States, has for many years granted funds to universities with no strings attached and no dire results. On the other hand, if Federal funds are made contingent on the pursuit of specific political objectives or reforms, medical education could suffer a serious setback.

The private medical schools, to double their income, will need an additional $750,000,000 capitalized at 4 per cent to yield $30,000,000 a year. That annual income is only one-fifth the sum Americans currently spend for vitamin pills and about 3 per cent of the expenditures for jewelry. The sum of $750,000,000 is probably one-tenth of our present contribution to European rehabilitation and about one-nineteenth of the budget recently recommended to Congress for the armed forces for a single fiscal year. The private schools should clarify their ideas on the extent to which they will request Federal aid, and they should accept that aid for special projects or for only a limited period until they can develop progressively other means of support and ascertain more clearly the part that local and private agencies will play in the entire medical program. If, however, Federal funds were granted for a limited period or on a basis of decreasing amounts year by year, private donors might be unwilling to pick up the burden when Federal support ceased.

The financial situation of state-supported medical schools appears to be less acute than that of the private schools, but even they cannot afford to be complacent. They will need either to receive more per student in appropriations for medical education or to act on the alternative of raising tuition fees or seeking Federal aid. That aid, if land-grant experience is applicable, need not give rise to fear of Federal control. In fact, state-supported institutions are probably subject to no greater pressure than that of a different kind which private colleges face. A capital sum from the Federal government as an endowment would obviate the need for annual or biennial requests for funds.

Cost to students. Although tuition fees have greatly increased in the past few years, they now cover less than one-third of the cost of medical education. Available scholarships and loan funds are entirely inadequate to help the large number of promising students who are financially unable to study medicine or even to go beyond secondary school. A recent study in New York State indicated that 57 per cent of the students who graduated in the highest fourth of their high-school classes were not entering college, mainly for financial reasons. College entrants were proportionately more numerous among the group of high-school graduates who stood in the lower half of the class and came from families with incomes of $9,000 or more a year than among the group who stood in the highest fourth and whose family incomes were $2,500-$5,000.[13]

Many promising medical-school candidates, asked when they had decided to study medicine, replied that they had always wanted to, but until the G. I. Bill of Rights or V-12 and AST programs made it possible they had felt they could not even consider the idea. Relatively large percentages of medical students are in need of financial aid; that need will be greatly intensified when the G.I. Bill of Rights expires. There is also need for a system of medical fellowships, preferably for interns, who during their graduate training in hospitals are usually faced with increased expenses for mounting family and other obligations.

The whole problem of scholarships deserves thoughtful study. Perhaps they should be administered not by a Federal agency but by individual medical schools in accordance with the needs and promise of individual students. Having Federal agencies provide scholarships to students who would agree to practice medicine in designated rural areas or in a specified Federal service for a given period after graduation and internship might constitute an entirely unjustified regimentation. The first few years after graduation are the most important in a physician's career. To force a potentially great physiologist or promising research worker to serve in any other field of work by exacting his promise to do so before he has even begun his medical studies seems both unwise and unfair. A compromise proposal suggests that student loan funds might be made available to be liquidated at some agreed rate (1) by medical practice in areas certified by a state health department as in need of physicians, (2) by service in a Federal, state, or local health agency, or (3) by teaching or research. The student would then be free to do what he wished but at the same time might have more incentive to enter an area of medical service for which there is definite need and in which the financial returns are relatively less than in private practice. On the other hand, even the need to liquidate a loan might put a student in bondage and deter him from going into the field of medicine which he really preferred. Although the subcommittee report recommends that Federal aid to students should carry no obligation for them to serve in any specified capacity after graduation, it was agreed that the Chairman's supplementary statement could incorporate the alternative viewpoint.

Postgraduate education. Medical schools with adequate resources have conducted refresher courses to keep physicians in touch with recent developments in medicine. The 1,500 such courses given in 1947 had an attendance of more than 60,000 physicians, or about one-third of the total in the United States. Many physicians, particularly those in rural communities, however, find it difficult to leave their practice for postgraduate work. The Section on a National Program for Rural Health strongly advocates establishing opportunities for refresher courses and postgraduate study to meet this need. The medical schools are expanding their activities in these fields and are carrying courses to physicians in Colorado, Michigan, and other states. Osteopaths are required in eight states to register each year in a course approved by the State Board of Examiners or by their professional association, and no difficulty has been met in enforcing this requirement. A parallel requirement, conditioning the renewal of licenses to practice medicine on periodic refresher courses, was not accepted by the Section on the Need for Health and Medical Personnel as advisable or necessary for physicians.

The American Academy of Pediatrics recommends the use of public funds for medical fellowships. These fellowships would provide training in medical centers and service at outlying affiliated hospitals on a rotation basis. Such a plan, which would furnish bedside training of varied types, might be far more effective than extension courses. The holder of a fellowship would receive a salary, and the hospital would be reimbursed for the expenses of residency training. Largely because of the G.I. Bill of Rights, hospitals approved for residencies by the Council on Medical Education and the various specialty boards now have a surplus of physicians taking this training.

DENTISTS

Supply and Demand

Though some estimates indicate that the need for dental care in the United States calls for at least twice the present number of active dentists, it seems unrealistic to expect that increase to occur or to assume that present methods of financing dental care will create an effective demand sufficient to warrant doubling the number of dentists. The 1940 ratio of dentists to the population is therefore taken as the basis for computing the adequacy of the probable future supply, with due allowance for growth of the population, its increasing concentration in the higher age groups, a continuation of the trend toward greater appreciation of the value of dental health, and a decrease in the total service effectiveness as the median age of active dentists advances.

The 1940 Census enumerated 70,417 active dentists, or a ratio of one to each 1,870 of the population. Considering the losses by death and retirement (estimated as 24 per 1,000) and the prevailing rates of graduation from the dental schools, the number of active dentists will probably reach 76,560 by July, 1950, producing a ratio of one dentist to 1,900 persons if the 1950 population numbers 145,460,000.[14] The supply of dentists will therefore not keep pace with population growth. Assuming the same rate of population increase, 82,016 dentists will be needed in 1960 to maintain the 1940 ratio, as indicated in the tabulation below for this and two higher estimates of the population in that year:

Population in 1960	Assumptions			Dentists needed to maintain 1940 dentist population ratio
	Fertility	*Mortality*	*Immigration*	
153,375,000....	medium	medium	none	82,016
155,075,000....	medium	medium	500,000[15]	82,927
157,609,000....	high	low	none	84,230

For a 1960 population of 153,375,000, an average of 2,500 dental graduates a year will be required to compensate for retirements and deaths and maintain the 1940 dentist-population ratio; for higher estimated populations 2,600-2,700 a year will be needed. Graduating classes of this size will require average annual enrollments of 10,600-11,500 in the dental schools of the United States, or 2,200-3,200 more than the average for 1941-47 when enrollment was highest. The present capacity of our forty dental schools is about 12,000 students, or just about enough to maintain the 1940 ratio of dentists to population. To obtain any material increase in the proportionate number of active dentists in the population will therefore necessitate an increase in that capacity.

As the population ages, an increase in the prevalence of dental disorders and an increase in the effective demand for dentists may be assumed. General and dental health education should also stimulate

[14] Projected by the Census, assuming medium fertility, medium mortality, and no net immigration.
[15] Over a five-year period.

that demand. Studies of patient loads carried by dentists[16] indicate that the peak is reached when the dentist is aged 35-39. Though the decline in service capacity thereafter will be partially compensated for by future improvements in materials, equipment, and techniques, the fact that many dentists will be older men seems worth consideration. The median age of dentists in 1960 will be higher than at present, largely because of extension of the time spent in preprofessional and dental education and the deferment of dental studies until after the war. Programs for the control of dental caries will probably not diminish the demand for dentists but instead will require many additional hours of dental service if children are to benefit from these measures. A conservative estimate of the effect of all these factors affecting the relationship of supply to demand appears to warrant an increase of at least 0.5 per cent a year in the number of dentists needed, and an average of at least 2,900 dental school graduates a year through 1960.

The current pressure of qualified students for admission to dental schools is unprecedented. In September and October, 1947, more than 10,300 candidates filed nearly 17,700 sets of credentials in thirty-nine of the forty schools. The schools had places available for only 2,942. Though some of the nearly 7,400 disappointed candidates doubtless lacked full qualifications, many admission officers expressed the belief that they had turned away at least as many qualified applicants as the number admitted. All forty dental schools enforce the minimum predental requirements for admission prescribed by the Council on Dental Education of the American Dental Association, specifying successful completion of two years' work in an accredited liberal arts college, with a year's credit in biology, physics, and inorganic chemistry, plus a half year's credit in organic chemistry.[17] As of October 15, 1946, less than half (48.1 per cent) of the 8,287 undergraduates enrolled in these schools had offered merely the minimum admission requirements; more than a fourth (27.6 per cent) had baccalaureate or other degrees on admission and nearly a fourth (24.3 per cent) had completed three or four years of college without a degree.

Special Problems of Supply and Distribution

Dentists in Federal service. An Army and Air Force of 1,339,000 strength maintained for twenty years needs 2,700 dentists, with an annual replacement of about 1,000. An additional 1,250 dentists will be required under

[16] Henry Klein, "Civilian Dentistry in Wartime," *Journal American Dental Association*, 31:648 (May, 1944).

[17] Biology or physics may be waived for occasional students with high scholarship and at least three years of college credit.

the national service training program. The Navy and Marine Corps requirements for dental officers represent 0.2 per cent of active personnel; at present the 555 dentists in the regular Navy and the 385 reserve officers fall 400 short of the authorized allowance of 1,340. So far as the Veterans Administration is concerned, little if any increase is anticipated in the number of dentists required, for any additional number made necessary by the enlarged hospital program will doubtless be offset by a decline in the requirements for the out-patient program.

Negro dentists. In 1940 the Negro population per Negro dentist in the South Atlantic and East and West South Central areas ranged from 12,000 to 14,000. Because few Negroes have graduated from dental school since then, only slight improvement can be assumed. Of 313 Negro students in dental schools in 1947, 87 per cent were in two institutions. Immediate action is needed to increase the number of qualified Negro applicants and to expand their opportunities for dental education.

Auxiliary workers. The patient load of dentists can be substantially increased if they employ dental hygienists or dental assistants. A dental hygienist conserves an estimated 1,500 hours per year of a dentist's time, and an assistant provides the equivalent of 750 to 1,000 hours. In 1946 there were about 4,400 active dental hygienists in the United States, or one to every seventeen dentists. There are fifteen schools for training these workers; they are permitted to practice in thirty-nine states and in the District of Columbia. Dental assistants usually receive their training in a dentist's office and are employed by slightly more than half the active dentists in the country.

State and regional differences. The need for dental personnel is not uniformly distributed over the United States, and there are marked regional differences in rates of population growth, the median age of the population, the resources for dental education, and the effective demand for dental care. State and regional studies should be undertaken to evaluate these differences as a basis for planning. Since many dental schools are restricting their enrollment to residents of the state in which they are located or those of adjacent states, some states are finding difficulty in maintaining an adequate supply of dentists. Existing evidence indicates that there is need for the expansion of existing schools or for the establishment of a new school in each of the nine geographic regions, particularly in the South Atlantic, East and West South Central, and Mountain areas. Action must also be taken to encourage graduates to locate in rural and low-income areas which now lack dentists.

Financing Dental Education

The proprietary dental school disappeared in the United States more than twenty-five years ago, never to return. Moreover, only one of the forty schools in the country lacks formal affiliation with a university or medical school, and that independent institution is hopeful of absorption by a large, privately endowed university. All forty schools give the four-year professional course prescribed by the Council on Dental Education.

The great over-all need in dental education today is additional support for all levels of teaching and research. A survey of thirty-eight schools by the Council on Dental Education in 1942-43 showed that the income of the preceding year averaged about $170,000 per school, from the following sources:

Source	Total Amount	Per cent of Total
Tuition and other fees	$2,791,868	43.2
Clinics	1,824,751	28.2
Parent institutions	1,524,975	23.6
Endowments	94,934[18]	1.5
Miscellaneous	229,508	3.5
Total	$6,466,036	100.0

Expenditures in that year, about equaling income, ranged from $2,285 to $415 per student and averaged $811. Increased costs of operation would bring that average today to $1,000-$1,200. Though tuition fees, which currently range from about $250 to $600 per student, are somewhat higher than formerly, they represent about the same proportion of income as in the year of the survey. Parent institutions have made heroic efforts in the past five years to supply funds to meet the increased costs of dental education.

The widening difference between the incomes of publicly supported dental schools and others presents a major current problem. The percentage distribution of the income of the two groups as revealed in the same survey was as follows:

Source	Privately Supported	Publicly Supported
Students	49.5	31.0
Clinics	33.5	18.0
Other	17.0	51.0
Total (per cent)	100.0	100.0

[18] Only twelve schools.

At that time, eleven publicly supported schools had 23 per cent of the students, 31 per cent of the total income of all dental schools, and an average income of $1,105 per student; in contrast, the twenty-seven privately supported schools had 77 per cent of the students, 69 per cent of the income, and an average income of $737 per student. Privately supported schools are now facing the most severe hardships; both publicly and privately supported schools have basic needs that cannot be met with their present income. Those needs, in summary, are: (1) adequate buildings and equipment for twelve schools now housed in outmoded quarters; (2) higher ratios of teachers to students, and salary scales that will attract a sufficient number of thoroughly competent full-time teachers; (3) better staffing and equipment for two-thirds of the schools, to permit intensive research and investigation of the basic causes and treatment of dental caries and other diseases of the oral cavity; (4) provision of graduate, postgraduate, and refresher courses; and (5) financial aid for undergraduate and graduate students, to permit wider opportunity for dental education among promising candidates. Adequate Federal aid in the form of scholarships, graduate fellowships, construction grants, and grants to schools for operating expenses might meet these basic needs. Almost all other sources of aid seem to be exhausted.

The graduate, postgraduate, and refresher courses which the dental schools of the United States can now offer are filled to capacity and cannot begin to meet the demand of dentists for admission. Tufts College Dental School has developed a plan of conducting refresher courses in all New England States through three centers in each state. These courses, arranged in collaboration with the state dental associations, cover nearly all aspects of dental practice and are booked ahead for at least two and a half years. They need to be greatly extended if they are to satisfy the demand in this region alone.

NURSES

Supply and Demand

An inventory taken during the war indicated that the country needed some 42,000 more nurses than were available in 1946;[19] the Committee on Higher Education has estimated that in 1960 we shall need 200,000 more nurses than are required today.[20] The need for nurses will of

[19] *Facts About Nursing* (New York: Nursing Information Bureau of the American Nurses' Association, 1947), pp. 8-9.
[20] *Higher Education for American Democracy*, Report of the President's Commission on Higher Education (Washington: Government Printing Office, 1947), Vol. 1, pp. 78-79.

course depend on the following factors: medical advances and the development of the hospital construction program; programs for the control of specific diseases like cancer and tuberculosis; programs for mental hygiene, immunization, maternal and child health, and rehabilitation; adequate staffing of local public health agencies; and the division of labor among members of the health team—physicians, nurses, social workers, and nursing aides. The report of the subcommittee on nurses (p. 27) indicates the needs for nurses in 1960 estimated by the President's Commission for Higher Education and the National Nursing Council as compared with current rates of supply.

In viewing the function of nurses, moreover, we must consider their roles in the areas of administration and teaching in hospital nursing services, in public health agencies, and in nursing schools. The role of every nurse in the prevention of illness and in teaching health, including mental health, should be emphasized.

The American Nurses' Association, in co-operation with other nursing groups, is making a sample study to determine the age, education, and fields of activity of all registered nurses within the United States and its territories. If census data were to classify all nurses in the country by type—registered nurses, students, and practical nurses—it would be far easier to determine the country's resources. Since the 1940 Census listed graduate nurses with students, it was impossible, when war came, to estimate our supply of nurses.

Public health nurses. The Maternal and Child Health Section of the Assembly, as well as the subcommittee on nursing in the Personnel Section, recommends an increase in the number of public health nurses within the next five years to a ratio of one nurse to each 5,000 people and in the following five years to one nurse to each 2,500. Through utilization of all educational resources, more teachers, supervisors, and consultants should be provided as soon as possible. An adequate number of public health nurses and nursing specialists in maternal and child health should be directed to strategic positions in administration and teaching in the basic nursing schools to give student nurses better training in prevention and in positive health in maternal and child care. Public health nurses already in the field should have in-service and on-the-job training in public health and in maternal and child health.

Nurses for Federal services. The Army and Air Force will need 8,000 nurses for 1,339,000 officers and men; the replacement rate for this strength will average 1,000 nurses a year over a twenty-year span, because of the high attrition rate from marriage, early retirement, and other factors. For the national service training program an additional 2,000 nurses will be required. The law provides 3,428 nurses as the normal allowance for the Navy, or 0.6 per cent of the active force of the Navy and Marine Corps. At present there is a deficit of 1,485 nurses. The Navy also is short about 1,000 of its allowance of 15,500 enlisted hospital corpsmen. The Navy's allowance for the Medical Service Corps—pharmacists, scientists, and administrative officers in medical and hospital work—represents 20 per cent of the medical officers. The Veterans Administration, with about 11,000 nurses now on duty, still requires an increase of about 30 per cent for proper staffing. As a result of the hospital construction program, the next few years will require an increase of at least 4,000 more.

Practical nurses. The 1940 Census listed more than 200,000 people who thought they were practical nurses, but the number of those in active practice who have graduated from a school of practical nursing is perhaps 9,000-12,000. The fifty-three schools now operating graduate about 2,000 a year. About a dozen schools have been established within the last few years, most of them in connection with the vocational school system. The services of well-trained practical nurses are most useful in hospital or home care of persons with minor illness, convalescents, the aged or infirm, and certain chronic cases. By 1960 we may need some 100,000 of these nurses, though the requirements will depend on the ability of the medical and nursing profession to use practical nurses to advantage. A job analysis of the occupation has been made by a representative committee, and a suggested curriculum for schools of practical nurses is in preparation to standardize their training. To determine their maximum usefulness, an analysis of the needs of individual patients should be repeated periodically, and practical nurses and nurses' aides should work under the careful supervision of professional nurses.

Financing Nursing Education

The Bellevue School of Nursing, established in New York City some seventy-five years ago, set the pattern of nursing education in the United States, "training yearly a band of experienced, obedient, devoted nurses for service in private cases and amongst the poor." The benefits which accrued to the patients and hospital from the nursing care provided were so evident that, when the school committee found difficulty in raising funds, the hospital gladly absorbed the costs of training nurses. Neither nurses nor the general public have challenged the wisdom of this arrangement for financing the education and maintenance of nurses. The apprenticeship system has thus become stereotyped in nursing, despite its serious drawback. It leads to educational inefficiency by diverting a third or a half of the students' time toward housekeeping activities that have little relation to nursing problems. It limits the scope of the educational program to the needs of the hospital and restricts extension to community programs for health and the prevention of illness. It deters many qualified persons from choosing a nursing career, because they and their parents resent the fact that student nurses must earn their maintenance by non-educational work.

An analysis of costs and income in twenty hospital schools of nursing participating in the cadet nursing program[21] indicates that maintenance and education for the three-year term costs from $2,011 to $4,225 per student, with a median of $2,585. Of this cost only about one-third is for education. The median income of the schools is $2,767, comprising 10.7 per cent from students for tuition and fees, 1.2 per cent from gifts, endowments, and other sources, and 88.1 per cent from the value of the students' services. These hospitals, on the average, therefore made a profit from their schools, for the students paid in cash and services 111 per cent of the costs of their education.[22]

Some hospitals, on the other hand, lose money on their schools; in that event the patients help pay for nursing education—an allocation of costs that is no more just than having the student nurses help meet the costs of caring for patients. A broader basis of support by communities is needed here as in other fields of education. Although nursing is rapidly approximating full professional stature, only 6.3 per cent of the 1,253 schools of professional nursing in the United States are now under the control of colleges and universities, a few are independently organized, and 91 per cent are owned and conducted by hospitals.

During the war, Federal funds made available for the Cadet Nurse Corps rendered immeasurable benefits to nursing education as well as to the public. These funds represented 25-35 per cent of the total revenue of the nursing schools. Nursing is a public service, and nursing education, whether conducted in public or private institutions, deserves support from the same sources as those for other forms of education. Past support

[21] Louis Block, "The Nursing School—Its Costs," *Hospital Progress*, September, 1947, pp. 2-8.
[22] Lucile Petry, "Who Pays for Nursing Education?" *American Journal of Nursing*, December, 1946, p. 828, and "Student Services and Educational Costs," *American Journal of Nursing*, September, 1948, p. 590.

through endowments, grants, scholarships, and fellowships has been almost microscopic. Adequate financial provision for nursing education, however, must be preceded by more careful cost analysis and cost accounting to determine the value of the nursing service rendered by students and the actual cost of training.

Although affiliation of hospital schools with universities will not necessarily provide more money for nursing education, it will be a first step in determining financial needs and improving the quality of education. The nursing profession is now too small to furnish qualified faculties for the 1,253 schools now in existence. Some 500 schools, graduating a total of 50,000 students a year, might do a far better job. Small hospitals, under such a plan, could abolish their schools and receive students and perhaps faculty members from large medical centers for specified periods and specified training. Students not only should learn the complicated techniques of nursing in a large medical center but also should have experience in the rural hospitals of outlying communities and in psychiatric institutions, tuberculosis hospitals, public health agencies, and other community facilities such as nursery schools. Nursing schools centralized in this manner, independently administered as educational institutions, and soundly financed could prepare a larger number of nurses for a wide range of service.

It is important also that the universities provide opportunities for advanced study and research in all fields of nursing specialization. The cost of graduate courses is very high—in one advanced clinical program $50 per credit point as compared with a tuition fee of $15. Federal funds are already available as training grants to universities in certain special fields such as psychiatric nursing and cancer nursing, and a limited number of scholarships and fellowships are available to the nurses in these fields. More extensive financial aid to the universities for these purposes is sorely needed.

RECOMMENDATIONS[23]

Although the Section on the Nation's Need for Health and Medical Personnel endeavored to direct its considerations to man-power needs and resources throughout the entire field of health, it concentrated its energies in three major categories—physicians, nurses, and dentists. Moreover, it limited its efforts to the major problems of supply and of

[23] This concluding portion of the chapter is the final report of the chairman of the Personnel Section, Dr. Algo D. Henderson.

financing. The reason for this limitation is immediately obvious when one takes account of the complexities inherent in the problems besetting the enrollment, training, and professional development of an army of health workers. It was felt that time limitations required concentration on the basic elements of the problem if definite conclusions and recommendations were to result from the discussions. Similarly, this Section dealt only generally with the problems of the specialties—public health, pediatrics, psychiatry, and the like—and received information on personnel needs in particular areas from other sections considering those fields specifically. Separate subcommittees were established to consider supply and financing problems for physicians, dentists, and nurses. These three subcommittees submitted the following reports which were accepted and approved by the Personnel Section as a whole.

REPORTS OF SUBCOMMITTEES

SUBCOMMITTEE ON PHYSICIANS

Your committee finds that the following major forces are creating an increased demand for physicians:

(1) The increasing complexity of medical care
(2) An increasing health consciousness on the part of the people
(3) The increasing requirements of government service for physicians
(4) The increasing number of administrative, teaching, and research positions requiring physicians

In view of this increase in demand, attention should be devoted to increasing the output of physicians in the years ahead. There are several means by which this may be accomplished. Medical educators should carefully survey existing medical schools to determine how they may best increase the number of their graduates without lowering standards. Additional medical schools are another source of supply. Six new medical schools have been organized in the past six years and the development of several others is being planned.

Your committee recognizes that more Negro physicians should be trained. It also recognizes that this problem is part of the larger problem of improving the opportunities for the education of Negroes in general, in order that there may be a larger supply of Negroes qualified to enter medical schools. The Committee recommends that effective action to improve this situation at all levels be initiated.

Your committee calls attention to the fact that good medical education is fundamental to good medical care and that American medical education leads the world. Efforts to increase the supply of physicians must assure the continuance of these high standards. Medical education should be available to qualified applicants without discrimination as to race, color, or sex.

A continuing study of the extent to which existing medical schools are meeting the demands of the country for physicians is a responsibility of medical educators. The Committee is pleased to report that such a study is about to start under the sponsorship of the Council on Medical Education and Hospitals of the American Medical Association and the Association of American Medical Colleges. It is recommended that this study evaluate the extent to which expansion of existing schools is desirable and possible.

Intelligent planning with respect to the supply of physicians requires periodic analyses of the demand for physicians, both as to number and special qualifications. To this end studies should be developed which will furnish more precise indices for measuring the magnitude of demand.

The increasing complexity of medical education has markedly increased the cost. As a result, the problem of maintaining the present supply and quality of physicians is definitely a problem of financing.

Possible sources for additional financial support are:

(1) Private contributions
(2) State and community appropriations
(3) Federal appropriations

Your committee recommends that increased efforts be made to secure additional contributions from the public at large as well as from state and community governments. The general public does not fully appreciate their obligations to medical education in return for the benefits that they enjoy. There is evidence to indicate that local support will be insufficient to meet the financial needs of a sound and expanding program of medical education, and that some form of Federal support will be necessary. Federal appropriations should entail no Federal control of the administration, curriculum, and student admissions of the medical schools. Continuity of support should be assured. Funds should be granted in such a way as to increase rather than decrease the stimulus and responsibility for local support of the schools from both private and public sources.

Support will be needed in three areas: for general operation, for capital improvements, and for student support. In allocating funds for capital improvements, consideration should be given to improving the quality of medical education as well as the number of physicians trained.

With respect to student support, funds should be provided in such a way as to widen the opportunity for medical training of qualified individuals throughout the nation. Federal aid to students should carry no obligation to serve in any specified capacity after graduation.

RAYMOND E. ALLEN; WALTER L. BLOEDORN; DONALD G. ANDERSON; JOSEPH L. JOHNSON; DONAL SHEEHAN; DAVID D. RUTSTEIN, *Secretary*; LOWELL REED, *Chairman*.

SUBCOMMITTEE ON DENTAL PERSONNEL

For the first time in more than one hundred years the ratio of dentists to the population decreased during the decade from 1930 to 1940. Since 1940 there has been a marked increase in the population of the United States, and forecasts by the Bureau of the Census indicate a continuing increase for several decades. Accompanying the recent growth of population there has been an unprecedented interest in dental care as a means of promoting public health. It is now estimated that during the first seven years of the present decade the dentists-to-population ratio existing before 1930 has been restored. In order to maintain this ratio and to compensate for population growth, and for deaths and retirements in the dental profession, as well as the growing appreciation of dental care, serious consideration should be given at this time to the problem of providing adequate dental personnel. It is therefore recommended by the Dental Committee of the Section on Professional Personnel, after conference with a committee of the Section on Dental Health, that:

1. The forty existing dental schools in the United States should be administered at a maximum capacity consistent with sound educational principles.

2. Additional dental schools should be established in areas of demonstrated need as integral parts of universities qualified educationally and financially to sustain them.

3. Encouragement should be given to the establishment of additional courses for the training of dental hygienists, dental laboratory technicians, and dental assistants under the direction of accredited dental schools or other accredited educational institutions organized and operated on a non-profit basis.

4. Studies of state and regional needs for dental care and of personnel should be promoted throughout the United States under the auspices of or in conjunction with the American Dental Association.

5. Provision should be made for increasing the number of qualified Negro applicants for dental education, and opportunities for such applicants should be extended throughout the United States.

It is well known that many qualified young men and women are for financial reasons unable to take up the study of dentistry. For the same reason, many capable and ambitious dental graduates are unable to elect advanced studies. The relation of these facts to the problem of securing personnel for dental practice, teaching, and research is obvious and compelling. The supply of dental teachers is inadequate, and the wide prevalence of dental diseases demands continued, and more comprehensive, research in the dental schools.

The greatest over-all problem in dental education in both publicly and privately controlled schools is the lack of adequate financial support. Modern dental schools are not self-sustaining, and the total endowments for dental education are not significant. Consequently the problem of improving the quality of dental care is closely associated with the need for extensive financial support to dental education.

In terms of dental care, personnel, and education, there is a marked need throughout the United States for studies conducted on a state or regional basis.

In the light of the foregoing facts, it is recommended that:

1. Federal scholarships for undergraduate students in accredited dental schools should be awarded on merit through state educational authority on the basis of population.

2. Federal or state funds should be provided for the support of fellowships to graduate students in accredited dental schools, the fellowships to be awarded on merit and directly through the schools.

3. Federal funds should be provided to aid accredited dental schools, and new schools established on equivalent levels, in the construction of buildings and the installation of equipment.

4. Federal funds should be provided to aid accredited dental schools in meeting annual maintenance and operation costs.

5. Additional Federal grants should be provided to accredited dental schools and other acceptable institutions for research.

6. Federal grants should be made for the purpose of providing greater opportunities in postgraduate training for dental practitioners in the United States.

7. Federal support should be made available for studies of dental needs and dental personnel on a state and regional basis throughout the United States, under the auspices of or in conjunction with the American Dental Association.

8. The Federal subventions as proposed above should not imply Federal intervention in the management and control of recipient institutions.

HARLAN H. HORNER; JOHN T. O'ROURKE

SUBCOMMITTEE ON NURSING[24]

In the interests of national health and welfare, the nurses meeting in this Health Assembly make the following statement:

Present health programs, as well as anticipated expansion in health services, make it imperative to increase the amount of nursing service of high quality.

Nurses make their most effective contribution as members of a health team. This team concept implies participation in planning and administration, as well as in the operation of health programs.

In view of the increased services required of professional nurses, their educational program must be broadened to prepare them for the complex services required of them in large medical centers, in rural hospitals, and in public health and other community programs.

The following data are presented to show the increase in the supply of nursing service in recent years:

The ratio of graduate and student nurses to the population was in

1910	1 per 1,116 people
1930	1 per 416 "
1940	1 per 357 "
1946	1 per 316 "

There were 36,200 students graduated from schools of nursing in 1946, as compared with 23,600 in 1940. Furthermore, 128,800 students were enrolled in

[24] *Facts About Nursing* (New York: Nursing Information Bureau, 1947); "Hospital Service in the United States, 1947," *Journal of American Medical Association*, April 12, 1947; *Higher Education for American Democracy*, Report of the President's Commission on Higher Education (Washington: Government Printing Office, 1947); "Report of Study made by the National League of Nursing Education, Department of Studies," *American Journal of Nursing*, June, 1948.

schools of nursing in 1946, as compared with 85,200 in 1940. There were 106,900 students enrolled in 1947.

The number of graduate nurses employed by hosptials with schools of nursing has increased by 270 per cent since 1945. In the hospitals associated with schools of nursing there were 20,500 graduate nurses in 1946, as compared with 50,700 in 1948.

Concomitant with the increased supply of nurses, there has been a phenomenal increase in demands for service. Admissions to general and allied hospitals jumped from 9,897,172 in 1940 to 14,882,243 in 1946. The daily average census in these hospitals rose from 435,459 to 603,685 over the same period.

Public health services are expanding rapidly. It is estimated that public health nurses make more than 16 million home visits annually. The number of nurses employed by all public health agencies on January 1, 1947, was 21,500. An indication of future needs for public health nurses is noted in the fact that 1,087 counties had no nurse engaged in full-time public health work in rural areas on January 1, 1947.

The following are estimates of nursing needs:

| | Estimated Numbers of Nurses Needed | |
Place of Service	*1946*[25]	*1960*[26]
Federal services	24,200	36,800
Non-Federal hospitals	190,900	315,700
Private duty	91,400	100,000
Public health	28,000	76,700
Industrial	10,000	25,000
Total	344,500	554,200

In addition, the National Nursing Council estimated that 15,000 nurses were needed in other fields. The President's Commission on Higher Education makes no estimate of the number that would be needed in other fields, such as office service.

The projected estimates were made on the basis of current standards of nursing practice. Any major change in nursing practice would of course affect the picture. Changes in practices in the medical and allied professions may also affect the amount of nursing service required.

In the light of this background, the following recommendations are made:

1. Nursing education must prepare the nurse to render the health services required in any health program.

2. Nursing education should be the responsibility of institutions of higher learning whose primary function is education. Nursing education should be available to qualified applicants without discrimination as to race, color, or sex. Two years of general education beyond the high-school level is recommended.

[25] *Facts About Nursing* (New York: Nursing Information Bureau of the American Nurses' Association, 1947), pp. 8-9.

[26] *Higher Education for American Democracy*, Report of the President's Commission on Higher Education (Washington: Government Printing Office, 1947), Vol. 1, pp. 78-79.

The number of schools should be commensurate with social, economic, and educational planning. (A smaller number of schools could more economically produce the number of professional nurses needed.)

3. A sound system of financing nursing education should be established.

4. A sound system of financing nursing service should be established.

5. Financial aid for qualified schools should be secured from local, state, and Federal sources as well as from gifts and endowments.

6. Scholarships for qualified students otherwise unable to finance their nursing education should be made available through the schools.

7. Fellowships should be made available through the schools to encourage advanced training of teachers and research workers in nursing.

8. Research funds should be secured to:
   (a) Improve the practice of nursing,
   (b) Improve the education of nurses,
   (c) Investigate the use and need for professional nurses, practical nurses, and other auxiliary workers, and
   (d) Study the role of the nurse in the health team.

9. Classification in the 1950 Census should be secured to differentiate between:
   (a) Graduate nurses,
   (b) Student nurses, and
   (c) Practical nurses and attendants.[27]

10. Biennial reregistration should be secured on a comparable basis in each state in order to obtain accurate, up-to-date information concerning the supply and distribution of nurses.

11. Educational facilities in this country, as well as the results of research in nursing, should be made available to nurses in other countries.

The most immediate problems facing the nursing profession are:

(1) The need for interpreting to the public the increased demand for nursing services.

(2) The need for improvement of employment practices.

The solution of these problems is necessary in order to secure a sufficient number of desirable applicants for schools of nursing. To this end, we urge joint planning and the support of all groups participating in this Assembly.

> KATHERINE DENSFORD; RUTH SLEEPER; RUTH HUBBARD; ELIZABETH PHILLIPS; LULU K. WOLF; SISTER OLIVIA GOWAN; LOUISE McMANUS; RUTH KUEHN, *Chairman*

PHARMACISTS

Although no special subcommittee was set up to deal with the problems of the supply of pharmacists, the Personnel Section accepted, for incorporation as a supplement to its recommendation, the following statement:

[27] Recommendations for practical nursing service are available in the report of the Joint Committee on Auxiliary Nursing Service, published by the American Nurses Association in 1947 and in *The Analysis of Practical Nurse Occupation, with Suggestions for the Organization of Training Programs* (Washington: Vocational Education Division of the U.S. Office of Education).

In determining the nation's need for health and medical personnel, consideration must be given to the need for pharmacists—a health group which practices its profession in hospital and other institutional pharmacies, in drug-manufacturing laboratories, and in more than 50,000 pharmacies or drug stores strategically located throughout the United States in a ratio of approximately 1 per 2,700 of the population. More than 10 million people visit these establishments each day.

About 85,000 pharmacists are licensed in the forty-eight states and the District of Columbia. Of these a sufficient number is available to supply about 1.5 pharmacists per pharmacy. Considering the hours per day during which pharmaceutical service is expected to be available and the fact that the pharmacy laws of the several states require a licensed pharmacist to be in charge of a pharmacy at all times, at least 100,000 pharmacists would be needed to provide the services demanded by the public. An annual replacement of between 2,500 and 3,000 pharmacists is required to cover losses by death and by retirement for various causes.

Enrollment in colleges of pharmacy for the academic year 1934-35 was 7,154, and the number of graduates 1,428. Ten years later the enrollment was 4,144, with 604 graduated. Beginning in the fall of 1946, enrollment increased to 16,000 and rose to nearly 18,000 in 1947.

To ascertain the actual needs and avoid the evils stemming from both under-supply and oversupply, a national pharmaceutical survey has been in progress for nearly two years and will be completed shortly.

The complex nature of modern drugs, along with the dangers accompanying their indiscriminate use, calls for adequate protection of the public at the point of sale. This can be supplied only by well-educated, ethical, and public-spirited pharmacists, keyed to co-operate with public health agencies in making known to prospective buyers the limitations of self-medication and the availability of good diagnostic and treatment facilities. Support of pharmaceutical education is being provided to a laudable degree by the drug industry through the American Foundation for Pharmaceutical Education. Additional funds from public or private sources are needed, however, especially to provide for graduate training for research workers and teachers of pharmacy, since the supply of these has been reduced to a dangerously low level.

ROBERT P. FISCHELIS, Member, Executive Committee National Health Assembly; Secretary, American Pharmaceutical Association

CONCLUSIONS AND SUPPLEMENTARY OBSERVATIONS

The foregoing subcommittee reports address themselves to the problems of providing basic training for physicians, dentists, and nurses, three great groups of health personnel which are in short supply. Although adequate supplies of these groups are essential to the maintenance of minimal health services, the Personnel Section recognizes that these reports do not by themselves constitute an adequate approach to the total problem of professional personnel. There was unanimous agree-ment, not only in this Section but also in all the other sections of the Assembly, that the provision of a continuing and adequate supply of personnel with a balanced basic training, supplemented by various types of specialty training, and continuing education throughout the professional career constitutes the number one health need of the nation.

The need for inculcating a proper understanding and appreciation of preventive medicine, particularly in the undergraduate medical student, is recognized. The need for strengthening and expanding facilities for academic and supervised field training in medical and public health techniques and administrative practice was emphasized not only in the Personnel Section but also in the sections concerned with maternal and child health, mental health, rural health, and medical care. Other rapidly developing areas of specialization which report urgent need for recognition, both in undergraduate and graduate training, are mental hygiene, nutrition, pediatrics, and physical medicine. Greater emphasis should be placed also on training in sufficient numbers other types of professional health personnel such as social workers, both general and psychiatric, clinical psychologists, physical therapists, nutritionists, and dietitians.

This Section emphasizes the essentiality of the highest caliber of in-struction in our teaching institutions and the need for personnel trained in the administrative phases of health services and of research. Extern-ships and preceptorships for medical students and interns in rural areas to improve training and appreciation of rural health problems among physicians were advocated, and serious consideration was given to means for providing opportunities and encouragement for refresher and post-graduate training for all categories of personnel.

Some disagreement was expressed with the statement of the subcom-mittee on physicians to the effect that "Federal aid to students should carry no obligation to serve in any specified capacity after graduation." A compromise suggestion proposes that funds be made available to the student as a loan which he could elect to repay as (1) a loan to be liquidated at a rate to be agreed upon or (2) a loan to be liquidated by service in (a) areas certified by the state department of health as in need of physicians' services, (b) Federal, state, or local governmental work, or (c) teaching and research. This arrangement would permit freedom of choice upon graduation and might, in fact, offer encouragement without duress for the student to enter areas of medical service such as teaching, research, governmental service, or rural practice.

The shortages of trained personnel appear to be proportionately greater in mental hygiene than in any other specialized field. These shortages include psychiatrists, clinical psychologists, psychiatric nurses, and psychiatric social workers. The need for improvement in the quality of training for mental health personnel is recognized.

As a means of alleviating acute shortages in some fields, a plan was submitted for establishing fellowships to individuals who agree to practice in special medical fields in areas of need. The plan involves fellowships for hospital residency training, linked to extension services from medical centers to outlying hospitals in which the resident would serve two months on a rotation basis. Both the hospital and the resident would be reimbursed. Money would be allocated to the states, and they in turn would allocate it to individuals and hospitals, the physician agreeing to practice in an area of need in the state. Such fellowships would eliminate the expressed objection to undergraduate scholarships in which an individual is committed to a given field before he knows his field of interest. This plan has the approval of the executive board of the American Academy of Pediatrics.

The provision of adequately trained and qualified personnel was repeatedly stressed as a most urgent problem of public health. Facilities and personnel for training public health personnel should be at least doubled for each of the professional public health categories, a continuing evaluation of basic needs should be established, and training programs should be developed in accordance with such evaluations. The training programs proposed would include academic education as well as field training and would cover all categories of professional public health personnel. Federal funds, to be administered through state health departments and schools of public health, are recommended for recruitment and training programs.

A representative of the osteopaths suggests that osteopaths be included in any estimate of the nation's health man power and that any provision for Federal aid to medical education be extended to osteopathic education. All agree that Negroes should have greater opportunities for education in the health professions. Due recognition should also be given to the importance of the pharmaceutical profession as an adjunct to the nation's medical and health man power and in the field of health education, and funds from public and private sources are needed, particularly to provide for graduate training of research workers and for teachers of pharmacy.

As the reports of each of the Personnel Section's subcommittees show, the need for Federal assistance in financing health and medical education is well recognized. It was the consensus of this Section that an effective mechanism for continuing the discussion and for the eventual implementation of possible Federal participation in financing medical, dental, and nursing education would be provided if Federal agencies, including Congressional committees, were requested to confer with the American Medical Association, the Association of American Medical Colleges, and the National Medical Association and with the appropriate bodies of the dental and nursing professions. Probably state and local government agencies with responsibilities in the fields of education and public health should also be included.

APPENDIX A

METHODS OF COMPUTING THE FUTURE SUPPLY OF PHYSICIANS AND THE DEMAND FOR THEIR SERVICES

NOTES ON TABLE 1

Line 1. The total number listed in the 1940 American Medical Directory; of the 175,146 so listed, 9,873 reported they were retired or not in practice.

Line 2. Represents the sum of the following figures:

Graduates of approved schools, 1940-50, inclusive[28]	65,326
Graduates of approved schools, 1951-59 (estimate 5,600 a year for 9 years)	50,400
Additions from unapproved and foreign schools, 1940-46[29]	6,878
Additions from unapproved and foreign schools, 1947-59 (500 a year for 13 years)	6,500
Estimated graduates from newly authorized schools	3,000
	132,104

Line 3. Based on 1930-39 life table for white males.

Line 4. Sum of the first two figures minus the third.

Line 5. Obtained by multiplying the total estimated number in 1960 (223,270) by the fraction gainfully employed.[30]

[28] Donald G. Anderson, F. H. Arestad, and Anne Tipner, "Medical Education in the United States and Canada," *Journal of the American Medical Association*, 134:1299-1425 (August 16, 1947), plus estimates from size of undergraduate classes.

[29] State Board numbers, 1941-47, *Journal of the American Medical Association.*

[30] Elliott H. Pennell, *Public Health Reports*, 59:281-305 (March 3, 1944).

Line 1, Column I. Computed by multiplying the total number of active, non-Federal physicians in 1940 (160,480) by the ratio of the estimated civilian population in 1960 to the civilian population in 1940: $160,480 \times 156,153,000 / 131,669,000 = 190,321$. From this figure is subtracted 5,052 to avoid duplication with the figure in line 3 (see below).

Line 1, Column II. In 1940, the ratio in the twelve best states (Joseph W. Mountin, Elliott H. Pennell, and Anne G. Berger, "Health Service Areas—Physician Requirements," Public Health Bulletin, in preparation) was 149.92 non-Federal physicians per 100,000 population, or 667 persons per physician: $156,153,000 \times 149.92 / 100,000 = 234,105$. That figure includes physicians engaged in teaching, public health, research, and other non-Federal services.

Line 1, Column III. The ratio in Roger I. Lee, and Lewis Webster Jones, *The Fundamentals of Good Medical Care,* Publication No. 22, Committee on the Costs of Medical Care (Chicago: University of Chicago Press), table 7, p. 15, is 134.71 physicians per 100,000 population. The physicians include all general practitioners and specialists engaged in the care of individual patients, except the staff physicians employed in tuberculosis sanatoriums and hospitals for mental disease, but exclude physicians engaged full-time in research, teaching, and administration. The total consists of the following:

Type of Service	*Physicians per 100,000 Population*
Preventive services for the individual	37.69
Puerperal state	13.64
Diagnosis and treatment	83.38
Subtotal	134.71
Refractions	6.86
Grand total	141.57

Using the subtotal and omitting refractions gives the following estimate for 1960: $156,153,000 \times 134.71 / 100,000 = 210,354$.

Line 2, Columns I, II, III. This figure contains the following estimates: Army and Navy for armed forces of 1,456,000, a total of 8,500; Veterans Administration, 8,400; U. S. Public Health Service, 2,200; other Federal agencies, 900.

Line 3, Columns I and II. Health Officers: The number needed in 1940 is estimated by adding to the known number of local health officers in that year (2,313) an additional number (519) to provide a ratio of 1 local health officer to 50,000 population in areas not covered by health officers in that year. A similar process for state health officers brings the 1940 number from 282 to 344. The total for local and state health officers is then raised in proportion to the increase in population: $3,176 \times 156,153,000 / 131,669,000 = 3,767$.

Tuberculosis Specialists: These physicians would presumably serve full time in hospitals. The Tuberculosis Control Division of the Public Health Service estimates a total of 40,000 deaths from tuberculosis in 1960. A standard of 2.5 beds per death is found in the Hill-Burton Act (P.L. 725, 79th Cong.); a standard of 1 physician for 50 beds is set in "Minimum Medical and Administrative Standards for Tuberculosis Hospitals and Sanatoria," *Am. Rev. Tuberculosis,* 52:4 (May, 1945). The number of physicians needed is therefore 40,000×2.5 /50=2,000.

Psychiatrists and Other Full-time Physicians in Mental Hospitals: The Mental Hygiene Division of the Public Health Service estimates that 7.5 physicians per 1,000 patients is a conservative figure. The standard found in the Hill-Burton Act is 5 beds per 1,000 population. Assuming full occupancy, the number of physicians needed in 1960 is therefore 5×156,153,000/1,000×7.5/1,000= 5,856. The total for the group, including the 5,052 health officers and tuberculosis and mental specialists subtracted from item 1, is 3,767+2,000+5,856=11,623.

Line 4, Column I. The Hill-Burton Act sets for general hospitals a goal of 4.5 beds per 1,000 population. Assuming that these hospitals will be staffed by specialists in the ratio prevailing in the twelve best states in 1940, there would be 74.784 specialists per 1,000 beds. The total therefore would be 4.5×156,153,000/1,000×74.784/1,000=52,550. The figure in item 1, however, includes 37,732 specialists in hospitals—the number in 1940 increased in proportion to the population increase (31,816×156,153,000/131,669,000=37,732). The additional number needed is therefore 52,550 minus 37,732, or 14,818. As a modest allowance for physicians to staff health centers, the last figure is raised by 1,500, giving a total increase of 16,318.

APPENDIX B

PLANNING COMMITTEE

Algo D. Henderson, *Chairman*	Associate Commissioner of Education New York State Department of Education
David D. Rutstein, M.D.	Professor of Preventive Medicine Harvard Medical School
Joseph C. Hinsey	Dean, College of Medicine Cornell University
Joseph L. Johnson, M.D.	Dean, College of Medicine Howard University
Mrs. Ruth Kuehn	Dean, School of Nursing University of Pittsburgh
John T. O'Rourke, D.D.S.	Director, Graduate Studies Tufts College Dental School
Donal Sheehan, M.D.	Director, Commonwealth Fund
Herman G. Weiskotten, M.D.	Dean, College of Medicine Syracuse University

STAFF ASSISTANTS

G. St. J. Perrott	Chief, Division of Public Health Methods Public Health Service, Federal Security 　Agency
W. Palmer Dearing, M.D.	Chief, Division of Commissioned Officers Public Health Service, Federal Security 　Agency

REGISTRANTS

Raymond B. Allen, M.D.	President, University of Washington
Donald G. Anderson, M.D.	Secretary, Council on Medical Education 　and Hospitals American Medical Association
Brig. Gen. George E. Armstrong	Deputy Surgeon General United States Army
Creighton Barker, M.D.	Executive Secretary Connecticut State Medical Society
Raymond F. Barnes, M.D.	Medical Director Midwestern Area, American Red Cross
James J. Berna, S.J.	Jesuit Educational Association Georgetown University
Walter L. Bierring, M.D.	Commissioner of Health Iowa State Department of Health
Walter A. Bloedorn, M.D.	Dean, George Washington University School 　of Medicine
B. Harvie Branscomb	Chancellor, Vanderbilt University
John E. Buhler, D.D.S.	School of Dentistry Temple University
Mrs. Alida C. Dailey	Superintendent of Nurses Harlem Hospital New York, New York
Wilburt C. Davison, M.D.	Dean, Duke University School of Medicine
Harold S. Diehl, M.D.	Dean, School of Medicine University of Minnesota
Thomas D. Dublin, M.D.	Long Island College of Medicine
Andrew G. Dumez	Dean, School of Pharmacy University of Maryland
Norman A. Durfee	Administrator for Personnel Services American National Red Cross
John Edelman	Textile Workers Union of America Congress of Industrial Organizations
George Frates	National Association of Retail Druggists
Sidney R. Garfield, M.D.	Director, Permanente Foundation

R. H. Graham	Executive Secretary, Oklahoma State Medical Association
Virgil M. Hancher	President, State University of Iowa
Ira V. Hiscock	Department of Public Health Yale University
Harlan Horner	Secretary, Council on Dental Education American Dental Association
Victor Johnson, M.D.	Mayo Clinic Rochester, Minnesota
Miss Elizabeth S. La Perle	Consultant on Research New York, New York
Walter J. Lear, M.D.	Association of Internes and Medical Students
R. C. McCaughan, D.O.	Executive Secretary, American Osteopathic Association
Edward G. McGavran, M.D.	Dean, School of Public Health University of North Carolina
Mrs. Louise McManus	Department of Nursing Education Teachers College Columbia University
Sister Agnes Miriam	School of Nursing Georgetown University
John McK. Mitchell, M.D.	Associate Director, Study of Child Health Services American Academy of Pediatrics
Sister M. Olivia	Dean, School of Nursing Catholic University
Capt. Robert P. Parsons	Medical Officer in Command Naval Medical School Bethesda, Maryland
Miss Blanche Pfeffekorn	Director of Studies National League of Nursing Education
Miss Elizabeth C. Phillips	Executive Director Visiting Nurses Association Rochester, New York
Justin L. Powers	Editor, *Journal of the American Pharmaceutical Association*
H. A. Press, M.D.	Director, Management and Planning Staff Department of Medicine and Surgery Veterans Administration
Lowell J. Reed	Vice-President, Johns Hopkins University
C. P. Roberts	Towson, Maryland

J. Ben Robinson, D.D.S.   Dean, Dental School
                                     University of Maryland

Col. Paul I. Robinson   Chief of Personnel
                                     Office of the Surgeon General
                                     United States Army

Mrs. Corina Rogers   Secretary, Public Opinion Engineers
                                     Washington, D. C.

Charles A. Rovetta   Associate Director
                                     Hospital Administration Program
                                     University of Chicago

Miss Ruth Sleeper   President, National League of Nursing
                                         Education

Capt. Gordon B. Tayloe   Bureau of Medicine and Surgery
                                     United States Navy

Miss Lulu K. Wolf   Director of Education
                                     School of Nursing
                                     Vanderbilt University

II

What Is the Nation's Need
for Hospital Facilities, Health Centers,
and Diagnostic Clinics?

TO EVALUATE soundly the existing and future needs for hospital and health facilities in the United States, it is essential to consider the remarkable growth of hospital services throughout the years. In the formulation of recommendations for the coming decade, the present scope and significance of these services also must be carefully determined. In accordance with these principles, this report of the National Health Assembly's Section on Hospital Facilities, Health Centers, and Diagnostic Clinics attempts to outline the development of the American hospital, to consider its present status, and to help chart its course for the future.

THE NEED AND ITS BACKGROUND

The hospital, a place where the sick and injured are cared for and restored to health and strength, is as old as civilization itself. Through the centuries it has kept abreast of the onward march of human progress and has played a most significant part in man's triumph over barbarism.

Today the hospital is as inseparable a part of our social fabric as the church and school. The typical American hospital serves humanity without regard to race, creed, or economic status. Fifteen million persons, more than one in every ten Americans, were admitted to hospitals in 1946. On an average day, 1,240,000 patients occupied hospital beds. Within hospital walls, two million babies were born—more than 70 per cent of the total births.

The grand total of hospitals in the United States is 6,280, which includes all clinical types. These institutions have nearly one and one-half million beds.

Seventy-two per cent of all hospitals are what is known as general

39

hospitals—that is, they are equipped to meet all kinds of medical demands. Such hospitals have 44 per cent of all hospital beds. For the most part, their purpose is to care for short-term illness.

Eighteen per cent of all hospitals, with 52 per cent of all the beds, are intended for long-term illnesses, of which mental disease constitutes the great majority.

In terms of service rendered, the general hospitals care for 92 per cent of all patients admitted in any year, including the two-million hospital births per year. Measured in terms of patient days of care, the general hospitals fall behind the mental hospitals: 40 per cent of all patient days are accounted for by the general hospitals, whereas more than half of all patient days are accounted for by the mental hospitals.

The funds invested in hospital buildings and fixtures in this country exceed four billion, four hundred million dollars. The annual expenditures for operating costs run to almost two billion dollars. The great majority of hospitals are operated under non-profit auspices—either church, government, or special associations. Only about one-fifth of the nation's hospitals, with 3.3 per cent of the total beds, are proprietary or profit-making institutions.

The hospital is, by any reckoning, the keystone of our health structure, the instrument by which medical science is brought to the people, and the fountain of scientific knowledge from which young people go forth to practice the healing arts.

Yet this country has slightly less than half the number of acceptable hospital beds and only a small percentage of the health centers it needs, by today's standards, to provide adequate hospital facilities for all Americans. Millions of persons in remote and rural areas are so distant from existing facilities that it is either impossible or inpracticable for them to obtain the full benefits of modern medical and hospital care. In many places present facilities are overcrowded and so burdened in providing emergency care that they are unable to render the fullest measure of quality hospital service to all who need it.

The present deficiency in the nation's hospital facilities presents a serious obstacle to the goal of more abundant health for all. Sound planning to overcome this obstacle can be accomplished only when due regard is given to the influences and events which in the historical growth of the American hospital have contributed to the existing deficiency.

Forces Impeding Hospital Development

Not only do hospitals reflect social and scientific progress, but they also are extremely sensitive to economic conditions. During the high level of economic prosperity following the First World War, the nation saw an unprecedented boom in hospital construction. By 1928 there were more hospitals and more hospital beds in operation than ever before.

The following decade of depression brought many changes of a lasting nature in the hospital pattern. Many hospitals, particularly among the proprietary group, were forced to close their doors. The occupancy in voluntary hospitals declined and the use of tax-supported institutions greatly increased. Although there was a small annual net increase in the number of hospital beds in the country, the building of new hospitals almost came to a standstill. During this period changes in the tax and inheritance laws operated to reduce the traditional source of funds for the construction of voluntary hospitals.

All during the depression years, the public health services and public health education operated to increase the public's appreciation of the value of hospital care. As the nation emerged from the depression in the late 1930's the hospital facilities of the country were inadequate to meet the demand. But the rapid transition from a state of depression to a state of emergency rearming allowed little time in which to remedy these deficiencies. With the onset of the Second World War, rigid building restrictions prevented all but emergency hospital construction.

The end of the war therefore found the nation's hospitals suffering from virtually fifteen years of neglect both as to expansion in relation to increased demand and as to the proper maintenance of existing plants. The hospital, meanwhile, had become more important than ever to the practice of modern medicine. Yet, as a result of inadequate planning in the past, hospital facilities were found to be inadequate or totally lacking to meet the needs of many localities. These factors, and the rapid increase in construction costs, made unthinkable a continuation of the haphazard expansion of the past.

FUTURE OBJECTIVES

It is axiomatic that the best interests of the hospitals and of the public are identical. Broadly stated, the future objective of the hospitals of the United States must be to make available to every individual the curative and preventive benefits of medical science at its best. This accomplishment will require leadership, imagination, and co-operative effort of the highest order. The human values that have brought our hospitals into being must be preserved at all costs lest the hospitals become impersonal machines. On the other hand, these values must be amenable to change and adaptation as required by changing demands and changing times.

In order to achieve the goal of adequate hospital care for all, four essentials appear to be necessary:

(1) Modern facilities properly distributed

(2) Adequate trained personnel

(3) Sound financial support

(4) Integration

Facilities

For reasons mentioned earlier in the present chapter, the problem of adequate facilities is now one of major proportions. Under the leadership of the Commission on Hospital Care during the years 1944 to 1946, practically all the states undertook careful and thorough surveys of their existing hospital and health facilities. Later these surveys were extended under the National Hospital Survey and Construction Act and are now for the most part complete. Under present accepted standards of adequacy and under standards set forth by the Federal Act, these surveys disclose a huge backlog of unmet need in terms of distribution, quality, and quantity. Hundreds of communities are found not to have hospital facilities readily available. Others have hospitals so obsolete or otherwise inadequate as to be unsuited for future use. Many other communities have entirely too small a number of beds to meet the all-time-high demand. It is the purpose of the National Hospital Survey and Construction Act to correct these inequities by placing new hospitals in communities where they are now needed, to add to the facilities in communities where they are now deficient, and eventually to replace those hospitals which are inadequate to perform their required services.

Public Law 725, 79th Congress, became law in August, 1946. It differed from all previous acts granting Federal aid to hospitals in several major respects. It was sponsored primarily by hospital, medical, and public health officials. It required the designation of a single state agency to administer the program at the state level (in contrast to all previous programs in which the Federal government had dealt directly with the local communities). It required a survey to determine the adequacy of all existing hospitals and health centers and the preparation of an expansion program based strictly on relative needs. The Act further required that advisory councils be set up at both the Federal and the state levels to assist the official agencies in the administration of the program.

Public Law 725 sets forth certain formulae of need for the various categories of facilities. The ratios prescribed in the Act are those accepted as representing adequacy at the time the Act was passed. These are: for general hospital beds, 4.5 per thousand persons; for mental-hospital beds, 5 per thousand persons; for tuberculosis beds, 2½ per average annual death from that disease; for chronic-disease beds, 2 per thousand persons; and for health centers, 1 for each 30,000 persons.

It is gratifying to note that the states have undertaken their new responsibilities under the hospital program in a most enthusiastic manner. A tremendous amount of organizational work had to be done before any progress could be made on the actual program. It was necessary to designate or create new agencies to administer the program. New types of personnel had to be employed, and several types of enabling legislation had to be enacted. Up to this time, twenty-one months after the enactment of Public Law 725, forty-seven out of the fifty-two states and territories have completed their state programs and have had them approved.[1] It is expected that the programs of all the others will be submitted before the end of June, 1948.

All state plans follow a basic pattern set forth by the Federal Act and are supplemented by state regulations. They are built around a pattern of base areas, intermediate areas, and rural areas, thus lending themselves to the basic concept of an integrated hospital service system. Under this co-ordinated system, every service area in the nation would have its own network of hospitals all working together to bring the best kind of medical service to everyone regardless of where he lives. The remote or rural hospital would be linked with the nearest hospital offering wider services, and this hospital in turn would be connected with the central or base hospital—a large research and training institution with complete facilities for complex diagnosis and treatment.

The need for new facilities is based on three general types of findings. The first is for hospitals in areas now having none; the second is for the augmentation of facilities in areas now inadequately served; and the third is for the replacement of existing hospitals considered at present to be a hazard to the safety of patients. Under these findings and the formulae contained in the law, the bed deficiencies are disclosed to be as follows:

General	256,000
Mental	310,000
Tuberculosis	85,000
Chronic disease	246,000

[1] The 80th Congress brought the Virgin Islands into the program, thus making a total of fifty-three jurisdictions. By June 30, 1948, fifty-two of these had state or territorial plans approved by the Surgeon General.

The Federal Act as constituted at present authorizes $75,000,000 annually for five years, or a total of $375,000,000, toward meeting these needs. When matched at the required rate of two dollars on the state and local level for every dollar from Federal funds, the total will apparently meet only between 12 and 13 per cent of the estimated deficiency. This figure is based on an over-all average estimate of $10,000 per bed.

With the ever increasing emphasis on preventive medicine, the health center should play an important part in future health activities and should be an important item in the hospital construction program. There are about 450 acceptable health centers in the United States and its territories today, with some 2,000 more now planned for future consideration. Most official local health departments are grossly ill housed and thereby greatly handicapped in the efficient performance of their functions. Since there are relatively few health centers now in existence, most of them concentrated in metropolitan areas, the health-center concept is relatively new to the public. The stress placed on health centers in this program has tended to create some confusion as to the meaning and purpose of a health center. It should be made clear that the health center, under Public Law 725, implies no administrative change in the practice of public health. Health centers will be recommended and approved only where there is a going, organized public health department. The health center is therefore no more and no less than a modern facility in which organized health services, as defined locally, may be more effectively carried out. The scope and the type of these activities are in no way dictated either by the health center or by the Federal Act; on the contrary, the structure is planned to fit the present or future contemplated activities of the public health organization and will therefore demand community understanding and participation.

The huge backlog of need disclosed by the state surveys may be ascribed to a number of causes. The most important perhaps is the fifteen years of relative neglect occasioned by the depression and war periods; another is the normal population increase of 17 per cent since 1930; still another cause is the greatly increased use of hospitals through a better public understanding; and a fourth is the greater use occasioned by a higher level of economic income at the present time. It is not believed, however, that this deficit reasonably can be or should be met within the next ten years.

The Hospital Facilities Section of the National Health Assembly feels that Public Law 725 is one of the most soundly conceived health statutes ever enacted by the Federal Congress. Its provisions for the allotment of Federal funds places more money per capita in the poorest states where the relative need is the greatest. Since the Federal government pays only one-third of the cost, the local communities still have the incentive for local initiative, which is indispensable to the successful operation of a community hospital. Its administration on a state level, with major state responsibility, removes any danger of Federal domination of what is essentially a state and local community enterprise. The additional device of contractual authorization added by the 80th Congress in its 1948 appropriation act gives still more flexibility to the program in that it allows the program to proceed at maximum speed without the necessity of tying up large sums of money over an indefinite period.

Public Law 725 is therefore a flexible and efficient device for assisting in the future expansion of our hospital system. It is believed that this flexibility should be taken advantage of and that expansion should be carried forth in an orderly and well-planned manner. A precipitous attack upon the problem of unmet need would be ill-advised for many reasons. Trained personnel could not be provided rapidly enough to meet the need under a greatly accelerated expansion program. Much of the deficit in facilities occurs in areas where special attention must be given to ways of insuring adequate finances for maintenance and operation once a hospital is built.

Present needs are based on present concepts of adequacy. There are many imponderables which will undoubtedly affect and change these concepts within the next ten years. Changes in medical practice, such as early ambulation of surgical and obstetrical cases, are already operating to reduce the average length of stay in acute-disease hospitals. The dramatic curative effects of certain new drugs recently introduced and of others which will probably be discovered likewise operate to reduce the length of stay. The home nursing care now being tried in a limited, experimental way by a few hospitals may prove an important factor in reducing hospital bed requirements.

Tuberculosis, in many states, is already on the decline. There now seems a reasonable likelihood that specific chemotherapy may soon effectively be employed in the treatment of tuberculosis. This factor may even still more rapidly reduce the need for tuberculosis beds.

More emphasis upon preventive treatment in mental disease and more intensive treatment in the early stages should in time operate to reduce the need for long-term mental-disease hospitals.

The long-time need for chronic-disease beds is likely to be less affected by scientific advances and changes in medical practice than the needs for other types of beds. A large number of acute-disease beds in general hospitals are now occupied by chronic cases. The increasing age level of the population points to a still greater case load of long-term illness. It is highly improbable that any of the developments now operating to reduce the incidence and duration of other diseases will be effective in this class. The chances are, therefore, that the need for chronic-disease facilities will prove to be less changeable than the need for other types of facilities.

Still other imponderables affect the future program under Public Law 725. The amount of private construction without Federal aid cannot be predicted with any degree of accuracy. In all probability it will make up a considerable proportion of the deficit in the larger centers of population. The effect of the future policy of the Veterans Administration cannot at this time be fully determined. It will, however, have an important bearing on the number of facilities ultimately to be provided under Public Law 725, should its duration be extended considerably. The present authorized Veterans Administration program apparently calls for an eventual complement of 150,000 beds embracing all categories of illness, but veterans' organizations are demanding 300,000 beds. These facilities may offset the known deficit by that amount.

The Hospital Facilities Section feels that the programs under Public Law 725 and the Veterans Administration should be closely integrated in the interest of good hospital services. The Veterans Administration program is planned by the Federal government for a restricted class of beneficiaries, whereas the program under Public Law 725 is planned by the states and communities for all the population, including veterans. Hospital facilities for veterans should be integrated into and become a part of the state hospital plan for everybody, and any additional beds for veterans should be constructed in accordance with that plan. That is what Canada is doing. Most of its beds for veterans are being constructed as additions to community general hospitals. In that way the hospital construction program for veterans is used to strengthen the existing hospital system rather than to tear it down. The same thing can be done in this country. This would assure continued high standards of service, and when facilities constructed to last one hundred years or more are no longer needed for veterans they can be used for other patients.

It is believed that Public Law 725 is the best plan yet devised for extending Federal aid to community hospitals. The program should be continued and extended. A policy of flexibility should be maintained. Should the cost of construction continue to rise, the basic authorization should be increased in order that the rate of expansion will not be diminished. Should it appear that local funds in high-priority areas are sufficient and the demand sufficiently great to warrant some increase in the basic authorization, this should be provided for. In other words, the program under Public Law 725 should be kept flexible so as to meet the changing needs in the hospital field in the most effective possible manner.

Personnel

The basic concept of Public Law 725 contemplates an orderly planned expansion of the national hospital structure. The rapidity with which the hospital pattern can be expanded is limited, among other things, by the availability of doctors, nurses, and auxiliary workers. During the war the shortage in hospital personnel was both actual and relative. It was actual because many doctors, nurses, medical social workers, and other personnel were drawn into the armed forces as well as into war industry. It was relative because of the rapid increase in the demand for hospital care. There is every reason to believe that this shortage will be corrected in time. Hospital salaries, which have always been low, have now been raised to a point where they more nearly compete with salaries paid in business and industry. Nurse recruitment, which was at an all-time high during the war but rapidly fell off after victory, is now on the upgrade again as a result of extensive recruitment efforts. Increased training facilities for interns, nurses, and other personnel will become a natural part of the expanding hospital structure.

Finances

Hospital income normally derives from four principal sources: (1) paying patients, either directly or through prepaid insurance plans; (2) endowment income; (3) community funds, gifts, bequests, community chests, and other types of local contribution; and (4) tax funds from Federal, state, or local governmental sources in reimbursement for the care of indigent patients or other public beneficiaries.

The philanthropic concept of hospitals is as old as are the hospitals themselves, but this concept in voluntary hospitals now requires re-examination in the light of present-day realities. Endowment funds and the contributed services of religious and volunteer workers have heretofore been important resources from which charity was dispensed. But decreasing endowment income and increasing costs of operation have greatly restricted these means of charity. Other expenditures in the name of charity come from community gifts and contributions and from excess charges over cost to private patients. Community gifts and contributions constitute a worthy endeavor to be encouraged and perpetuated. But charges to private patients in excess of cost of care is at best a policy requiring careful examination. However, adequate service can be provided by the hospital only when it receives at least the cost of the services rendered. Services for which the hospital is not paid probably constitute the greatest threat to the economic stability of the voluntary hospital.

As a general principle the financing of hospital care should be provided by the community to the fullest extent possible. The greatest financial liability in most voluntary hospitals is the inadequate payment for services rendered to public beneficiaries and for service to patients who are not public beneficiaries but are unable to pay the complete cost of their care.

The failure of public governmental agencies to pay the full cost of the care of public beneficiaries is in part the fault of the hospitals themselves. Every effort should be made to place hospital administration on a more businesslike basis so that the entire cost of the service rendered can be readily shown to public officials. On the other hand, governmental agencies must be ready to accept responsibility for the full cost of care for public beneficiaries. There is no such thing as free care; it must be paid for by somebody. If government does not pay its full cost, the deficiency must be made up from other sources or the effectiveness of the hospital will be reduced.

The Blue Cross prepaid hospital insurance plans, with a rapidly increasing membership now amounting to more than thirty million subscribers, is the most stabilizing financial force in the voluntary hospital field. Every effort should be made to increase membership in this and other prepayment plans.

If the present sources of hospital income prove to be inadequate in the face of rising costs, then higher levels of government, the states and the Federal government, must assume part of the responsibility.

Integration

Hospitals traditionally have been isolationists in their development. Both the quality and the quantity of hospital service has been limited largely to the local resources. Within recent years, however, a different viewpoint has arisen in many parts of the country. It is becoming increasingly apparent that the complexities of both hospital administration and medical care exceed the capacities of the local hospital, particularly in the smaller-sized group.

The Commission on Hospital Care recognized this fact and recommended that hospitals be organically associated with each other in order that each might benefit from the technical and intellectual resources of the other. It is desirable that funds, either public or private, be made available to facilitate the exchange of personnel needed for high-quality service in an integrated hospital system. Public Law 725 sets up the physical framework for such an organic interrelationship. The realization of this objective through administrative organization is essential to the development of a true hospital system. Its success will depend to a large degree on how fully hospital boards and trustees meet their responsibility for leadership toward this end.

THE NEXT TEN YEARS

As progress is made in carrying out these basic objectives, the next ten years should see the realization of a third major stage in the development of the nation's hospital services. In the first, the hospitals provided meager care almost exclusively for the sick poor. The second stage witnessed the hospital's evolution into the workshop of medicine to which the sick and injured came largely for curative measures. The third developmental phase, which has already begun, should bring a marked extension of hospital services both into and throughout the country. In the development of this third stage the hospital should become more and more an important health agency, not only in providing the best in therapeutic measures but also in taking active steps toward the prevention of illness. The new hospitals will keep abreast of new developments in medical science and in the changing patterns of the times. Particularly, they will be aware continually of the changing needs for hospital services and will afford the flexibility of operations necessary to adapt the services readily to meet new needs without unnecessary delay. In these and all other activities, the hospitals will cooperate still more closely with members of the medical profession so that the best interests of all will be carried forward in the provision of improved hospital and medical care.

The traditional functions of the general hospital have been care of the patient, research, and medical education. In the new stage at least two more functions should be added. These are preventive medicine and public health education.

Care of the Patient

Care of the patient is the primary function of the hospital, and it is also an area in which considerable development may be expected in the years ahead. General hospitals should strive continually to provide essential services for all physicians and patients through the adoption of the newly developed techniques and the acquisition of more efficient equipment. The general hospital should provide as far as possible for all types of illness. Such service would include facilities for the treatment of acute communicable disease, nervous and mental disease, tuberculosis, and long-term illness. The inclusion of all possible types of cases in the general hospital service has many obvious advantages. Few patients suffer from one condition exclusively. The general hospital staff is in a better position to treat the patient as a whole than is the specialized staff of the special hospital.

Beyond question, one of the greatest needs today is for facilities for the care of the patient with a long-term illness. This need will increase progressively in the years ahead. From the national health survey of 1935 it was computed that twenty-three million persons were suffering from some form of chronic illness. In 1900 only one person in twenty-five was sixty-five years of age or older. It is estimated that in 1980 the ratio will be one in ten. In 1940, 26.5 per cent of the nation's population was over forty-five years of age, and this group required over half of the medical services rendered. By 1980 it is expected that the number of persons over forty-five will constitute nearly half of our population. This change will add enormously to medical and hospital care requirements.

Much attention has been directed to the great need for more adequate care of the mentally ill. Careful and comprehensive study should be given to this problem. General hospitals should be stimulated to provide facilities and personnel for the diagnosis of mental diseases and for the treatment of those patients who are not in need of long-term institutional care. Mental hygiene clinics should be established in the outpatient departments of general hospitals wherever competent professional service is available. Due attention should be given to the need for expansion of the services of special hospitals for nervous and mental diseases.

The problem of providing an integrated service for the chronically ill is a complex one. Most general hospitals accept chronic patients, although relatively few have specialized departments for their care. Not only are these patients an economic drain on the hospital but they occupy beds badly needed for acute cases.

Many or perhaps most chronic-disease patients require intermittent acute care. This fact points to the advisability of providing chronic facilities either as a part of or under the supervision of the general hospital. Also, in view of the increasing incidence of chronic illness, its study should become of increasing interest and importance to the general hospital staff.

Medical social service will likewise become increasingly important, especially in connection with the care of all chronic illness. Hospitals should establish medical social-work departments or activities to assist patients in meeting social and economic problems relating to their illness, to help them carry out the physician's instructions, and to provide physicians with helpful information regarding the patient's socio-economic environment. The medical social worker should function with the doctor in research, either as part of a medical research project or in the study of social factors in illness. She also shares in the hospital teaching program in supervising the field work of medical social-work students and in teaching the social component in illness to the professional groups—nurses, dietitians, undergraduate medical students, interns, and residents.

Research

The research activities of hospitals should continue at an even faster tempo. The spectacular discoveries and developments of medical science over the past few years have aroused public interest in research activities to an all-time high. The physician in his day-to-day contact with hospital patients is in an excellent position to add to the sum total of medical knowledge. The present emphasis on research in great specialized institutions in no way lessens the need for clinical research in hospitals.

Medical Education

The expanding pattern of hospital and medical services throughout the country requires an ever increasing number of physicians, dentists, nurses, technicians, and other professional personnel. Since hospitals are essential to the training of such personnel, the teaching resources of hospitals should continue to be used to the fullest possible extent.

Preventive Medicine

Although preventive medicine in its narrowest sense is usually considered the function of official public health officers, it is in fact a function of every physician and every health organization, including the hospital. With a realization of economic value as an important end result of disease prevention and the promotion of health, hospitals and out-patient departments should concern themselves with the support and maintenance of worth-while programs in this field. This function may be exercised effectively in many areas such as out-patient services, diagnostic clinics, community services, and co-operation with local health departments.

Public Health Education

Few hospitals have any planned community-wide programs of health education. This field has been left almost entirely to organized departments of public health and voluntary health organizations. Increased effort should be directed toward achieving a better community understanding of the value of hospital care and other means of illness prevention. A better public understanding of hospital values will result in greater utilization and public support of hospitals. The individual should be made aware that better hospitals mean better care for himself and his family. He must understand that the skill of his own doctor and that of other physicians can be developed only in a good hospital.

Other Considerations

Board of managers. The boards of management of voluntary hospitals should be composed of members who are broadly representative of the public. Definite liaison arrangements should be made among the members of the managing board, the administrator, and the medical staff for the discussion of professional affairs and the establishment of administrative and professional relationships.

Training in hospital administration. Until relatively recent times formal training in hospital administration has been almost unknown. Training at best has been almost entirely by the apprenticeship method. The complex organization of the modern hospital and the enlarged scope of its function demand that the administrator be a well-trained, competent individual who will insure provision of the essential services as well as efficient administration. The first formal scholastic course in hospital administration was established by the University of Chicago only fourteen years ago. More recently eight other universities have also instituted formal courses in hospital management. One state has already enacted laws requiring the registration of hospital administrators, such registration contingent on their fulfilling certain qualifications. This may well become a trend which will make the value of formal administrative training even more immediately apparent. Formal training in hospital administration prepares the individual not only for institutional management but also for a broader field of medical administration in which opportunities are continually on the increase.

Staff organization. In view of the hospital's responsibility to the community for the provision of a high quality of care, it is essential that it have a formal staff organization. Formal medical-staff organization is essential to assure the best care of the patient in any hospital, as well as to insure supervision and evaluation of the medical care provided.

Licensure. Over the years through which the hospitals have served the American public, they have remained remarkably free from any governmental controls. No other public service agency has been so favored. This fact is a tribute to the character of the men and women who have built our hospital system. The great majority of the hospitals have not and do not now need any official regulations to insure the best possible service. Nevertheless freedom from control, desirable as it may be in principle, has permitted some abuses in hospital practice. These can be corrected effectively only through the enforcement of minimum standards by means of the mechanism of licensure. Hospital licensure statutes should be such as to develop an effective hospital service adequate to meet the public need and to provide maximum opportunities for the training of medical and nursing personnel. The effective administration of licensure statutes should be directed primarily toward the education of hospitals in the essentials of good practice. The police power of licensure should play a minor role in the main purpose of the procedure.

Out-Patient Services

Care of the ambulatory patient in the out-patient department should be extended as a means of preventing hospitalization and providing service to the general public as well as to patients before or after their stay in the hospital. Such services provide advice, supervision, assistance, and direction for convalescents and the chronically ill who do not need institutional care. The follow-up services are valuable to both patient and physician in determining the effectiveness of the therapy provided during hospitalization and ambulant care. Out-patient service provides one of the best means for hospital participation in preventive medicine, particularly in the fields of mental illness, venereal disease, tuberculosis, and dental care. The out-patient department, incidentally, is one of the most effective public health educational devices a hospital can use.

Diagnostic Clinics

Medicine as taught today by the medical school is best practiced in group organizations such as the diagnostic or group-practice clinic. The trend toward specialization in medicine creates an ever increasing need for consultation if the patient is to receive complete service. Comprehensive diagnostic service can therefore be furnished most effectively in a group-practice or diagnostic clinic where all the specialities are represented. The facilities available in a modern hospital lend themselves to this type of service and greatly increase the hospital's opportunity to serve its community.

Co-operation with Local Health Departments

Hospitals and health departments have a common responsibility in promoting the health of a community. They should seek every method for co-ordinating their efforts and integrating their functions. This can be done in part through the joint use of certain personnel and of such facilities as laboratories, out-patient departments, and other diagnostic equipment and, wherever it appears logical and feasible, through the use of common physical facilities. Such co-operation lends itself particularly well to maternal and child-health programs, communicable-disease control, tuberculosis, and mental-hygiene case findings. The integrated activity should include the general health education of the community, the visiting nurse service, and social service programs. At the present time about 25 per cent of all organized public health departments carry on some of this work in local hospitals.

Health of Minority Groups

There are in the United States a number of large minority groups. Their health needs are greater than those of the population as a whole, and in general there is not now available to them the same quality or quantity of medical and hospital care as there is for the balance of the population. The need for an expanded and improved health service for these groups, and particularly for Negroes, is recognized. They should have the same high quality of professional and institutional care as all other segments of the population, and there should be an increased and broadened opportunity for the education and training of professional personnel to serve them.

The Rural Problem

Because of the social and economic conditions surrounding rural life, special problems are involved in providing good rural hospital care. In the horse-and-buggy days, when the doctor's entire equipment was carried in his saddle bags, almost every rural community had its family doctor. As wealth and population gravitated more and more to the urban centers and as hospitals became an essential in the practice of medicine, the country doctor began to disappear from the scene. Although hard-surfaced roads and automotive transportation have mitigated this loss in part, it is a fact nevertheless that medical care is for all practical purposes almost non-existent in many rural areas today. The question therefore is one not of hospitals alone but of hospitals and medical care.

The problem of extending medical care and the services of the modern hospital into rural areas is one which requires careful planning and co-ordination of effort on the part of all concerned—the professions and the general public. Public health services, health centers, community clinics, and small hospitals—all properly correlated and integrated with the diagnostic and therapeutic services of larger hospitals and their specialized personnel—appear to offer the best solution of the problem.

CONCLUSIONS AND RECOMMENDATIONS

Full recognition is given to the vast strides made by the American hospital in attaining its present vital and strategic place among the nation's health resources. Yet much remains to be accomplished in achieving the ultimate aim of adequate services for all people without regard to race, creed, color, or economic circumstances. In order that maximum progress toward this goal may be realized in the next ten years, it is recommended that:

1. The program under the Hospital Survey and Construction Act should be continued and extended under a policy of flexibility permitting such adaptation as may be required to meet changing needs. The present authorization of $75,000,000 per year should be increased in view of the urgent needs for the establishment of additional hospital beds and clinics and health centers in many areas of the country.

2. The program under Public Law 725 and the hospital program of the Veterans Administration should be closely integrated in the interest of good planning.

3. Hospitals within service areas should be functionally or organically associated with one another so that the patient may benefit from the resources of all.

4. The full cost of hospital services for those patients for whom governmental agencies have assumed responsibility should be paid from tax

funds. This same principle should be observed by non-governmental agencies purchasing hospital care.

5. Hospitals, health departments and all other health agencies should seek every method for co-ordinating their efforts and integrating their functions in the interests of greater efficiency and service to the patient.

6. Diagnostic clinics, out-patient services, and home medical care and allied programs should be developed more extensively in extending health services for all.

7. Hospitals should intensify and extend their basic activities in research and education.

8. Preventive medical and dental service and public health education should be carried out more widely as regular functions of the modern hospital.

9. As far as possible, the general hospital should provide facilities for the care of all types of illness and should give increased attention to the care of the patient with a long-term illness.

10. The pressing need for additional facilities for the care of the mentally ill and those suffering from chronic diseases in general hospitals makes it necessary that special emphasis be given to this problem in the original state hospital plans and any revision of these plans under Public Law 725. A careful study to develop recommended standards is needed in this area for the guidance of state organizations under this Act.

11. In order to develop and adequately meet good standards of patient care, it is recommended that all hospitals, nursing homes, and other facilities for the care of the sick should meet at least minimum standards through the mechanism of licensure.

12. The control of local facilities should be exercised by the people in each locality on a co-operative or community basis, where possible with an elected board of directors representative of both lay and professional groups.

13. Lay and professional organizations and governmental agencies should join in conducting a health education program and in developing plans for adequate facilities and health services which will include well-co-ordinated and highly integrated networks of mobile units, clinics, community hospitals, district hospitals, regional hospitals, and great medical centers.

APPENDIX

PLANNING COMMITTEE

Charles F. Wilinsky, M.D.,
   Chairman

Executive Director
Beth Israel Hospital
Boston, Massachusetts

Arthur C. Bachmeyer, M.D.

Medical Director
University of Chicago Clinics

George Bugbee

Executive Director
American Hospital Association

Msgr. Maurice F. Griffin

President, Catholic Hospital Association

Miss Katherine Hardwick

Director, School of Social Work
Simmons College

Malcolm T. MacEachern, M.D.

Associate Director
American College of Surgeons

Rev. John G. Martin

Superintendent, Hospital of St. Barnabas
Newark, New Jersey

STAFF ASSISTANTS

David Wilson, M.D.

Chief, Office of Special Services
Division of Hospital Facilities
Public Health Service, Federal Security
   Agency

Louis Block

Acting Chief, Office of Hospital Services
Division of Hospital Facilities
Public Health Service, Federal Security
   Agency

REGISTRANTS

John J. Bourke, M.D.

Executive Director
New York State Joint Hospital Survey and
   Planning Commission

Andrew W. L. Brown

Council of Social Agencies
Detroit, Michigan

L. E. Burney, M.D.

Health Commissioner
State of Indiana

John H. Cauley, M.D.

Health Commissioner
Commonwealth of Massachusetts

Miss Ethel Cohen

Director, Social Service
Beth Israel Hospital
Boston, Massachusetts

Paul B. Cornely, M.D.   Medical Director
                                     Howard University

William A. Coventry, M.D.   Duluth, Minnesota

Paul A. Davis, M.D.   President, American Academy of General
                                         Practice

John A. Ferrell, M.D.   Executive Secretary
                                     North Carolina Medical Care Commission

Warren E. Forsythe, M.D.   Director, Student Health Service
                                     University of Michigan

John J. Griffin   Bureau of Old Age Assistance
                                     Board of Public Welfare
                                     Somerville, Massachusetts

C. L. Guyton, M.D.   Director, Hospital Division
                                     South Carolina State Department of Health

James A. Hamilton   Hospital Consultant
                                     University of Minnesota

Henrietta Herbolsheimer, M.D.   Chief, Division of Hospital Service
                                     Illinois State Health Department

Frank J. Houghton, D.D.S.   Dental Director
                                     Jersey City Medical Center
                                     Jersey City, New Jersey

S. P. Kingston   Executive Engineer
                                     St. Mary's Hospital
                                     Rochester, Minnesota

Robert Kinney   Assistant to Director
                                     Community Services Committee
                                     Congress of Industrial Organizations

M. Ray Kneiff   Executive Secretary
                                     Catholic Hospital Association

William Wallace Lanahan   President, Board of Trustees
                                     Johns Hopkins Hospital
                                     Baltimore, Maryland

Ralph F. Lindberg, D.O.N.   Secretary, Osteopathic Hospital Association

Miss Margaret A. Losty   Consultant Public Health Nurse
                                     New York City Department of Health

Rev. Donald A. McGowan   Director, Health and Hospital Bureau
                                     National Catholic Welfare Conference

Edward P. McNamee, M.D.   American College of Radiology

William S. McNary   Executive Vice-President
                                     Michigan Hospital Service

Miss Julia M. Miller   Dean, School of Nursing
                                     Emory University

H. J. Mohler	President, Missouri Pacific Hospital Association
J. Solon Mordell	Assistant Director, Pharmaceutical Survey American Council on Education
Charles H. Pemberton, M.D.	Senior Physician Lone Star State Hospital Houston, Texas
Oliver G. Pratt	President, Rhode Island Hospital Providence, Rhode Island
W. Arthur Purdum	Chief Pharmacist, Johns Hopkins Hospital Baltimore, Maryland
John E. Ransom	Director, Hospital Division Georgia State Department of Health
Paul Sifton	United Automobile Workers Congress of Industrial Organizations
Miss Junice Dalen Sondergaard	Director of Education Minnesota Farmers Union
Norbert A. Wilhelm, M.D.	Director, Peter Bent Brigham Hospital Boston, Massachusetts
Frank E. Wing	Director, New England Medical Center Boston, Massachusetts
W. Franklin Wood, M.D.	Director, McLean Hospital Waverley, Massachusetts

III

What Is the Nation's
Need for Local Health Units?

LOCAL health units are the cornerstone of the nation's health. The performance of all specialized public health programs depends ultimately on adequately staffed local health units which provide the people with the benefits of modern medical science. Where full-time local health units do not exist, preventive medical services and community sanitation programs are applied only sporadically. People look to the local health officer, the nurse, and the sanitarian for those direct services which, in the mind of the public at least, represent the community's bulwark against epidemics and preventable illness.

The first local county health unit was established in 1907, approximately fifty years after the establishment of the first state board of health in Boston, Massachusetts. From 1907 to 1935 the number of full-time county health units grew from 1 to 561. These 561 local units served 762 counties. The passage of social security legislation in 1935 gave added impetus to the growth of our network of local health services so that by 1947 there were 1,284 local health areas accredited as having full-time units. These 1,284 units served 1,874 of the 3,070 counties in the United States. This picture is modified somewhat by the fact that 309 of the 1,284 full-time county health departments had no health officer, and these 309 local health units served 655, or over one-third, of the 1,874 counties allegedly covered by full-time local health units in 1947.

The quantitative adequacy of local full-time health-unit coverage was further studied in the light of the basic minimum staffing standards set up by the American Public Health Association. This basic minimum coverage required the following personnel:

One physician (health officer) per local health unit

One nurse per 5,000 people

One sanitarian per 25,000 people

One clerk per 15,000 people

The study showed that only forty-seven counties and seventeen cities in the United States were served by full-time local health units which employed the basic minimum number of public health workers recommended by the American Public Health Association. It was further found that only 3.4 per cent of the population of the country lived in areas served by those local health units which met the minimum standards. The reports from which these statistics were derived were received from health departments, both state and local, which served a total area in which only 74 per cent of the population of the United States resided. Several entire states sent in no reports. Since reporting areas are generally better covered with local health units than non-reporting areas, it is evident that something less than 3.4 per cent of the entire population of the country actually is served by acceptable full-time local health departments.

The size of the population in the area served is another factor which affects the efficiency of a local health unit. It has been found that such units function more effectively when they serve a population that exceeds 50,000. Of the 1,284 full-time local health units reported, 521 served populations of less than 35,000. When a small population comprises a local health-unit jurisdiction, it is impractical to maintain a sufficiently large or diversified staff of public health workers to meet the many and varied public health needs of the people. There is duplication of effort, specialization is impeded, and salaries tend to remain at less than competitive levels.

The minimum standards set by the American Public Health Association and widely accepted by public health administrators mention only four categories of public health workers. It was not the intention here to minimize the importance of having on local health-unit staffs other types of public health workers such as health educators, nutritionists, psychologists, medical social workers, sanitary engineers, laboratory workers, and others. The judicious use of such specialists, however, will require a concentration of at least 50,000 people within a local health jurisdiction. In the case of units serving smaller population groups, arrangements may have to be made for utilizing on a co-operative basis the services of specialists employed by a neighboring unit. This has been done successfully in various places throughout the country.

Of all of the essential public health workers, the supply of nurses is most limited. Eleven million people in the United States live in areas served by full-time local health units employing nurses in a ratio of one nurse to every 5,000 persons. This ratio is not ideal. Practical public health administrators even claim that, if the nurses employed by full-time local health units were asked to do bedside nursing as well as administrative and educational public health nursing, the ratio would have to be increased to one nurse for each 3,000 or 2,000 persons depending on local conditions and the density of the population. Reports for the fiscal year 1946 indicate that approximately 11,136 nurses were employed by local health units, whereas the estimated need was approximately 30,000; there was therefore a shortage of some 19,000 nurses.

The shortage of sanitarians, though less acute than the shortage of nurses, is nevertheless a source of anxiety. In 1946 approximately 5,000 were employed, whereas there was a need for 7,000. That need, estimated on the basis of one sanitarian to every 25,000 persons, is undoubtedly overly conservative. It is believed by many public health administrators that with the newer methods of rodent and insect control, malaria control, and restaurant sanitation this ratio should be dropped to one sanitarian to 15,000 persons. If the latter criterion is accepted the estimated need for sanitarians would rise to 9,000.

Established minimum personnel standards for full-time local health units require only one full-time physician acting as health officer for each unit. Local health units serving large population groups have need of additional staff physicians—at least one physician, in addition to the full-time health officer, for each population unit of 50,000 persons. Communities that have progressed to the stage of supporting programs for cancer control, mental health, chronic disease control, and the like have need for additional physicians on the staff of the local health unit. On this basis it is estimated that the basic minimum need for physicians under full-time employment in local health departments is approximately 3,000. This figure is double the number of physicians employed by local health units in 1946.

Since approximately 80 per cent of the funds spent by local health units is for the employment of personnel, additional funds will obviously be needed to finance the expanded staffs that are immediately called for. Prior to the war it was estimated that basic minimum public health services could be provided in a community by the expenditure of $1.00 per capita. Inflation, plus the need to move public health salaries up to a realistic competitive level, has brought about an upward revision of this estimate to $1.50 per capita. Even $1.50 per capita will provide only the basic minimum services. The total cost of the minimum basic local health services proposed for the nation, anticipating the existence of about 1,200 full-time local health units, will be in the neighborhood of $210 million per year, supplemented by the amount spent by most local health units for specialized services. Statutory and economic limitations imposed on the taxing ability of local communities make it impractical to look to the local communities for the entire $210 million. Assistance will have to be obtained from the state and Federal governments, where taxing power is less circumscribed.

During the fiscal year 1946 it was estimated that $67,952,036 was spent for the support of local health services. Of this the Federal government contributed $12,628,001, state governments $5,761,058, and local governments $49,562,977. It is apparent from these figures that the local governments are aware of the need for adequate local public health services and that the future expansion of these services will depend, in some degree at least, upon the willingness of the state and Federal governments to contribute more substantially to their support.

The provision and administration of local public health services is fundamentally the responsibility of the local and state governments. Nevertheless the need for the Federal government to supplement these state and local services has been proved. The principle of such supplementary support has been accepted. Federal grants-in-aid have played an important role in encouraging the development of local health services and in maintaining them once they have been started. The greatest asset of a community, of a state, or of the United States as a whole is the good health of its citizens. Healthy people are productive, require less care from others, are better able to defend their country, and make better and more responsible citizens. It is on this basis that the tripartite union of local, state, and Federal governments was evolved for the development and support of a nation-wide system of local health units designed to afford every citizen, regardless of race, creed, or color, the protection made available by science against the ravages of preventable diseases.

It is difficult to estimate in dollars and cents the value of public health services. Many of the values are intangible or accrue so indirectly that they are not easily discernible by the unskilled eye. What record is there of the increased amount of work done by the farm worker who has long suffered from malaria and then is cured? Are there any statistics which show conclusively the decrease in the admission to mental institutions of patients with paresis or tabes dorsalis following the passage of pre-marital and prenatal laws for the control of syphilis? How many hundreds of thousands of persons, but for the protection rendered by public health departments, would have died in epidemics of smallpox, plague, typhoid fever, and diphtheria? What is the financial value of the thousands of children who have grown to healthy manhood and productive womanhood because of the protection afforded by modern maternal and child-health services?

A very fragmentary evaluation of the need for additional public health services can be developed statistically. It is estimated, for example, that between 1941 and 1946 in the United States 23,379 people died of diphtheria, measles, whooping cough, syphilis, smallpox, salmonellosis, typhoid fever, bacillary dysentery, tetanus, and undulant fever; almost all of these deaths were preventable. During these same years 233,538 Americans died of tuberculosis, pneumonia, premature birth, accidents, meningitis, scarlet fever, puerperal fever, diarrhea, and enteritis. At least half of these deaths could have been prevented. The annual deaths from cancer numbered 168,979, of which approximately one-third could have been prevented. There were annually 23,379 deaths from preventable causes, 116,769 from controllable causes, and 56,326 from cancer—a total of 196,474 deaths which could have been prevented if modern scientific knowledge and skills had been properly applied. The needless loss of almost 200,000 lives a year is a wanton and preventable waste of our greatest national resource—healthy human beings.

Each year research workers, clinicians, laboratory workers, and other men and women of science are discovering or perfecting new techniques and methods of preventing or controlling disease and ameliorating its crippling effects. These new discoveries are only partially utilized because the development of our local public health services has lagged behind technological progress. This gap can be filled only by the combined and concentrated efforts of all public health workers and agencies, whether local, state, or Federal—either voluntary or official. The most serious needs at the moment are additional financial support for local health units and trained personnel in adequate numbers.

WHAT LOCAL HEALTH SERVICES HAS THE PUBLIC A RIGHT TO EXPECT?

There has been a substantial failure on the part of public health administrators to inform the public of the public health services which they, as citizens, have a right to expect. This is probably the most important factor responsible for the relative slowness with which full-time local health units have been and are being developed throughout the country. Coincidental with this is the failure to acquaint the public with the cost of not having adequate local health services. The average citizen has not been told forcibly enough that he cannot afford *not to have* a good local health department.

Few realize the extent of the public health program, the fields in which public health services are effective, or the many new avenues of activity that are rapidly being opened to health departments. In the 1946 budgets submitted to the Public Health Service by the state health departments, funds were allocated for twenty-six separate and distinct public health programs. These services include vital statistics, health education, preventable disease control, tuberculosis control, venereal disease control, local health administration, laboratory services, environmental sanitation, public health nursing, industrial hygiene, dental hygiene, cancer control, mental hygiene, maternal and child health, service to crippled children, school medical service, nutrition, food and drugs, hospital surveys, surveys and studies, hospital inspection, licensure, medical care, training, general administration, and personnel administration.

Even this rather long list does not fully delineate the many areas of public health endeavor. Preventable disease control, for example, depending upon local circumstances, may require a further breakdown of activities into sections concerned with malaria control, hookworm control, dysentery control, and the like. Environmental sanitation may include fairly large and discrete programs dealing with stream pollution, housing sanitation, smoke abatement, rodent and air-pollution control, in addition to the more traditional activities such as milk, water, and food sanitation.

Not every state health department, and surely none but the larger municipal health departments, will be found to have well-developed public health programs in every field of public health. The basic activities that should be incorporated into every local health department have been defined, however. These are: vital statistics, the control of communicable diseases, environmental sanitation, laboratory services, maternal and child health services, chronic disease control, and health education. In addition to such basic services, it is the responsibility of communities themselves to determine what additional public health programs should be added in the light of local needs and local resources.

There are certain essentials which are basic to the establishment of efficient and economically operated local health units. These are:

(1) A health education program that will keep the people informed of public health needs, potential resources, and what other communities are doing to solve their public health problems.

(2) A capably administered state department of health to provide the leadership necessary for the establishment of a state-wide network of good local health units.

(3) Legislation that will permit and encourage the establishment of local health units of efficient size, with acceptable personnel standards, and with sufficient financial resources.

(4) A state subsidy for local health units that will permit the development of local health units of sufficient size and quality to meet adequately the needs of the people. This subsidy should be distributed on a formula basis designed to give to each community its equitable share of the total sum available and to give most assistance to those communities having the greatest financial need.

(5) Federal financial assistance in an amount sufficient to permit the development of local health units to serve every community in the country.

(6) An adequate staff of public health workers qualified by training and experience to do the work for which they are employed.

(7) A salary scale sufficiently high to attract qualified public health workers to fill existing positions and positions likely to become available in the future.

(8) An opportunity for advancement. The morale of the worker depends as much on the knowledge that his efficiency will be rewarded by promotion as on the actual salary he is receiving.

(9) A recruitment program designed to provide at all times a full complement of workers. This program must begin early in the professional life of the potential recruit—in his pre-medical, pre-nursing, and pre-engineering days.

(10) As much local autonomy as is consistent with the efficient administration of a state-wide program.

(11) Field training centers for the in-service training of employed personnel.

(12) A method of continuous evaluation of local health services by means of which the shortcomings of the local departments may be

corrected and the strong points brought to the attention of other local departments. One method of evaluating the work of local health departments is by the use of the evaluation schedule designed by the American Public Health Association.

From the viewpoint of the public health administrator, diseases are more costly to find and to control in rural areas than in urban areas. Where the density of population per square mile is low, public health nurses may make only three visits a day instead of the ten or more visits commonly made in metropolitan areas. Here the water supply for each family is a separate problem, whereas in a large city the purification of one source of water, large though it may be, results in the provision of safe water to hundreds of thousands of consumers. In rural areas it is extremely difficult for people to attend clinics, to travel to urban areas for meetings, and to accept responsible positions in organized community health groups. In sparsely settled areas, local health units of necessity serve smaller population groups and as a result have on their staffs fewer specialists than are found in urban areas. This makes for a more generalized approach to public health problems in rural areas; nurses must be acquainted with the rudiments of sanitation, and sanitarians must know enough to recognize the need for the services of a public health nurse. More public health workers are needed per person in rural areas than in urban areas, and the cost of rural public health services will be proportionately higher.

The role of the private practitioner of medicine in protecting the health of the community cannot be overestimated. Many local health units have been formed as a direct result of the guidance and leadership of local physicians. By training, physicians are the persons who should best recognize the need for protective public health services and be able to give guidance and assistance to the local health officer and his staff in building a sound local health program. The health officer depends on local physicians to report communicable diseases to the health department. The nurse can be much more valuable to the community if her services are utilized by the local physicians. Physicians are also needed to act as clinicians in the local health departments. In their own offices they can perform a valuable service in educating patients to guard their health. The health officer in providing health services to any community must work hand in hand with the local medical practitioners.

When a community lacks a full-time local health unit there is a fairly

definite course of action that may be taken to lead to its development. The first step, as a rule, is taken by an individual who for personal reasons has had his attention called to the need for community action. The second step is the calling together of other people within the community who are or might be interested in community betterment. The third step is the establishment of a formal committee whose goal will be to see that the community is provided with the type of local health service that will protect it from preventable diseases. The fourth step is to obtain outside professional assistance from the state health department or elsewhere in order to survey the need for health services and to delineate the extent of the problem. The fifth step is to make a survey of community resources in terms of personnel, equipment, and finances. The sixth step is to seek from the state health department or elsewhere those resources which are needed to establish an adequate local health unit but are not available in the community. The seventh step is to formulate a concrete plan of action, enlist the aid of all civic-minded individuals, and inaugurate a health education program designed to secure public support. The eighth step is to set up criteria by which the local health program may be evaluated from time to time to determine whether or not it is efficiently and economically meeting the health needs of the community.

Once a community has provided itself with a good local health unit it may expect fairly specific types of service from the several members of the health department staff. The public health nurse centers her service around the family as the basic, economic, social, and health unit of the community. In her family work the nurse teaches as she nurses. She helps find early cases of disease and reports them to the proper source. Although she is never officially a diagnostician, she is always a "suspectician." It is her duty to ferret out untreated cases of disease and see to it that community resources for caring for disease are fully utilized. Her role in helping mothers and children is important. She interprets to them the diagnostic tests they have undergone, provides nursing care for the sick and the convalescent, and often acts as the confidante of people who would take their personal problems to no one else. To maintain her scientific skill she must attend training courses at regular intervals, seeking ever to increase the breadth of her public health knowledge. She must establish harmonious public relations, keep accurate and complete records, and work co-operatively with private physicians and the staffs of public agencies with whom she deals. There is no other member of the staff of the local health unit who can challenge her importance in community life.

As it is with the public health nurse, so it is with the sanitarian and the sanitary engineer. Each has his own particular duties and responsibilities. Few people realize the importance of the fact that during the past fifty years sanitarians and engineers have made our water fit to drink, have succeeded in obtaining the pasteurization of approximately 80 per cent of our milk supply, and have introduced good restaurant sanitation. Since they seldom deal directly with the consumer of public health services, they are the forgotten group in public health work.

Where good local health services exist, the public may reasonably expect that its environment will not be detrimental to health. Local environments differ widely. In rural areas smoke abatement is no problem. In city areas wells are of little concern. Most cities have pasteurized milk ordinances, so that undulant fever is now non-existent in these places. The public does have a right, however, to expect that whatever types of environmental sanitation are needed will be provided. Among the sanitation services which the public has a right to expect through a good local health department are:

(1) Close supervision over all water supplies
(2) Sanitary disposal of human and other wastes
(3) An adequate garbage disposal system
(4) An insect and rodent control program that will keep the community free from flies, mosquitoes, and rats
(5) Supervision of the sanitary cleanliness of swimming pools and beaches
(6) Protection of the milk supply
(7) Sanitation of restaurants and sources of food and ice
(8) Provision of laboratory services for the analysis of water, milk, and food
(9) School programs designed to make schools healthful places for children
(10) Control of tourist and trailer camps and of picnic areas
(11) Investigation and amelioration of nuisances
(12) Home-accident prevention program
(13) Health education program
(14) Control of environmental conditions that cause allergic disorders such as asthma and hay fever
(15) Control of air pollution

(16) A local housing program

(17) Protection of industrial workers from occupational and other diseases

(18) An emergency sanitation program designed to become immediately effective in times of disaster

From the health officer the community must expect, first of all, enlightened leadership in all health matters. A health officer, properly trained and sufficiently experienced, should assume leadership within the community in all matters and activities pertaining to its health. He should be wise enough to utilize fully the many services available from private physicians, voluntary health agencies, and other public agencies. He should obtain as much support as he can generate from the people themselves. The health officer must take the lead in determining what the health problems are within the community, what resources are available to meet those problems, and what needs to be done to obtain additional resources.

Today there are two shortages that continually face almost every local health officer in the country. One is the shortage of money. The other is the shortage of trained personnel. Once a community has been made aware of its public health needs it can, in part at least, be depended upon to increase its health appropriations. The shortage of trained personnel is more serious. Many things have to be done to overcome this impediment to the advancement of public health in our country.

In the first place, more physicians will have to be trained in public health work. The total number trained in our schools of public health during 1947 was only 290. With a present-day deficit of at least 1,400 physicians trained for public health services, it is apparent that facilities are inadequate for the education of health officers. The same situation exists for public health nurses. Present facilities could not begin to provide the opportunities necessary for the training of the additional 16,000 public health nurses needed at the present time.

Local health units have more or less depended on the state and Federal governments to supply them with trained personnel, since the training process is costly and the local health departments do not have adequate training facilities. If there is to be a rapid expansion of local health-unit staffs within the next ten years, the Federal government may have to provide field-training funds as well as grants-in-aid to meet part of the cost of developing and operating local health units, so that present field-training facilities may be expanded and new facilities established.

Unless available field-training facilities are expanded to meet the demand for additional personnel, any attempt to expand our system of local health units may be thwarted at the very outset.

In addition to the need for more academic or professional training opportunities, there is a need for additional field-training centers, for the expansion of which funds are required. The considered opinion of experts in the training field is that Federal as well as other funds will be needed in substantial amounts before sufficient field-training areas are developed to insure that all public health workers can meet minimum standards of performance.

The recruitment of personnel is an even more fundamental need. Admittedly few people know enough of the activities of local health units to desire to become members of a health department staff. Disregarding this apathy on the part of young people toward public health as a career, because of their lack of understanding of what health departments do, there are more serious obstacles to be overcome before recruitment programs can be successful. Public health positions must be made more attractive. Today many areas of the country are unable to offer attractions equal to those offered by employment in private industry. To make public health positions competitive with positions in other walks of life the following changes must be made:

1. Salaries must be increased so that public health workers receive remuneration equivalent to that received by workers doing similar work in private employment.

2. Professional standards must be raised to the point where competency can be assured.

3. To insure the professional growth of public health workers, training opportunities must be made available.

4. Opportunities for advancement must also be available.

5. A retirement system must exist so that employment in health departments becomes a career.

6. Arbitrary dismissal must be precluded by suitable personnel practices.

7. There must be no partisan political interference with the reasonable activities of the health department staff.

Another incentive to local recruitment is the existence of a modern health center. Except in small areas of the country, health departments are poorly housed. A modern health center not only provides a respectable office place for professional people, it also offers a convenient place for the citizens to assemble for public meetings and provides clean, sanitary, and comfortable quarters for health department clinics. As the home of the health department staff, it should be attractive, sufficiently commodious, and efficiently designed. A shabbily dressed physician would command the respect of few of his patients. A shabbily attired local health department has great difficulty in commanding the respect of the people it is intended to serve.

THE PEOPLE'S PLACE IN
LOCAL HEALTH WORK

The success or failure of a local health department depends primarily on the interest of the people in their own health and on the understanding they have of their own health problems. Professional leadership can create a continuing demand for good health services in a community by raising the level of the public's understanding of its health problems and how best to meet them. This leadership must be exercised in such a way that the individual accepts responsibility for his own, his family's, and his community's health. If the people of a community feel that garbage removal is the most important health activity in that community, then the health program should stress garbage removal until such a time as the people have been educated to emphasize some other and much more productive phase of community health activity. The important thing is that the people themselves, and not solely the professionals, should be involved in determining where their interests lie.

Unfortunately in many communities there are large groups of professional people who do not sufficiently believe in the need for local health units to assume an aggressive role in encouraging their development. Some are afraid that the health department will encroach on private enterprise; others fear that health-department activities will make unnecessary the work of the community's voluntary agencies; some have less respect for public health workers than for other professional people because of their lower salary scale and their shabby quarters; still others are just selfishly indifferent.

There are several ways of overcoming this indifference. Improvement of courses in preventive medicine in our professional schools can give students a better understanding of the value of health departments. Better publicity can be obtained by the use of skilled educators and information specialists. Good health departments can overcome much of the current professional indifference by maintaining an "open door" policy under which local professional groups are encouraged to visit the local health department. Health councils may be established with broad professional as well as lay representation. Finally, improved personnel practices will result in a satisfied staff and a more congenial relationship between the health department and the community.

More important even than professional leadership is the existence or non-existence of lay leadership for health in a community. Unless and until people are vitally concerned with their own health problems, little can be done to obtain or maintain a good local health department. To secure solid and substantial lay support, the local health department must be successful in developing interest and leadership of inspired, qualified lay leaders. There are leaders in thought and there are leaders in action. The leaders in thought have vision a little beyond that of the masses; such leaders, through their personal, family, and business lives, through their organization affiliations, and through regular channels of publicity, will point out to the community its deficiencies in health and the means by which these deficiencies may be corrected. The leaders in action are of a different type; they are the men and women who will organize a campaign for a local health unit or do what has to be done to obtain larger local appropriations, adequate local health ordinances, or a bond issue for a health center. Neither of these two types of leaders alone is sufficient; the one must supplement the other. It is the wise health officer who is discriminating enough to recognize the difference between the two and has both types working on his team.

Just as there are individuals who are leaders in thought and others who are leaders in action, in every community there are organizations that lead in thought and those that lead in action. The health officer must know the personality of all the organizations in the community and must use their several talents wisely if he is to conduct a long-range health program successfully.

Lay leadership, upon which the permanent success of a local health unit depends for much of its productiveness, is difficult to secure. Successful leaders have many demands for their services. When such leadership has been secured it must be husbanded as carefully as possible by supplementing it with the services of less dynamic leaders who can do much of the prosaic work connected with community organization. Lay leadership can be encouraged and at the same time conserved by the development of a representative local health council of civic-minded individuals and representatives of community organizations—essentially a council of public health consumers.

There are two basic concepts of the way in which a local health council should operate. One is that the council should organize first and then discover and meet the public health needs of the community. The second is that the public health needs of the community should be fairly well determined first and the council then formed to meet these needs. Each of these methods has its merit, depending on local conditions and the type of public health program most urgently needed.

Since lay health councils are composed of people, the value of a council to an individual health officer will depend to a large extent on the personal relationships which are developed between the health officer and the council members. If these relationships are unpleasant much of the value of the council will be dissipated, but if they are pleasant the council can be of great assistance to the health officer.

The lay health council serves many functions in a community. It provides opportunities for free discussion and the interchange of ideas. The executive and lay members serve as co-ordinating links between their special interests and the health program of the entire community. The inclusion of representatives of professional organizations and interested lay persons adds much to the value of the council. Health councils are essentially co-ordinating bodies. They promote the efficient operation of public health work through the co-ordination of health activities within the area served—whether they are local, community, state, or national—by eliminating duplication of effort and by stimulating new and needed services. The health council is the best device yet found for developing public opinion with respect to public health needs, programs, and legislation.

In order to be effective a health council should be autonomous. To take action it should not have to obtain the consent of any other group. It should employ its own executive secretary even though the secretary may serve other community organizations on a part-time basis. By studying the vital statistics of a community continuously, the members of a health council can emphasize from time to time those parts of the health program which need strengthening. They can be used by the local health officer to spearhead a drive for greater participation in special programs (such as a diphtheria immunization program or the prevention of infant mortality by the provision of better prenatal care). The decision of the council to promote a particular health program should be unbiased, since the council has no special program which it feels impelled to promote. By a discreet use of praise and criticism it tends to maintain the community's interest in and support of a balanced, efficient, and economic public health program.

One of the foremost weapons of the health council is health education. When properly used, health educational devices and techniques play a leading role in molding community interest into a pattern that permits co-ordinated action to achieve health goals. To obtain community support, people have to know from the very beginning what the local health department is doing or proposes to do, how much it will cost, and how soon the desired results can be shown. Even before the public is approached, the staffs of the health department, of voluntary health agencies, and of other public agencies must be reasonably well oriented in the functions of the local health department. The difficulty of awakening public interest should not be underestimated. The constant barrage of propaganda and sales talk via radio, motion pictures, the press, and the magazines has made people indifferent to the usual educational approaches. The health officer and the health council must consider seriously the need to use all of the available media for health educational purposes. Many health departments and organizations are producing modern motion pictures dealing with various aspects of public health. The state health departments often have on their staffs experts in health education whose advice will save community public health workers a great deal of time and labor. Executives of local radio chains and editors of newspapers should be represented on the council, so that these modern methods of audience appeal may be used to carry the public health message. Finally, public school teachers should receive sufficient training during their normal-school days to interest them in incorporating public health into every course they teach in school.

The most convincing proof of a good health department, however, is a health job well done. Many health departments have expanded and survived through many years merely because they did a good job year after year. No matter how good their publicity, no health department can command public support for long if its programs are ineffective, if its staff is indolent or poorly trained, or if its attitude is defeatist.

CONCLUSIONS AND RECOMMENDATIONS

The need for local health units is growing apace with the rapid advances made by scientists in the prevention, diagnosis, and treatment of preventable diseases. Having passed through the era of environmental sanitation and then through one of immunization against some major communicable diseases, public health is now entering its third era, which will be more and more concerned with the management of the chronic diseases. Heretofore little has been known about the early diagnosis of these diseases, even less about their treatment, and little if anything about their prevention. With substantial sums being appropriated for research into the origins of some of the long-term or chronic diseases, there is some reason to believe that within the next decade a new and bigger job will be handed down to our local health departments. They will have to undertake control programs against chronic diseases.

Today local health departments are too often either non-existent or skeletonized. This condition must be remedied before local health departments can do the work at present assigned to them and certainly before they can begin the costly and time-consuming task of preventing and controlling all the preventable diseases of infancy, youth, maturity, and old age.

The most valuable resource any country can possess is healthy citizens. Public health administered through a nation-wide system of adequately staffed and adequately financed local health departments could salvage many of our people rendered non-productive because of chronic disease and could do much more than has been done to prevent crippling by other diseases.

No community can afford *not to have* a good local health department.

The recommendations of the Local Health Units Section of the National Health Assembly, as embodied in the report submitted by its Resolutions Committee, are as follows:

1. It is the firm conviction of the Section on Local Health Units that the *complete coverage of the nation with full-time local health units*, capable of applying the science of preventive medicine directly to individuals and families, is fundamental to the effective functioning of all health programs. We therefore recommend that the attainment of this goal be given first consideration in any popularly desired and federally assisted nation-wide program for national health.

2. The attainment of complete coverage of the nation with full-time local health units is a *joint responsibility of the local, state, and Federal governments*. We recommend that every effort be made to obtain *adequate local, state, and Federal appropriations* for the establishment, operation, and maintenance of full-time, adequately staffed local health units throughout the nation.

3. Recognizing the fact that, even if the preceding recommendations are put into effect, complete coverage with full-time, adequately staffed local health departments will not result unless there are effective *continuous recruitment and training programs,* it is recommended that facilities and personnel for training be *at least doubled immediately* for each of the professional public health categories, and that thereafter the program be developed in accordance with a continuous evaluation of basic needs. The Local Health Units Section is convinced that a recruitment program to be successful must include five basic factors:

(a) Salaries commensurate with the remuneration received by the same basic professional groups in private practice or other fields;
(b) Professional recognition and standing;
(c) Security and tenure of office;
(d) The supplying of information to high-school students on the opportunities in public health; and
(e) Adequate fellowships providing basic professional training for persons agreeing to enter and serve in the field of public health.

4. This Section of the National Health Assembly endorses the present efforts of the State and Territorial Health Officers, the National Congress of Parents and Teachers, and many other national organizations in *supporting legislation* that is designed to achieve the objectives set forth in the foregoing recommendations.

5. The Section on Local Health Units recommends that every local area endeavor to establish some voluntary, over-all, co-ordinating health agency, such as a health council or health committee. Such an organization should, as a minimum, provide for:

(a) Membership from all official and voluntary health agencies, from the professional groups, and from among civic-minded individuals as members at large;
(b) The gathering of factual material as a basis for defining local public health problems and unmet needs;
(c) Professional interpretation of the material gathered in these studies of local facilities and services;
(d) Participation in planning to meet such needs as are found to exist;
(e) Participation in initiating programs designed to meet these needs;
(f) Opportunities for mutual understanding; and
(g) The focusing of attention in such a manner as to bring about a widespread understanding of the full-time local health department as the basic essential for any community health program.

Further, this Section is convinced that professional and technical training must include not only academic training but also field training for all the professional public health categories and in each of the generally accepted types of field training, including orientation, field experience, observation, apprenticeship, internship, and in-service training.

6. It is further recommended that new Federal funds be made available immediately, designated specifically for the development of these recruitment and training programs.

The Local Health Units Section believes that the responsibility for developing recruitment and training programs is shared by the local, state, and Federal health agencies, the professional organizations involved, and the accredited schools for public health training. We recommend that funds be administered through state health departments and schools of public health. The administration of the field-training center should be a responsibility of the local health officer.

As an answer to the question "What local health services has the public a right to expect?" the Local Health Units Section, in accordance with the report of its Resolutions Committee, recommends that the local health unit be responsible for providing or seeking the adequate provision of the following services for all the people within the area of its jurisdiction:

1. *Vital statistics.* People need and should be able to obtain certified copies of birth and death certificates. (These are frequently necessary for entrance to school, for obtaining work, for entering the armed forces, for collecting insurance, for settling estates, and so on.)

2. *Control and prevention of the communicable diseases.* These include both diseases of the acute and epidemic type and diseases of long duration and recurrence such as tuberculosis and malaria.

3. *Environmental sanitation.* The people have a right to expect an adequate, safe, potable water supply; an adequate, clean, safely pasteurized milk supply; the supervision of foods and food handling, including instruction in personal hygiene and the hygiene of food handling; a safe method of excreta disposal; control and supervision of swimming pools and bathing areas and of the health aspects of housing; insect and rodent control; proper sanitation of schools; a program of accident prevention; and a co-operative effort with industry to assure the health protection of workers.

4. *Laboratory services* providing aids to the diagnosis of disease and the examination of water, milk, and other foods.

5. *Protection of maternal and child health.* This should extend through the pre-natal, parturient, and post-natal periods and through the infant, pre-school, and school ages. Adequate hospital, medical, and nursing services should be locally available. If not available, they should be actively sought by the local health officer.

6. Development of an educational and diagnostic program for the prevention, arrest, amelioration, and cure of *chronic diseases and their complications.*

7. *Health education.* The people have a right to expect their health department to be a source of authentic information on generally accepted procedures for health protection and the maintenance of optimal health.

The people of the area under the jurisdiction of a local health unit have a right to expect their health department to employ a well-qualified health officer, an adequate staff of qualified nurses and sanitary personnel, and a sufficient number of clerical personnel.

The public should expect that its health department be conveniently located and adequately and decently housed, as essential to rendering efficient services.

All full-time local health departments should have available consultant services from the state health department, in all the basic fields as well as in such special fields as nutrition, public health, dentistry, health education, mental health, and industrial hygiene. Local health departments should also be able to rely upon the state department of health for such direct services as are unfeasible or uneconomic of local procurement.

It should be emphasized that these are minimum services and that many health areas will want to be able to increase the scope of their interest and activity.

APPENDIX

PLANNING COMMITTEE

Haven Emerson, M.D.,
   Chairman

Committee on Local Health Units
American Public Health Association

Reginald Atwater, M.D.

Executive Secretary
American Public Health Association

Carl Buck, M.D.	School of Public Health University of Michigan
John W. Ferree, M.D.	Associate Director National Health Council
Robert H. Riley, M.D.	Director of Public Health Maryland State Health Department

STAFF ASSISTANT

| A. L. Chapman, M.D. | Assistant Chief, States Relations Division
Public Health Service, Federal Security Agency |

REGISTRANTS

J. K. Altland, M.D.	Director of Local Health Service Michigan Department of Health
Miss Lillian Anderson	Nutrition Director Community Service Society New York, New York
Albert N. Baggs	American Legion Indianapolis, Indiana
L. Banov, M.D.	Health Officer Charleston City-County Charleston, South Carolina
William W. Bolton, M.D.	Associate Director Bureau of Education American Medical Association
Mrs. Stanley G. Cook	Chairman, Committee on Legislation National Congress of Parents and Teachers
Paul Cornely, M.D.	Professor of Public Health Howard University
Mrs. Margaret Cowdin	Executive Secretary Illinois State-wide Health Committee
Miss Vivian Drenckhahn	Health Educator National Tuberculosis Association
L. L. Duncan	Community Services Committee Congress of Industrial Organizations Kansas City, Missouri
Willard E. Goslin	Superintendent of Schools Minneapolis, Minnesota
Howard Green	Secretary, Health Council Cleveland, Ohio
Miss Alma C. Haupt	Director, Nursing Bureau Metropolitan Life Insurance Company

Frank J. Hill, M.D.	Health Officer Minneapolis, Minnesota
Clarence W. Klassen	Director, Sanitary Engineering Illinois State Department of Public Health
David B. Lee	Director, Bureau of Sanitary Engineering Florida State Board of Health
George F. Moench, M.D.	Health Officer Oak Ridge, Tennessee
John D. Porterfield, M.D.	Director of Health Ohio State Health Department
Lee A. Rademaker, M.D.	President, Lions International Salisbury, Maryland
Baxter K. Richardson	Senior Administrative Officer Illinois Department of Health
Thomas De C. Ruth	Assistant to Vice-President for Health Services American National Red Cross
Clarence S. Scammon, M.D.	Director of Health Division Commonwealth Fund
T. F. Sellers, M.D.	State Health Officer Georgia State Health Department
Cecil A. Z. Sharp, M.D.	Commissioner of Health St. Louis County Health Department Clayton, Missouri
Ernest Stebbins, M.D.	Dean, School of Public Health Johns Hopkins University
George M. Uhl, M.D.	Health Officer Los Angeles, California
Carl A. Wilzbach, M.D.	Commissioner of Health City of Cincinnati, Ohio

《 IV 》

Chronic Disease
and the Aging Process

A BASIC change is required in society's traditional attitude toward chronic illness and its victims. The realization that much illness of this type can be prevented and that many persons heretofore regarded as inevitably disabled can be rehabilitated to lead useful, happy lives must become the starting point for any genuine program of chronic-disease control. If society is to ameliorate the vast burden of sickness and disability caused by chronic diseases, the known facts concerning them must be widely publicized and thoroughly understood by both professional health personnel and the general public.

The Nature and Extent of the Chronic-Disease Problem

Differentiation between acute and chronic diseases is not difficult. The former are largely short-term illnesses—such as lobar pneumonia and measles and the other familiar communicable diseases of childhood—which recede within a period of a few days or, at most, two or three weeks. The latter are characterized essentially by their long-term nature. Symptoms may be undetected, intermittent, or continuous. Furthermore, chronic diseases tend to result in periods of disability of varying length and severity. They require medical supervision or care for months, years, or even an entire lifetime.

In the National Health Survey of 1936[1] it was estimated that some 25 million persons in the United States are suffering from a chronic illness; more recent research has demonstrated that this figure is probably grossly underestimated. It was also estimated, on the basis of the 1936 Survey, that 7 million persons—or more than one-quarter of the total number afflicted with a chronic disease—are disabled by their ailment

---

[1] National Health Survey, 1935-1936, *The Magnitude of the Chronic Disease Problem in the United States*, Bulletin 6, Preliminary Reports, Sickness and Medical Care Series (Washington: U.S. Public Health Service, 1938).

for at least seven consecutive days in every twelve-month period and that, among these persons, at least 1½ million are chronic invalids.

Although chronic disease was defined, in the National Health Survey, in part on the basis of an informant's awareness of the symptoms of his chronic ailment, it is now known—as a result of mass chest surveys, recent diabetes investigations, and the work of cancer-detection clinics— that there exists in the nation a tremendous amount of chronic illness the victims of which are unaware of their condition during the period when preventive measures could be most effective.

What are the most important diseases which can properly be described as having a chronic nature? Ranked in order—in terms of combined indices of prevalence, resulting disability and invalidism, and mortality— they are: heart disease, arteriosclerosis and hypertension, nervous and mental diseases, the rheumatic ailments—including arthritis, neuritis, and similar conditions—kidney diseases, tuberculosis, cancer and other tumors, diabetes, asthma and hay fever, and hernia.

Active efforts to combat chronic disease in the United States probably date from the 1920's, when the New Jersey Department of Institutions and Agencies first undertook organized steps to improve care of that state's chronically ill. Subsequently, in the early 1930's, a chronic-disease control program was inaugurated in Massachusetts, following a state-wide survey which revealed that one person in eight was afflicted with some form of chronic disease. It is only in the last five years, however, that there has been a widespread development of such efforts, paralleling a marked increase in public and professional interest in the chronic-disease problem. As a consequence of this newly awakened interest, control programs were initiated in Connecticut,[2] Illinois,[3] and Maryland,[4] in 1943; in New York State,[5] in 1944; in Indiana,[6] in 1945, when a division of adult hygiene and geriatrics was established in the State Health Department; and in California, in 1947. During the same period, a Central Service for the Chronically Ill was organized in three of our great metropolitan centers—in Chicago, in 1944, and in Philadelphia and Mil-

[2] *Planning for the Care of the Chronically Ill in New York State—Some Medical-Social and Institutional Aspects*, Legislative Document (1946) No. 66A (Albany: New York State Health Preparedness Commission, 1947), pp. 75-78.

[3] *Ibid.*, pp. 78-81.

[4] *Ibid.*, pp. 82-83.

[5] *A Program for the Care of the Chronically Ill in New York State*, Legislative Document (1947) No. 69 (Albany: New York State Health Preparedness Commission, 1947).

[6] *Planning for the Care of the Chronically Ill in New York State—Some Medical-Social and Institutional Aspects*, pp. 81-82.

waukee, in 1947. Community studies of chronic disease have also been made recently in a number of cities, including Cleveland,[7] Pittsburgh,[8] St. Louis,[9] New Haven,[10] and Chicago.[11]

Of primary importance in stimulating this recent upsurge of interest in the chronic-disease problem was the lamentable lack of adequate hospital and nursing-home facilities for care of chronic patients. This phenomenon was only a surface indication of a fundamental long-term factor characterizing our society—the progressive aging of the population in the United States.[12] It is this factor which is largely responsible for the increasing prevalence of chronic illness and, therefore, for the growing hiatus between the number of chronic patients and the facilities available for caring for them. The changing age composition of the American population can be attributed to several causes: a decreasing national birth rate;[13] curtailment of immigration; and, particularly, the success of modern science in preventing maternal and infant mortality and deaths from communicable and other infectious diseases.

Public health agencies are beginning seriously to recognize the fact that chronic disease is becoming a major public health problem, now that many acute communicable diseases have been conquered and a greater proportion of the total population is surviving into middle and later life. It would be a grave mistake, however, if they were to attack this problem largely in terms of the need for more institutional facilities for the care of patients in advanced stages of long-term illness; over-concentration on the provision of institutional facilities for the chronically ill might well mean the postponement for many years of real efforts to grapple with the chronic-disease problem. For the progressive

[7] Mary C. Jarrett, *Care of the Chronically Ill of Cleveland and Cuyahoga County* (Cleveland: Benjamin Rose Institute, 1944).

[8] Mary C. Jarrett, and Claude W. Munger, *The Care of Chronic Disease in Pittsburgh and Allegheny County* (Pittsburgh: Health Division, Federation of Social Agencies of Pittsburgh and Allegheny County, 1947).

[9] *Control and Treatment of Chronic Disease in St. Louis and St. Louis County, Missouri: A Study of Existing Resources and Unmet Needs* (St. Louis: Health and Hospital Division, Social Planning Council, 1946).

[10] Preliminary report in process of publication. Survey begun in 1947.

[11] *Chronic Illness in Metropolitan Chicago* (Chicago: Central Service for the Chronically Ill, Institute of Medicine, 1947).

[12] P. K. Whelpton, *Forecasts of the Population of the United States, 1945-1975* (Washington: Bureau of the Census, U. S. Department of Commerce, 1947).

[13] Although from 1936 to 1943 "the [gross reproduction] rate rose 25 per cent and the 1943 rate . . . was the highest since 1927," and although there was a "record-breaking rise in the number of births during the last half of 1946," census data recorded for the years from 1800 to 1947 "show clearly that the long-time trend of fertility in the United States has been downward and that a great decrease has occurred." (*Ibid.*, pp. 17-18.)

aging of the population means that this country will be faced in the coming years with a constantly increasing need for institutional facilities for the chronically ill—no matter how many new facilities are provided—unless steps are undertaken to decrease the incidence of disability resulting from chronic illness, to develop adequate non-institutional facilities, and to enhance the effectiveness of institutional programs.

Adoption of a new approach to chronic illness is essential. Such an approach should include appropriate emphasis on prevention of chronic illness; on continued study of its causation; on early detection, diagnosis, and treatment; and on planned convalescence and rehabilitation.

Furthermore, despite the importance of the progressive change in the age composition of the population as an underlying factor in the increasing incidence of chronic illness, it should be stressed that chronic disease is not merely a problem of old age. Careful study should be devoted to the question of whether, necessarily, chronic disease is closely related to the aging process. It is true that the highest rate of prevalence of chronic disease and disability occurs among the older persons in the population; but, as the National Health Survey discovered, more than three-quarters of those with a chronic illness and two-thirds of the invalids are between the ages of fifteen and sixty-four and more than half the chronic-disease victims and one-third of the chronic invalids are under the age of forty-five.

It is probably among chronically ill persons sixty-five years of age and older that the greatest need exists for institutional care. If the problem of chronic disease is to be tackled intelligently, provision of more institutional facilities for persons afflicted with chronic illnesses in advanced stages will not be sufficient. In the long run, greater attention to prevention of chronic disease holds far more promise as a means of eventually solving the problem than mere construction of new institutional facilities, and in cases where prevention cannot be accomplished successfully it will be found profitable so to organize medical and social services and facilities as at least to delay the progress of chronic ailments toward permanent or prolonged disability.

A Democratic Solution to the Problem

Any attempt to solve the problem of chronic illness must be made in terms of the individual, for in a democracy the solution of the individual's problem becomes the solution of the problem as a whole.

Although in an over-all program of chronic-disease control the primary emphasis must be placed on prevention, it is obvious that, with the limited medical knowledge at our command at present, the years to come will bring millions of new victims of chronic illness. Arresting the progress of a chronic ailment, once it is incurred, and enabling the victim of such an ailment to become again a useful and productive member of society as rapidly as possible are equally important objectives of a chronic-disease control program. In other words, if we are not wholly successful in attacking the problem of chronic disease at one end of the scale by preventing its occurrence, we must redouble our efforts to lessen its devastation at the other end by concentrating on the use of dynamic techniques for rehabilitating as many chronically ill persons as possible. With a correct understanding of the medical, social, and economic implications of chronic disease, virtual miracles can be accomplished in rehabilitating its victims.

A good example of how such understanding can be geared to an organized program of convalescence and rehabilitation for the chronically ill is furnished by the activities of the department of medical rehabilitation of Bellevue Hospital in New York City—a department which has been in operation for only a little longer than a year. The department conceives its function as that of training permanently diseased or disabled persons to live and work to the best of their ability and, with whatever faculties remain to them, to make themselves as independent as possible in order to regain self-respect and personal dignity. The physicians who work in Bellevue's rehabilitation department like to call their work "dynamic therapeutics in chronic disease" or "the third phase of medical care"; they concentrate, in other words, on what happens to a chronic patient between the bed and the job.

The rehabilitation department at Bellevue is regarded as a service unit for all the other divisions of the hospital. Only 80 of Bellevue's 3,000 beds are allotted to it, and it admits no patients directly. Patients are admitted to the department only after they have been examined by the department's staff, so that the feasibility of training them can be determined. Training, in this connection, does not necessarily mean vocational training; vocational instruction is given only after the patient is taught how to take care of his daily needs and how to become ambulatory to the best of his ability. In the physical-medicine section of the department, occupational therapy, physical therapy, corrective physical education, and instruction in speech are offered; in the rehabilitation section proper, emphasis is placed on the patient's socio-economic problems, vocational future, and personality difficulties and on giving him an opportunity to engage in voluntary activity around the hospital.

The relationship of such a rehabilitation program to the total program of a general hospital is clearly indicated by the fact that the department requires for its work the assistance of consulting specialists in psychiatry, neurology, urology, plastic surgery, orthopedic surgery, and cardiovascular diseases. When a patient is admitted to the department, he gets a routine physical and medical examination; in addition, he is given a test for range of motion, muscle strength, and the like; he is also tested for his ability to perform the numerous functions inherent in daily living.

The case of Jimmy ———— furnishes a good example of what can be accomplished for the individual patient by a many-faceted rehabilitation program of this type. Jimmy was recently transformed from a bed-ridden cripple to a productive member of society within several months as a result of the imaginative application to his case of the dynamic concept of rehabilitation which has been outlined.

He had been a bed patient in Bellevue Hospital in New York for about five years, with a particularly crippling form of arthritis, when he was brought to the attention of the hospital's newly organized rehabilitation department. During those five years there had been no appreciable improvement in his condition, which had been diagnosed as incurable. His ankles, knees, hips, and back were rigidly immobile, his legs fixed permanently at an angle of 45 degrees to his body.

Since his arms and hands were unaffected, the rehabilitation staff felt that something could be done to help him. Under their guidance, Jimmy soon learned to get out of bed by holding the bedstead, swinging his legs over the side and—using them as a counterweight—dropping to the floor. Picking his crutches off the bed, he was then able to walk around stiff-leggedly.

After a month of instruction and treatment, he could walk throughout the hospital. He was then placed in the training course conducted at Bellevue by a well-known watch company. His finger dexterity was extraordinary—so good, in fact, that after he had been in training for only three months the company offered to set up a watch assembly plant for him at home, so that he might leave the hospital and be self-supporting. Physicians of Bellevue's rehabilitation department expect, however, that Jimmy will easily be able to hold down a competitive job in private industry when the plastic surgery operations they are currently performing on his hip joints are completed.

Members of Bellevue's rehabilitation staff feel that a program such as theirs has a definite place in a general hospital and that it is an essential part of total medical care. The New York City Department of Hospitals strongly supports this view as indicated by its having had the blueprints for several new general hospitals in the city redrawn to permit allocation of 20 per cent of the beds in each institution for the convalescent care and rehabilitation of chronically ill patients. That care of this kind for the chronically ill should be furnished by general hospitals is, in fact, a concept now widely accepted by hospital administrators and authorities in the field of chronic illness.

A fully rounded chronic-disease control program in an urban community should be organized in such a way as to take account of the rehabilitation needs of the chronically ill. A certain proportion of[14] the general hospital beds in such a community should be used for convalescence. When chronic patients are over the acute stage of their illness, they should be "graduated" to the convalescence department and placed in a dynamic training program, so that they can be prepared to return to work as soon as possible. Associated with the general hospital there should be a chronic-disease evaluation unit where patients can receive training and have their potentialities for normal living appraised. After a period of evaluation and treatment not to exceed six months in an institution of this type, they should be transferred to a suitable institution or become active members of the community once again.

In the latter instance other services should be made available to them. Most important in this respect is a home-care program, which should be supported by ancillary services such as home-nursing visits and housekeeping assistance. A foster-home scheme should also be established in the community, with separate divisions for chronically ill and disabled children and for older persons. An adoption system for disabled children should be correlated with the foster-home program.

In addition, the community should provide a domiciliary home for chronically disabled patients who are able to live outside of an institution. Women's clubs, school groups, and community organizations of all kinds should be encouraged to plan programs of recreation—games, music, dancing, and lectures—for such homes. Also essential to a dynamic rehabilitation program in a community is a sheltered workshop, where

[14] Dr. Howard A. Rusk, who presented from personal experience the data on which the present section of this chapter is based, stated that he "would like" to set this proportion, for experimental purposes, as high as 20 per cent for a sample community having more than 100,000 population.

individuals of all ages can perform whatever work their ability or desire might permit.

Finally, community social and recreational centers where partially disabled persons can congregate for relaxation should be established.

It is not only economically feasible but economically necessary, in a democracy, that such opportunities for continued development of the personalities of chronically disabled individuals be provided, particularly in view of the proved potentialities of such persons as citizens.

The Role of Government

It cannot be questioned that the deficits with regard to provisions for care of the chronically ill are so great and so varied that joint action by both public and private agencies will be required in overcoming them. It is an accepted fact today that all levels of government—Federal, state, and local—are already engaged in chronic-disease control activities; it is likewise accepted that they will—and should—continue their efforts to ameliorate the chronic-disease problem.

The pages which follow—consisting of the conclusions arrived at by the Section on Chronic Disease and the Aging Process—are organized under seven subheadings. The first group of conclusions, "General Concepts," comprises those which are basic to any consideration of the problem of chronic disease as a whole. The other six groups consist of statements appropriate to each of the six main subtopics into which the delegates felt the subject matter to be discussed divided itself most logically, namely: "Role of Research, Training, and Clinical Techniques in Chronic-Disease Control"; "Non-Institutional Care of the Chronically Ill"; "Institutional Care of the Chronically Ill"; "Planned Convalescence and Rehabilitation"; "Utilization and Employment of the Chronically Disabled"; and "Co-ordination and Planning of Chronic-Disease Control Programs."

CONCLUSIONS AND RECOMMENDATIONS

The conquest of many of the acute communicable diseases has brought chronic or long-term illness into sharp focus as the major cause of death and disability today. The chronic diseases—heart disease, arteriosclerosis and high blood pressure, rheumatism, kidney disease, diabetes, cancer, and many others—affect practically every American family. At least 25 million persons are afflicted with a chronic illness, 7 million suffer some disability from chronic disease, and 1½ million are invalids. The chronic diseases cause the loss of nearly a billion man-days each year in productive activity.

Much of this staggering loss to our economy can be prevented. Indeed, prevention must be made the core of our attack on these diseases; otherwise, the changing age composition of our population will make the chronic-disease problem larger and more difficult in the coming years. If, however, we are to accomplish much in the way of prevention, our approach to the chronic-disease question must be based on a real appreciation of its major characteristics.

Of vital importance in this connection is the fact that chronic disease spares no age group. Although long-term illness and invalidism occur with greater frequency among older persons in the population, the *greatest volume* of illness and disability of a chronic nature is found among the younger adult age groups. More than three-fourths of the persons afflicted with a chronic illness and two-thirds of the invalids are between the ages of fifteen and sixty-five years; moreover, more than half the persons with chronic disease and one-third of the invalids are under the age of forty-five. It is obviously quite incorrect, therefore, to consider chronic disease as primarily a problem of the aging or of the aged. The progressive aging of the population of the United States, however, does make it all the more necessary that chronic disease be attacked vigorously in all age groups. For, although more of it is found in the younger adult age groups, the longer one lives the more apt he is to develop a chronic illness.

Consequently, in meeting the problem posed by the growing prevalence of chronic disease, emphasis should be placed by society on enabling everyone to attain and enjoy a healthy maturity. This objective can be approached through the application—to all individuals throughout their life span—of the principles of continued medical supervision and health guidance which have produced such striking improvement in recent years in the health of mothers and children. An effective program for fostering the attainment of a healthy maturity for everyone should center around such activities as health promotion and prevention of chronic illness at all ages; research on chronic-disease causation and therapy; early diagnosis and competent treatment of chronic ailments; and encouragement of planned convalescence and rapid rehabilitation for those who have been stricken with chronic illness. Of equal importance in such a program is the provision of opportunity to all persons to remain socially useful and economically productive throughout their life. Full utilization of the productive capacities of our human resources depends, in turn, on a recognition by society of the definite distinction between biological and chronological age. On the basis of this distinction, opportunities for older persons and those who are partially disabled to engage in worthwhile and satisfying work should be extended beyond the arbitrary limits set by present custom.

Only in terms of a dynamic approach of this kind can we begin to make real progress toward reducing the volume of chronic disease and disability which exists today at all age levels.[15]

General Concepts

1. *Definition*. In defining chronic disease, emphasis should be placed on *impairment of health* rather than on specific disease entities. On this basis an acceptable definition might be: *any impairment of health which persists, regardless of whether or not the patient is aware of its existence and irrespective of the degree of disability it induces, its tendency to progress, or its rate of progression*. Although disability from chronic disease is relative and variable, most chronic diseases, if neglected, tend to progress toward an increasing impairment of the patient's effectiveness.

2. *Relationship of general medical care to chronic care*. The type and quality of medical care required by the chronic patient cannot be separated from that required by the patient with an acute illness, regardless of whether the former is being treated at home, at work, in a hospital, or in a convalescent institution. The chronic patient, however, requires care for a more extended period of time; during this period, he may also develop acute exacerbations of his illness or contract a new and entirely independent acute disease.

3. *Need for new techniques*. The necessity for a readjustment in the techniques of conducting medical education and research, providing hospital service and home care, and planning convalescence and rehabilitation is emphasized by the fact that chronic diseases have become the major cause of illness and the greatest cause of disability and death in our nation. A large percentage of chronically ill persons, contrary to the prevailing opinion and attitudes, can be rehabilitated; they can be retrained to do gainful work or at least to care for themselves. They need

[15] The preceding paragraphs embody the sense of a suggestion, made in the course of the proceedings of this Section and approved by the delegates, that a statement on the relationship between chronic disease and the aging process be framed by the Section staff and included as an introduction to the conclusions officially adopted by the Section on Chronic Disease and the Aging Process.

not remain burdens to themselves, their families, and society. As the proportion of older persons in our population increases, the number of persons with protracted illness and permanent handicaps will also increase; it is imperative, therefore, that all possible means of preventing, mitigating, arresting, and curing disability be explored.

4. *Provision of services.* Since chronic illness affects all strata of our population, services for the chronically ill should be readily available for those who can afford to pay all or part of the cost of their care as well as for the indigent.

5. *Financial assistance.* It is essential that all persons interested in the sick should help in planning for care of the chronically ill; additional financial support of their efforts—from both tax-supported and philanthropic sources—will be necessary if the chronic-disease problem is to be handled more effectively than at present.

Role of Research, Training, and Clinical Techniques in Chronic-Disease Control

1. *Diagnostic principles.* Early diagnosis of incipient and/or asymptomatic chronic disease and control of it before disability sets in are important aspects of good medical care. Whenever possible, a *complete diagnosis* of all mental and physical factors involved in impairments of health should be attempted.

2. *Health inventory.* Emphasis should be placed on the *health inventory* or *health consultation* as the most valid technique for preventing disability from chronic disease. This diagnostic procedure should be applied particularly to persons *apparently* healthy but possibly harboring incipient, asymptomatic chronic disease, and should be employed on a highly individualized basis if worth-while results are to be obtained. Among the essential elements which an adequate health inventory should include are: (a) an analysis of the patient's habits and life objectives, as well as of the social factors affecting him; (b) instruction of the patient in general principles of hygiene and nutrition and in the value of "intangible" aspects of the advice and guidance given him by his physician; and (c) a description to the patient of his condition in as complete and comprehensible a manner as possible.

If the health inventory is to be properly employed as a preventive technique in medicine, it is essential that the lay public be made aware of the limitations of medical science with respect to diagnostic accuracy, application of research findings, and the like. No matter how thorough a particular examination may be, it cannot be *guaranteed* to elicit evidence of an existing asymptomatic or silent disease.

3. *Mass screening programs.* Mass screening examination programs for the detection of chronic diseases should be correlated rather than segregated—as at present—by specific disease categories. In a single adequate diagnostic study of a patient, any or all chronic disorders should be discovered; a complete study of this kind would also be more economical and meaningful. Separation of screening programs into different disease categories increases the expense and time involved in carrying them out, since in many instances the same individual must be screened for several diseases at different times. In addition, a person is likely to be given a false sense of security about his health if he is examined for only one specific disease and found to be free of it. Furthermore, screening examinations of this type usually omit consideration of emotional factors and personal habits which often have an important bearing on the total health of an individual.

The major chronic disorders for which physicians should be prepared to look in screening examinations are—in the order of their importance as sources of premature disability as well as death—cardiovascular, metabolic, and neuropsychiatric diseases, cancer, tuberculosis, and arthritis.

4. *Diagnostic facilities.* Improved facilities should be provided for the gathering of ancillary information essential to an adequate diagnosis of conditions revealed by a health inventory. X-ray apparatus and facilities for the collection and analysis of laboratory specimens should be readily available and accessible to both patients and physicians—whenever possible, at some central point such as a local health center.

5. *Need for special training.* Special training in problems and techniques of prevention, treatment, and rehabilitation in the field of chronic disease is needed particularly by the following groups: (a) physicians and medical students; (b) graduate and practical nurses, hospital and nursing-home administrators, administrators of homes for the aged, social workers, physiotherapists, occupational therapists, and others professionally involved in care of the aged and chronically ill; (c) persons among the general public who must care for a chronically ill or infirm relative at home; and (d) chronically ill persons themselves.

6. *Instruction of medical personnel.* Instruction of professional medical personnel in techniques of chronic-disease care should stress:

(a) Maintenance of an individual's *total health* instead of analysis of specific and isolated disease entities;

(b) The importance of early detection of insidious—and particularly asymptomatic—progressive impairments and methods of detecting such impairments;

(c) The probability that several diseases or defects will co-exist in any patient with a chronic disease, especially if he has already been found to have one of the functional impairments or chronic disorders characteristic of later maturity;

(d) Maintenance and construction of better health in general as the objective of a health inventory instead of mere treatment of a specific disease;

(e) Significance of emotional factors—especially ordinary personality problems and neuroses—in both the causation and therapy of chronic disease; and

(f) The need for physicians to undertake postgraduate and refresher training in the prevention and treatment of chronic disease and in methods of rehabilitating the chronically ill.

7. *Instruction of nursing-home operators.* Instruction of nursing-home operators in the proper methods of caring for the chronically ill should become one of the duties of nursing-home inspectors as soon as adequate standards of licensure for nursing homes are established at the state level. Inspection of a nursing home should not be limited to a review of its facilities and services alone but should include presentation by the inspector of educational material on such subjects as dietetics, occupational therapy, psychotherapy, and the qualifications of staff members.

8. *Instruction of the general public.* There is need on the part of the general public for a greater understanding of the nature, causation, treatment, and prospects of chronic illness, so that individuals may live more wisely and thus avoid many prematurely disabling disorders, seek proper medical attention promptly when they need it, and do a better job of caring for chronically ill members of their families at home. There is also need on the part of the public for a better appreciation of the mental and physical aspects of the aging process, so that constructive attitudes toward aging may be fostered.

Education of the public on factors involved in chronic as well as other diseases should be meticulously accurate. It should not be oversimplified or superficial, nor should it be fear-provoking. At the same time, the public—as well as the physicians—should be made fully aware of the limitations of medical science; physicians should state these limitations clearly and frankly to patients, for false promises of the impossible merely destroy a patient's confidence in his physician.

Instruction of the public in techniques of caring for the chronically ill can best be accomplished through local official and voluntary agencies such as the American Red Cross, local health councils, men's and women's clubs and fraternal organizations, schools, hospitals, labor unions, and community health departments.

9. *Instruction of patients.* Chronic-disease patients should be educated to assume personal responsibility for their health. A proper public health approach to the problem of chronic disease implies the development of initiative, effort, and a co-operative attitude by the patient himself. Since rehabilitation of a person disabled as a result of chronic illness requires great and continued effort on his part, he must have an adequate psychological motivation toward improvement. Nothing should be done to make continuance of disability from any cause profitable or desirable to a patient.

10. *Research in chronic disease.* Research in chronic disease should be encouraged by every means possible. Scientists and the general public should be kept informed regarding those aspects of the chronic-disease problem on which investigation is most urgently needed. These should be determined on the basis of periodic studies of morbidity and disability figures as well as mortality data, so that, in the future, funds and time for research purposes will be distributed among disease categories in a more equitable and logical manner than at present. This, however, should not be taken to mean that pure medical research, unrelated to specific disease statistics, should not also be fostered and encouraged. Furthermore, research and demonstrations, utilizing national and local resources, should be undertaken to develop a new concept of adequate care for chronically ill patients—one which will stress the social as well as the medical factors involved.

Areas in the field of chronic disease in which research and investigation are now most urgently needed are: (a) causation of progressive chronic disorders; and (b) development of diagnostic techniques for evaluation of total health and for detection of silent, asymptomatic diseases.

Research efforts might also profitably be devoted to: development of methods for collecting adequate morbidity statistics; evaluation of the advantages of including secondary diagnoses on death certificates; development of techniques for gathering useful data for chronic-disease control from operating plans providing disability insurance, medical care, and similar benefits; perfecting of procedures for employing area sampling as a tool in medical research; and determination of principles of psychological management of patients with chronic disorders, particularly in connection with their motivation toward rehabilitation.

With respect to the inclusion of secondary diagnoses on death certificates, the Federal government should undertake a study to determine
the desirability of such an innovation.

Although funds for the carrying out of research projects of this kind
will have to be forthcoming from various sources, no control should be
exercised over medical research by bodies distributing funds for research
purposes. Moreover, great discretion should be employed with regard to
procedures used in publicizing the results of medical research.

11. *Emotional factors and chronic disease.* In view of the important
role played by emotional factors in the causation, treatment, and control
of chronic disease, close collaboration on the development of techniques
of prevention and treatment between authorities in the fields of mental
hygiene and chronic disease is essential. Particularly necessary in this
connection is the organization of procedures for integrating public health
mental-hygiene programs—including those involving the education of
professional personnel as well as of patients—with chronic-disease control
programs.

Non-Institutional Care of the Chronically Ill

1. *Home care: a central concept.* Provision of care at home for persons
suffering from long-term illnesses is an essential element of a chronic-
disease control program. It has been estimated that about 70 per cent
of those afflicted with a long-term illness can best be cared for in their
own homes, provided adequate supervision and assistance are available.

2. *Basic aspects of home care.* A minimum program of sound home
care for the chronically ill should include provision of:

(a) A home environment for the patient which meets normal standards of
    comfortable living;
(b) Housing facilities which are adapted to his special needs;
(c) Assistance, when necessary, in housekeeping and in the procurement and
    preparation of the kind and quantity of food essential to good nutrition;
(d) Adequate medical care, including extramural hospital care and services
    of both private and clinic physicians;
(e) Professional and non-professional nursing care—on a full-time as well as
    a part-time basis—supervised by both official public health nursing agen-
    cies and voluntary visiting nurse societies;
(f) Assistance by social workers in family planning and adjustment, with
    full support from community resources; and
(g) Restorative services, including rehabilitation, physical and occupational
    therapy, vocational guidance, and recreational opportunities.

3. *Methods of providing home-care services.* Administration of a home-care program for chronically ill persons requires over-all co-operation in planning for and providing needed services. Such co-operation can be achieved by at least two means:

(a) Establishment of special community, state, and national committees to insure that existing home-care facilities will be used efficiently and new ones developed; and

(b) Provision of leadership in the development of a home-care program by a single agency in each community.[16]

4. *Financing home care.* The resources of government, private philanthropy, and individual patients are all needed for financing home-care services. All three groups should collaborate in meeting the cost of such services.

5. *Special housing facilities.* Government and private housing programs should include provisions for the construction of dwelling units designed especially to accommodate chronically ill persons who require home care.

6. *Role of the general hospital.* In the programs of general as well as special chronic-disease hospitals, arrangements should be made, as part of the total community plan, for continuation in the home of medical and rehabilitation measures begun in the hospital.

7. *Housekeeping assistance.* The American Red Cross and other appropriate voluntary and official agencies should be urged to give serious consideration to the training and employment of housekeeper aides to assist in caring for chronically ill and infirm aged persons in their homes. Provision of housekeeping service of this kind on an extensive scale is urgently necessary; at present there is practically no such service being provided, even though voluntary and public agencies in many communities furnish housekeeping assistance to families in which the mother is ill.

Institutional Care of the Chronically Ill

1. *Institutional care only one facet of the problem.* A comprehensive attack on all ramifications of the problem of chronic disease is required. Institutional care of patients with long-term illnesses is a very important area of need, but plans for an over-all approach to chronic-disease control

---

[16] The validity of this technique as a means of stimulating the provision of home-care services has been demonstrated in New York City, where leadership in this respect has been furnished for several years by the Montefiore Hospital for Chronic Diseases.

must include provision for scientific and administrative research and for education and the development of extramural programs of care for all categories of patients with extended illnesses. The Joint Statement on "Planning for the Chronically Ill,"[17] issued in 1947 by the American Hospital Association, American Medical Association, American Public Health Association, and American Public Welfare Association, should become a basis for action.

2. *What is involved in institutional care.* Institutional care of the chronically ill may necessitate not only the use of the diagnostic and therapeutic facilities of the general hospital, but also an emphasis on ancillary services such as medical social work, physical, recreational, and occupational therapy, and religious ministry.

3. *Relationship to hospital planning.* It would be desirable, in general, that the unmet needs of the chronically ill be provided for through existing planning agencies. State agencies already—or about to be—designated as state-wide planning bodies for the construction of new hospital facilities should focus their attention on the institutional requirements of long-term patients.

4. *Role of the hospital.* The hospital should be the central point in the structural and functional pattern of institutional care for the chronic sick—for the actively ill as well as for those long-term patients who require only custodial care. The simplest approach to the complex problem of the relationship between chronic disease and aging is to deal with the chronic sick of all age groups in appropriate types of facilities.

5. *Licensing procedures.* Universal and uniform licensing procedures for public, voluntary, and proprietary institutions offering care for the chronically ill should be adopted throughout the nation, and licensing bodies should be equipped to assist, in a consultative capacity, in elevating standards of care.

6. *Financial assistance.* Requirements in both urban and rural areas of the country for expanded and improved institutional facilities for care of the chronically ill are so great and so immediate that they cannot be met without financial assistance in the construction and maintenance of such facilities from local, state, and Federal governmental sources.

Planned Convalescence and Rehabilitation

1. *Work therapy as an adjunct to medical treatment.* Recent experience in the military services, the Veterans Administration, and certain

---

[17] Published in the *American Journal of Public Health*, Vol. 37, No. 10 (Oct. 1947), pp. 1256-1266. Adopted as an official statement by the four associations sponsoring the Joint Committee.

demonstration programs in civilian hospitals and institutions has shown that a large percentage of chronically ill persons can be rehabilitated and retrained to do some gainful work. Many can return to competitive employment; others will necessarily be forced to seek sheltered work; still others will be able to undertake productive activity only within the hospital or some other institution in which they are being treated. Work therapy, however, must be more widely used as an adjunct to medical treatment. A patient's ability to leave the institution or to be self-supporting is not the sole criterion of success in rehabilitation; "self care" is an equally valid rehabilitation objective from the medical, social, and economic standpoints.

2. *Better understanding of rehabilitation techniques needed.* Among physicians and other professional personnel working with the chronically ill and aged there must be a better understanding of the possibilities and techniques of rehabilitation; furthermore, the present critical shortage of personnel—both medical and ancillary—trained to perform rehabilitation must be overcome. Both of these objectives can be achieved by means of:

(a) Special orientation and instruction of physicians and ancillary personnel concerned with the chronically ill, through postgraduate training, professional meetings and publications, and similar methods; and

(b) Increased emphasis on the application of *dynamic therapeutics* to chronic disease in the undergraduate, graduate, and postgraduate education of physicians and ancillary personnel.

3. *Expansion of rehabilitation programs.* Greater stress must be placed on the establishment of rehabilitation programs in special and general hospitals, convalescent homes, nursing homes, homes for the aged, and other types of public and private institutions. Facilities must be expanded, but existing knowledge and techniques must also be imaginatively applied in present facilities. With careful planning, dynamic rehabilitation programs can be organized in many existing institutions without undue expense or loss of beds. Such programs can be set up most effectively through development of:

(a) Effective demonstrations in general and special hospitals and in convalescent, nursing, and public homes;

(b) Integrated post-hospital home services; and

(c) Specialized rehabilitation facilities, including separate convalescence sections in general hospitals; physical medicine, psychotherapy, and prevocational training services in all hospitals; community social and recreational centers; and domiciliary and foster homes for the partially disabled.

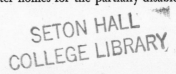

4. *Co-ordinated approach required.* Among the general public as well as among members of the medical and health professions there must be greater appreciation of the medical, social, and economic implications of the growing prevalence of chronic diseases and the progressive aging of the population. All known techniques of education should be directed toward creating an awareness of the necessity for adopting a co-ordinated approach to the planning of rehabilitation facilities for persons partially disabled by chronic disease. The most effective means for accomplishing this aim are actual demonstrations of what can be achieved through such an approach.

Utilization and Employment of the Chronically Disabled

1. *Normal life and useful work essential.* Both for persons who are disabled as a result of chronic illness and for those in the older age groups, society should make possible a life as nearly normal as their capacities permit; they should be allowed to live, preferably, in their own homes or in an otherwise familiar environment. It is also society's responsibility to provide an opportunity for such persons to do useful work.

2. *Employment of partially disabled workers economically sound.* It is imperative that industry and government prepare themselves to give employment to a larger number and proportion of older and partially disabled workers. Employers should not, however, be asked to hire persons of advanced years and those partially disabled merely as a charitable gesture, or to offer them artificial jobs or "made work." There is a wide latitude within which employment of such persons can be shown to be economically sound.

3. *Chronological versus physiological age.* Employers should judge the age of their employees on a physiological rather than a chronological basis and should not decide that an individual is unable to work simply because he is partially disabled as a result of chronic illness. Adjustment of the number of workers to the number of existing jobs should not be achieved at the expense of older or partially disabled workers.

4. *Functioning of retirement boards.* Retirement from work should take place on a selective basis rather than at a specific age. Retirement boards made up of medical (including psychiatric) and administrative personnel should be set up in government and industry. The basic function of such boards should be to determine whether an employee is sufficiently fit mentally and physically to perform his job, or a related job, effectively; their findings should describe the employee's specific

degree of fitness. Findings should be reviewed in the light of: (a) the nature of the employee's job; (b) any special skills or aptitudes, not to be readily duplicated, which he may possess; and (c) the existing supply of man power in the organization. The experience and functioning of retirement boards established in the Army, Navy, and Public Health Service should be studied as a background for the establishment of retirement boards in industry and elsewhere in government.

5. *Adequacy of retirement pensions.* Commendable progress has been made by both industry and government in the development of old-age and retirement programs, but these should be made more adequate with respect to the amounts of pensions paid to retired employees and the number of employees covered.

6. *"Tapering off" in employment.* The possibilities of a program of "tapering off" in public and private employment should be investigated; under such a program, an individual employee might be relieved of responsibility and the more taxing requirements of his work in graduated steps as he approaches retirement age, his pay remaining commensurate with his productivity during the "tapering off" period.

7. *Disability studies.* It will be economically worth while for industry and for government (in its capacity as an employer) to undertake further studies of the medical aspects of disability and the relationship of disability to the performance of productive work. In general terms, types of work which tend to be suitable for employees with varying types of disability should be determined as a prerequisite for an understanding of this relationship.

8. *Education of employers.* An educational program should be inaugurated to:

(a) Encourage employers to hire and retain in employment older workers and those partially disabled by pointing out to them the assets—including loyalty, lower labor turnover, and less absenteeism—which such workers bring to any business enterprise; and

(b) Demonstrate to employers the desirability of providing special equipment and apparatus, rest periods, adjusted hours of work, and similar concessions to their partially disabled and elderly employees in order to make it easier for these employees to continue to work.

Since such a program of education belongs in a democracy to all the people, government, private institutions and agencies, foundations, labor unions, and employers' organizations should participate in it.

9. *Revision of legislation.* A study should be made of existing laws

which, by penalizing employers who hire persons of advanced years and those who are partially disabled, in effect bar employment to such persons, and immediate steps should be taken to have laws of this kind revised.

10. *Protection against exploitation.* Adequate provision should be made to safeguard older workers and those who are partially disabled against exploitation by industry.

11. *Health maintenance services.* On-the-job health maintenance services should be made available to employees with chronic diseases, whether or not they are disabled, as a means of keeping them in productive employment.

12. *Re-evaluation of compensation and disability insurance practices.* Some of the current practices connected with payment of workmen's compensation and disability insurance should be re-evaluated in the light of modern therapeutic techniques and opportunities. At present, an employee's degree of disability is often determined by a review of the diagnosis of his case rather than by a thorough appraisal of his condition. On-the-job training and trial employment for disabled persons—as a means of encouraging those who are employable to return to work— might profitably be emphasized, rather than continuing compensation.

Co-ordination and Planning of Chronic-Disease Control Programs

1. *Importance of co-ordination of services.* Co-ordination and integration of services for the chronically ill, in co-operation with physicians, hospitals, nursing homes, and social agencies, is important not only for prudent community planning but also for proper guidance of families burdened with the medical problems and social and economic sequelae of chronic illness.

2. *Co-ordination and planning at the local level.*

a. Local planning committees should be established under the auspices of organized health and welfare bodies. Such committees should include among their members representatives of the health and welfare professions, of governmental and voluntary agencies and institutions, and of farm, labor, industrial, civic, and other community groups.

The functions of such committees should be: (1) to educate the community and to stimulate its interest in the chronic-disease problem; (2) to study the special needs of the chronically ill; (3) to encourage the provision of services and facilities; (4) to improve standards of care; (5) to provide information services; (6) to plan a co-ordinated program of chronic-disease control; (7) to interest official agencies in assuming leadership in the foregoing activities; and

(8) to assist in developing responsible and continuing citizen interest in the work of the official local health agency.

b. The various local governmental agencies having responsibilities toward the chronically ill should co-ordinate their activities either by participating in the work of these planning committees or by other appropriate means.

c. The local health department has a particularly important role to play in chronic-disease control in emphasizing prevention as the key to solution of the chronic-disease problem and in achieving integration of chronic-disease control activities with other health programs and functions, such as industrial hygiene, communicable disease control, school health, nutrition, and public health nursing.

d. Development of regional planning for the chronically ill on the basis of medical service regions and districts should be seriously considered. The region surrounding a large city cannot be separated from the city for purposes of medical care. Chronic-disease planning bodies already set up within large cities should therefore be expanded to include representatives from appropriate groups organized in surrounding suburban and rural areas.

3. Co-ordination and planning at the state level.

a. A single official state agency should be given the job of planning for care of the chronically ill. The state health department should be prepared to assume that responsibility in many instances. The state planning body should be charged with stimulating and developing among localities planning for care of the chronically ill on a regional basis.

b. The work of state-wide hospital facilities planning bodies should be supplemented by that of state and local voluntary organizations dedicated to the co-ordination of both institutional and non-institutional phases of the chronic-disease problem.

c. Co-ordination of the efforts of all such organizations can be achieved at the state level through establishment of a broad advisory committee to the official state chronic-disease planning agency; on this committee all private, professional, and public agencies working in the field of chronic disease should have representation.

4. Co-ordination and planning at the national level.

a. Formulation of a program of care for the chronically ill is an extremely complicated matter, involving every aspect of the provision of medical care; it is impossible, therefore, to outline too specifically, at present, a plan for care of the chronically ill which would be valid for the next ten years. It is essential, however—as one of the major elements in such a plan—that a national commission on chronic disease be established.

(1) The existing Joint Committee on Chronic Disease of the American Hospital Association, American Medical Association, American Public Health Association, and American Public Welfare Association should be continued and constituted as such a national commission, and its membership should be expanded to include appropriate representation from other disciplines, organiza-

tions, and interests in the field of chronic illness and from various geographical areas of the United States.

(2) Among others, the functions of a national commission on chronic disease would be:

(a) To advise and guide state, regional, and local agencies, both official and voluntary, engaged in planning for chronic-disease control and for care of the chronically ill;

(b) To co-ordinate nationally information now available regarding the nature and extent of the chronic-disease problem and to serve as a clearing house for information on new developments, experiments, and programs in care of the chronically ill;

(c) To co-ordinate public and voluntary planning activities; and

(d) To explore methods of implementing all pertinent recommendations made to it.

(3) The work of the commission should be encouraged by the provision of funds from private sources and by support from government in the form of both funds and personnel, so that it will be able to analyze more effectively the problem of chronic disease and make recommendations on its control and on the care of its victims to governmental agencies and other appropriate bodies, following the pattern set with respect to hospital care by the Commission on Hospital Care[18] of the American Hospital Association and with respect to child health by the Study of Child Health Services[19] conducted by the American Academy of Pediatrics.

b. An appropriate body should be set up in the Federal Security Agency to co-ordinate planning and program activities in the field of chronic disease carried out by the various subdivisions of the Agency concerned with health, social security, education, and rehabilitation. Through this body, the Agency should also co-ordinate its chronic-disease activities with those of other Federal agencies working in related fields.

c. The United States Public Health Service should study the possible advantages in and means of co-ordinating its several activities in the chronic-disease field, including program development and research.

d. Federal grants-in-aid to the states for research, control programs, services, and facilities are essential to meet the total chronic-disease problem. Such grants should permit the states to arrange for care to be given to a patient outside his home state when facilities in another state are more accessible to him or more suitable for treatment of his particular condition.

DISCUSSION HIGHLIGHTS

Relationship of Chronic Disease to the Aging Process

One of the liveliest discussions which took place in the course of the proceedings of the Section on Chronic Disease and the Aging Process centered

[18] Commission on Hospital Care, *Hospital Care in the United States* (New York: Commonwealth Fund, 1947).

[19] *Health Services for Children and Pediatric Education in the United States* (New York: Commonwealth Fund, 1949).

around the phrasing of the Section's title. As the discussion developed, it became clear that most of the delegates fell into one or the other of two clearly opposed camps on this issue. One group was firmly convinced that it was confusing, inaccurate, and misleading to imply—as the title of the Section did— that there was any close or necessary connection between chronic disease and either "the aging process," "old age," or "the aged." The opposing group maintained that, although the problems of chronic disease were not synonymous with those of the aging process, there was enough in common between them to justify the phrasing of the title as it stood.

It was agreed by all delegates, however, that some clarification of the relationship between chronic disease and aging should be included as part of the formal conclusions of this Section.

The discussion arose following Dr. Ferderber's remark that there appeared to be some confusion as to whether the delegates were considering "chronic disease in the aged and the aging" or "strictly . . . chronic disease." Dr. Masur took this opportunity to point out that confusion on this issue was running through all the deliberations of the Section, and suggested that it might be resolved if the title of the Section were changed so as to relate exclusively to chronic disease. Other delegates quickly endorsed this point of view.

Dr. Rogers joined the debate to observe that the title of the Section as it stood made "just the distinction we want to make" between problems of "old age" and those of "the aging process." He advocated, nevertheless, the insertion of a strong statement—to introduce the final report of the Section—which would emphasize the differences between chronic disease on the one hand and the problems of both the aging and the aged on the other. Support for Dr. Rogers's position was forthcoming from Dr. Klumpp, who pointed out that certain economic and employment difficulties of the chronically ill are closely related to those which older persons face. Dr. Stieglitz observed that in a formal medical sense, too, there is a relationship between chronic disease and aging in that aging and its processes impair physiological efficiency. Objecting to any attempt to change the Section's title, Dr. Rusk endorsed the idea of introducing the final report with a clarifying preamble which would specify that incidence of chronic disease is not limited to any age group but that special aspects of the chronic-disease problem are related particularly to an aging population.

Some merit in both points of view on the question was found by Dr. Terris. He maintained that a "constructive solution" which would prevent the Section from becoming known as "the Section on the aged" had to be worked out, since the preventive approach to chronic disease stresses treatment in early adult life as a means of avoiding disability later on. At the same time, he pointed out, the social and economic difficulties facing older persons are certainly important in the whole context of the chronic-disease problem.

Questioning whether the Section title as it stood was not creating more confusion than would be caused by changing it, Miss Jarrett moved that it be altered to "Section on Chronic Diseases." Her motion was seconded and, after further discussion, was put to a vote and defeated.

Dr. Rusk then moved that a clarifying preamble on the relationship between chronic disease and aging be included in the Section's final report to the Assembly. The motion was seconded and passed after a brief discussion on the manner in which such a preamble should be written.[20]

Non-Institutional Care of the Chronically Ill

The question which aroused most controversy in the course of debate on the preliminary report of the subcommittee considering the non-institutional aspects of chronic-disease care was one relating to the provision of housekeeping assistance for victims of chronic illness.

The discussion was initiated by Dr. Stieglitz's remark that the detrimental effects on a family of having to care for a chronic invalid at home should be given some study in view of the fact that welfare boards and similar agencies tend to insist that such a patient be kept at home as long as possible.

Miss Hubbard replied that if attempts were made to rehabilitate chronic invalids living at home, so that they could contribute something to the family either as wage-earners or by doing chores around the house, they would not constitute such a "psychological load" on its other members. Miss Jarrett then interposed the suggestion that chapters of the American Red Cross be urged to consider furnishing housekeeping services to the chronically ill. Housekeeping service is very costly, she said, and must therefore be supported by large and well-financed organizations such as the Red Cross; it is financially impossible for most voluntary organizations to offer such a service, and public agencies can rarely provide it in sufficient volume to meet the existing need. In formally moving that this suggestion be transmitted to the Red Cross, she remarked that current neglect of the chronically ill "constitutes a national emergency."

The sense of Miss Jarrett's motion was endorsed by Miss Hubbard and Miss Nicholson. The latter, however, questioned whether it should be specified by the Section that provision of housekeeper services ought to be the function of either the Red Cross or any other single agency.

Miss Jarrett contended that it is a "natural function" of the Red Cross to provide such service, but Miss Gimmestad declared that the purpose of the Red Cross is to supplement other resources and felt that it should not be asked to assume full responsibility for furnishing housekeeper aid to the chronically ill.

Further discussion on whether "other appropriate agencies" should also be requested to provide housekeeping services and on whether the Red Cross should be indicated by name, as Miss Jarrett had suggested, was concluded by the Section's adoption of a compromise statement urging other appropriate voluntary and official agencies as well as the Red Cross to give "serious consideration" to the provision of housekeeper services.[21]

[20] The preamble, as finally drawn up, appears above as the statement introducing the conclusions reached by the Section.

[21] This motion as adopted is included above as one of the final conclusions agreed upon by the Section.

Community Co-ordination and Planning of Chronic-Disease Control
   Programs

In the course of the discussion on methods of planning for chronic-disease control, a particularly spirited debate took place with regard to the specific manner in which a national commission on chronic disease should be created. The major point at issue was whether the predominant influence on such a commission should be exercised by official or by voluntary agencies concerned with chronic-disease control.

The draft report of the subcommittee on community planning activities contained a recommendation that some planning on a national scale should be conducted by the Federal Security Agency. Dr. Merrill took exception to this recommendation, maintaining that national planning could best be accomplished by a commission on which voluntary agencies as well as the Federal government would be represented, rather than by the Government itself.

Dr. Rogers asserted that the most important factor to be considered in this connection was the provision of a common forum at which both official and non-official agencies with an interest in planning for chronic-disease control could meet to discuss their respective programs. Nevertheless, he said, effectuation of such programs—that is, promotion of legislation, formulation of budgets, stimulation of public interest, and the like—would be a function similar to many of the activities now being carried out by the Federal Security Agency. It would be desirable, therefore, he contended, for some branch of the Agency to handle the technical details involved in such programs—to make grants-in-aid, perhaps, or to create other appropriate patterns for furnishing assistance to communities which might desire to undertake control activities.

Dr. Merrill replied that his remarks were intended only as a plea for the right of national voluntary hospital and professional associations to play an important role in the over-all planning program.

Speaking as a member of the Joint Committee on Chronic Disease,[22] Dr. Miller declared that it was the hope of some of the members of the Joint Committee that it might become the national planning body for a chronic-disease control program and serve, in addition, as "a reservoir of information and stimulation."

It was suggested by Miss Soule that, if such a development were to take place, there ought to be wider representation on the Joint Committee than could be supplied by the four associations which had established it. Dr. Bertner moved, at this point, that the Joint Committee be broadened at least to take in members from various sections of the country. Despite its excellence, he said, the Joint Committee as constituted represents only two or three states.

Dr. Masur remarked that some of the delegates to the Section on Chronic Disease and the Aging Process were thinking in terms of "something more" than a committee—"composed of extremely busy people who had many other obligations"—which would meet only at rare intervals. It would be quite

[22] Composed of representatives of the American Hospital Association, American Medical Association, American Public Health Association, and American Public Welfare Association.

possible, he asserted, for the working responsibility for planning activities to be centered in a national commission, with the Joint Committee serving in an advisory capacity.

Dr. Stieglitz, referring to Dr. Bertner's motion, reminded the delegates that, apart from the question of geographical representation, there were a number of significant disciplines not represented on the Joint Committee, among them nursing and psychiatry. He recommended that the Joint Committee be expanded to include more fields of professional interest. The Joint Committee then would have to be requested to expand itself, Dr. Miller cautioned; since it was created under the auspices of four private organizations, its composition could not be changed by any outside group. Dr. Rogers declared that it was his opinion that, in the interest of achieving co-ordinated activity in the field of chronic-disease control, the Joint Committee might be asked by some Federal authority to expand itself and then to accept responsibility for acting as a national commission on chronic disease.

As a voluntary organization, the Joint Committee might want to continue with its present representation, Dr. Merrill pointed out. He felt it was the Section's purpose, however, to attempt to establish a national commission on chronic disease which would be broadly representative geographically and would also include in its membership delegates from labor unions and other interested community groups. He would "dislike very much," he declared, to see a planning organization established which "does not have these broad potentialities."

Stressing the importance of retaining the "working forcefulness" of the original concept leading to the organization of the Joint Committee, Dr. Rogers asserted that there were adequate means of expression for the specialized interests which had been mentioned in the discussion through the four associations sponsoring the Joint Committee, even though all these interests were not specifically represented. Nevertheless, he added, the Joint Committee would undoubtedly support the suggestion that it should be more representative geographically.

As a means of reconciling these opposing points of view Dr. Terris proposed that the Joint Committee be made responsible for developing a commission on chronic disease and that all appropriate groups, public as well as professional, be represented on the commission.

Miss Hildegarde Wagner objected that, if a commission were appointed by the Federal government, the government would want to be officially represented on it. Dr. Terris explained, however, that he was not thinking of a government commission but of one which would merely receive governmental support.

The question before the house—Dr. Bertner's original motion on expansion of the Joint Committee—was then called for. With Dr. Bertner's consent, it was rephrased by Dr. Rogers to include some of the points raised in the discussion and then presented for consideration to the delegates in the following form:

The existing Joint Committee on Chronic Disease (should) be continued and constituted as a national commission on chronic disease, and appropriately expanded to include representatives of allied disciplines and organizations and various geographical areas.

The motion was voted on and approved in this form.[23]

APPENDIX

Planning Committee

James R. Miller, M.D., *Chairman*

Past President
Connecticut State Medical Society;
Board of Trustees
American Medical Association;
United States Delegate
World Health Assembly (1948)

Damon Kerby

St. Louis *Post-Dispatch*

Karl P. Meister

Executive Secretary
Board of Hospitals and Homes
Methodist Church

Miss Edna Nicholson

Director, Central Service for the
Chronically Ill
Institute of Medicine of Chicago

Howard A. Rusk, M.D.

Associate Editor, New York *Times*;
Chairman, Department of Rehabilitation
and Physical Medicine
New York University College of Medicine

Staff Assistants

Joseph W. Mountin, M.D.

Associate Chief, Bureau of State Services
Public Health Service, Federal Security
Agency

Mrs. Lucille M. Smith

Chief, Medical Needs Section
Bureau of Public Assistance
Social Security Administration
Federal Security Agency

Edward B. Kovar

Social Science Analyst
Bureau of State Services
Public Health Service, Federal Security
Agency

Registrants

Miss Elizabeth Andrews

Supervisor of Placement for Women
Air Reduction Company, Inc.

[23] It appears above, with certain minor editorial revisions, in the Section's conclusions on "co-ordination and planning at the national level."

Miss Ruth Baker	Supervisor, Inter-Agency Housekeeper Service for the Aged Family Service Association Cleveland, Ohio
E. W. Bertner, M.D.	President, Texas Medical Center Houston, Texas
Daniel G. Blain, M.D.	Medical Director American Psychiatric Association
E. M. Bluestone, M.D.	Director, Montefiore Hospital for Chronic Diseases New York, New York
Lester Breslow, M.D.	Chief, Chronic Disease Section California Department of Public Health
Miss Claire M. Burque	Administrator, Central Service for the Chronically Ill Health and Welfare Council, Inc. Philadelphia, Pennsylvania
Charles S. Cameron, M.D.	Medical and Scientific Director American Cancer Society, Inc.
Miss Mary F. Champlin	Executive Secretary, Health Division Federation of Social Agencies of Pittsburgh and Allegheny County, Pennsylvania
Llewellyn R. Cole, M.D.	Co-ordinator of Graduate Medical Education University of Wisconsin Medical School
George W. Cooley	Assistant Secretary, Council on Medical Service American Medical Association
Col. Wesley C. Cox	Medical Corps, United States Army; Chief, Army Industrial Hygiene Laboratory
Mrs. Ada Metcalfe Crouch	Publicity Department, Uplands Sanatorium Pleasant Hill, Tennessee
Russell J. N. Dean	Executive Assistant, Physical Medicine and Rehabilitation Service Veterans Administration
Warren F. Draper, M.D.	Assistant to the Vice-President for Health Services American Red Cross
Miss Martha H. Eddy	Administrative Extension Specialist New York State College of Home Economics Cornell University
Murray B. Ferderber, M.D.	Consultant in Physical Medicine Veterans Hospital Pittsburgh, Pennsylvania

Miss Ella B. Gimmestad	Assistant Director of Nursing Services American Red Cross
Samuel A. Goldsmith	Executive Director Jewish Charities of Chicago
John J. Griffin	Supervisor, Old Age Assistance Somerville, Massachusetts
Miss Hazel M. Halloran	Director of Social Service St. Vincent's Hospital New York, New York
Raymond M. Hilliard	Commissioner, New York City Department of Welfare
Miss Ruth W. Hubbard	General Director Philadelphia Visiting Nurse Society
Miss Mary C. Jarrett	Director, Poliomyelitis Research Project New York University College of Medicine
Hugh S. Jewett	California State Director American Cancer Society, Inc.
Theodore G. Klumpp, M.D.	President, Winthrop-Stearns, Inc.
Jack Masur, M.D.	National Institutes of Health Federal Security Agency
Rev. Donald A. McGowan	Assistant Director in Charge of Health and Hospitals Department of Social Action National Catholic Welfare Conference
Walter E. Merrick, M.D.	Chief, Department of Physical Medicine Harlem Hospital New York, New York
A. P. Merrill, M.D.	Superintendent, St. Barnabas Hospital for Chronic Diseases New York, New York
Sister Pacifica	Sisters of Charity Carney Hospital Boston, Massachusetts
James E. Perkins, M.D.	Managing Director National Tuberculosis Association
Mrs. Ruth Pierce	Chief, Division of Public Assistance Nebraska State Board of Control
Ellen C. Potter, M.D.	Deputy Commissioner for Welfare New Jersey Department of Institutions and Agencies
Leo Price, M.D.	Director, Union Health Center International Ladies' Garment Workers' Union New York, New York

Miss Ollie A. Randall   Consultant on Services for the Aged
Community Service Society
New York, New York

Dean W. Roberts, M.D.   Chief, Bureau of Medical Services
Maryland Department of Health

Edward S. Rogers, M.D.   Dean, University of California School of Public Health

Mrs. James P. Simonds   Editor, *Bulletin of the American Medical Association Auxiliary*

Miss Theodate S. Soule   Director of Social Service
New York Hospital

William E. Steckler   Attorney, Indiana Association of Licensed Nursing Homes

Edward J. Stieglitz, M.D.   Chairman, Membership and Education Committee
American Geriatrics Society

Eugene J. Taylor   Editorial Staff
New York *Times*

Milton Terris, M.D.   Medical Associate
Subcommittee on Medical Care
American Public Health Association

Sister Thecla   Catholic University
Washington, D. C.

A. L. Van Horn, M.D.   Medical Director
Kate Macy Ladd Fund

Miss Hildegarde Wagner   Assistant to the Director
New York State Joint Hospital Survey and Planning Commission

Miss Margaret W. Wagner   Executive Director
Benjamin Rose Institute
Cleveland, Ohio

James O. Watson, D.O.   Chief of Staff
Doctors' Hospital
Columbus, Ohio

Benjamin V. White, M.D.   Co-author, *Diagnosis in Daily Practice*
Hartford, Connecticut

William R. Willard, M.D.   Associate Professor of Public Health
Yale University Medical School

《 V 》

A National Program
for Maternal and Child Health

DURING the past three decades a great body of new knowledge about child growth and development has been made available to help parents in the rearing of their families. Much of this new knowledge is concerned with positive health, that is, not only freedom from disease but also a condition of well-being of body, emotions, and mind. We know today that illness is not merely a matter of germs, viruses, or physical deformities. It is *feeling* as much as being. A child's feeling about a test in school can produce as serious a stomach ache as eating a spoiled custard.

Although the saving of many hundred thousand lives among mothers and babies has been recorded in the annals of public health progress during the past two decades, the measure of success must not be looked upon only in terms of falling death rates. The important questions before the nation are: For what kind of a life are these mothers and babies being saved? Are we saving thousands from the grave merely to condemn them to limp through life half well? Are we bringing strong, healthy babies into weak, unhealthy, disturbed families? Do expectant parents really enjoy being expectant? Are young parents taking on the responsibilities of a family without knowledge of what these responsibilities really mean or how they originated in the biological mysteries of nature?

There is, as yet, no yardstick to measure the degree of success achieved in terms of positive health for the mother, the child, or the family. The following facts, however, indicate that portion of progress in maternal and child health which *is* measurable.

Maternal Care

The high tide in the number of births in the United States was reached in 1947, with 3,910,000 babies born. Nearly 80 per cent of all these babies were born in hospitals. Eighty-four per cent of white mothers had their babies in hospitals, as compared with only 40 per cent of non-white mothers; 2 per cent of white births were unattended by a physician, whereas 38 per cent of non-white had no medical care. City dwellers had 91 per cent of their babies in hospitals, but in the country this percentage fell to 61. A rapid increase in the hospitalization of maternity patients during the past decade took place without a similar increase in the number of hospital beds. This resulted in serious overcrowding in hospitals. In 1947 there were 84,000 maternity beds in hospitals approved by the American Medical Association and 7,300 more in unapproved hospitals. In 1945, 177,000 mothers had no medical attendance at childbirth, and 4 out of 5 of these mothers lived in rural areas. There are less than 1,900 obstetricians certified by the American Board of Obstetrics and Gynecology. Nearly half of these are in the twelve metropolitan areas of over 1,000,000 population. Two states have only one certified specialist in obstetrics; four others have only two each. The total number of doctors who limit their practice to obstetrics is 4,076. General practitioners with varying degrees of training in obstetrics deliver a large proportion of the mothers and usually without recourse to assistance when needed from specialists.

From 1933 to 1946 the maternal death rate in the United States fell from 62 to 21 per 10,000 live births. There is a striking difference in the maternal death rates as between whites and non-whites and as between states. For white mothers, the maternal death rate fell from 56 to 17 in the period from 1933 to 1945; for non-whites, from 97 to 45. In Wyoming, the maternal death rate in 1945 was 9. In Mississippi, it was 38. In Minnesota, the State Medical Association found in a survey that 9 out of 10 mothers who died in childbirth had inadequate care, and 7 out of 10 could have been saved by good care.

One of the most significant changes in recent years has been the growing awareness among expectant parents of the need for good care early in pregnancy. A large proportion now seek care by the third month and some are learning to select wisely their doctor and hospital.

The quality of obstetric care given by obstetricians and general practitioners has been responsible in a large measure for the great progress in the past decade, aided by such advances as the sulfas, penicillin, and streptomycin, the wider use of blood transfusions and plasma, X-ray examination of the pelvis, better nutrition, knowledge about the Rh factor, stricter hospital regulations, and higher qualifications for the training and licensing of midwives. The emphasis on breast feeding and on rooming the mother and baby together in the hospital, the growing concern for emotional security of mother and baby and the whole family, newer methods of anesthesia, and the growing interest in natural childbirth—all these have contributed to improving the health and well-being of mother and baby.

Another change in maternity care has been the shortening of the period of hospitalization. Some mothers are sent home as early as the first day after their babies are born, too often without regard to home conditions and without provision for medical or housekeeping service. Others stay until the fifth or sixth day. In only a few hospitals do mothers remain for more than ten days.

Care of Children

There are 45,000,000 children under eighteen years of age in the United States. They live in about one-half of the families of the nation. They are concentrated in low-income families and low-income states. Three out of five live in families with incomes of less than $2,100. Four out of five live in families with incomes of less than $3,000 a year. One-half of the nation's children live in thirty-two states with only one-third of the national income. Farm families have about 30 per cent of the children and only 11 per cent of the income.

Over 100,000 babies die every year in their first year of life. Two-thirds of these die in the first month of life. Although great progress has been made in reducing the death rate of children after one month of age, little headway has been made in cutting down on the deaths of younger infants. More infant deaths are attributed to premature birth than to any other factor. About 12 out of every 1,000 babies born alive die because they were born prematurely. In good hospitals where specialized facilities are available this rate has been cut to about 6.

From Pearl Harbor to VJ-Day, 281,000 Americans were killed in action. In the same period, 430,000 babies died in the first year of life. Many of these babies could have been saved.

The mortality rate for children of pre-school age has dropped more than the rate for any other age group. It was cut in half during the period from 1933 to 1945. The death rate of children from five to fourteen years of age has been almost halved in the same period. As deaths from other causes are prevented, accidents and rheumatic fever and heart disease move up on the list, with accidents now the most frequent killer of children after the age of one.

Over 1,400,000 children are handicapped by diabetes, tuberculosis, epilepsy, rheumatic fever and rheumatic heart disease, orthopedic and

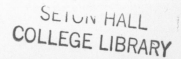

plastic defects. Another million have hearing defects, 4,000,000 have visual defects, and 20,000,000 have dental defects. The figures on mental health are not known, but 18 out of every 100 4-F's in the draft were rejected because of mental and personality disorders. Most of the problems of mental health start in childhood.

The number of employed children is considerably higher than before the war. Only one-third of the states have established a basic minimum age of sixteen years for employment outside school hours or in manufacturing. Employment of children in commercialized agriculture is for the most part unregulated. The war-time relaxation of child-labor standards and the lack of adequate legislative protection in the employment of children endanger their opportunity for physical and mental health and development.

There are 43,000 hospital beds for children in the United States, which comprise 9 per cent of the total. Experts believe that about 15 per cent of the beds in general hospitals should be set aside for children.

Of the 3,500 pediatricians in the country, more than half are in the twelve major metropolitan areas. Most children are cared for by general practitioners, and 46 per cent of these practitioners have had little or no hospital training in pediatrics. Only a few general practitioners have access to pediatric specialists in time of need.

Medical services for children throughout the country are spotty. This is true of general medical care; of well-child conferences; of public health nursing, social, dental, mental hygiene, and school health services; and of convalescent care. A sample study of eight states by the American Academy of Pediatrics showed that children in some states receive only one-half as much care as children in other states. It is safe to assume that no state provides too much care for its children, and there are areas that are grossly deficient in medical care for children.

Approximately 26,000,000 children are enrolled in elementary and secondary schools in the United States. It is impossible to know the total amount of money spent for school health services, but studies have shown that expenditures range from one cent to $3.00 per year per child. Many agencies are involved in providing this service. A report dated 1941 showed that health departments in the 48 states and 2 territories have full responsibility in 5 states, and the education department in one state; health and education departments share responsibility in 44 states. This does not mean, however, that school health services are available to all children. Some 4,000,000 children aged from five to fourteen are living in communities that have no medical service at all in their public elementary schools.

Similarly, a large number of schools are without health or physical education programs. For example, estimates indicate that only 20 per cent of the pupils in the last two years of high school are enrolled in health education and only 50 per cent, roughly, in physical education.

Nevertheless, gains have been made in the health practices of both families and students. Surveys indicate more positive attitudes toward good health practices, a greatly increased concern for safety, a livelier awareness of and more interest in health problems, and less reliance on quackery and superstition. Children are taller and heavier than they were formerly.

Expenditures and Programs

The total sum now spent in the United States for maternal and child health by the states, counties, and cities, by voluntary health agencies, hospitals, nursing agencies, and other organizations, and by individuals has never been computed, nor has the value of maternal and child health services provided by doctors in their private offices. From 1935 to 1946, Federal expenditures under the Social Security Act for these purposes increased from $6,650,000 to $18,500,000. Seven million children were aided by the national school-lunch program during 1946-47, at a cost of $71,000,000. The health care of mothers and children, nevertheless, is still provided on a hit-or-miss basis, with no complete program to provide complete family health care.

Implications. Confronted by such facts as these, the nation has two choices. One is to relax in pride over the gains we have made in the past. The other is to face up to our unfinished business.

It is clear that, as a nation, we have no plan to put health opportunities and safeguards within the reach of all mothers and children, white and Negro, urban and rural, rich and poor. It is time we had such a plan.

A nation that is ready to spend billions for past and future wars, that spends each year hundreds of millions to support and protect the prices of potatoes and other products, should gladly invest whatever is necessary to protect the health and strength of its mothers and children. This is not a job simply for the Federal government, nor just a job for our public servants. It is a job that must be done in the best American tradition with private enterprise, the voluntary agencies, the private practitioners in all professions, paired with government at Federal, state, and local levels. And success will come with the total participation of all the people in every local community.

Our task at this Assembly was to suggest how this teamwork can be developed and to mark the road ahead to positive health for all mothers and children.

CONCLUSIONS AND RECOMMENDATIONS

Because other sections of the National Health Assembly considered nutrition, dental care, environmental sanitation, mental hygiene, and the chronic diseases common in childhood, these important factors were not considered in the Section on a National Program for Maternal and Child Health.

Although detailed reports of the Section's subcommittees follow later in the chapter, certain recommendations were deemed of such importance that they are included in the following summary:

1. A vigorous program of research in matters related to child life should be established and supported, where necessary, by increased Federal grants. Such research should include a combined attack from the fields of medicine, psychology, anthropology, sociology, education, economics, and other related fields, with special emphasis on accidents, rheumatic fever, premature birth, child behavior, the ways of modifying the attitudes of parents, and the effects on children of the changing patterns of family life.

2. A central clearing house should be established in which research problems and projects may be recorded in order to maintain a free exchange of information for all workers, to avoid duplication of effort, and to suggest research needed to fill gaps in our knowledge.

3. Federal grants should be increased and extended to provide training of professional personnel responsible for medical care and health supervision of mothers and children.

4. The newer knowledge in child rearing, in pediatrics, in obstetrics, and in related fields must be brought to those on the job of caring for mothers and children—particularly to the general practitioner—through extension courses and other methods.

5. The Children's Bureau and other appropriate Federal agencies and professional organizations should expand their present work of developing standards of care for maternal and child health. The psychological, social, and physical needs of the individual should be taken into account. Standards should be set up, whenever possible, in a form that will make them useful to the local community that wishes to use them.

6. There should be only one standard of hospital care for all mothers and children—a standard which puts into practice the newest and best medical and nursing knowledge and techniques for each patient and uses every modern facility and service on the basis of medical need rather than on the basis of ability to pay or other barriers. This care must insure the emotional security as well as the personal dignity of each patient and family.

The development or revision of hospital licensing systems is recommended. Systems which provide merely inspections for sanitary and fire hazards and which emphasize minimum standards are inadequate. A revised licensing system, placing full authority in the hands of the health department, should aim at achieving standards, not minimum requirements. The enforcement of licensing laws is more effective in raising the level of service in hospitals when educational guidance, rather than mere inspection, is provided by highly qualified hospital consultants.

7. A positive program of mental health should permeate all services for mothers and children and should be an integral part of all community health programs for children, including those for adolescents.

8. A more vigorous program for the education of parents in child rearing should be undertaken. Although members of many professions and a variety of community agencies are concerned with this program, the prime responsibility for developing and maintaining extended programs for parent education must rest with the health and education authorities.

9. In the education of physicians, nurses, social workers, teachers, and other professional personnel who work with children, more information concerning the growth, development, and behavior of normal children should be included.

10. A comprehensive program of nutrition service and nutrition education should be an essential part of all health, education, and welfare programs for mothers and children. An adequate number of qualified nutritionists should be provided for this purpose.

11. Local communities should take the initiative in developing experimental projects designed to solve their own local problems, and a wide variety of methods of attack should be encouraged.

12. Since accidents are the chief cause of the death of children older than one year, it is recommended that accident prevention be considered a major responsibility of state and local health departments and that persons qualified in this field should be included on their staffs.

13. To have an adequate and sound national plan for the treatment,

care, and rehabilitation of children with physical and mental handicaps, a census of such children should be taken by the Federal government at regular intervals beginning with the census in 1950.

14. Services for the rehabilitation of physically and mentally handicapped children should be expanded with increased Federal and state support and should be co-ordinated with the programs of voluntary agencies. Current planning for the relation of medical centers to regional and community hospitals should be considered in connection with the development of more and better institutional, out-patient, and convalescent service and after-care of handicapped children.

15. Because of conflicting and restrictive laws and regulations, children are often prevented from securing available health services. A critical study should be made which should result in the removal of such legal limitations and promote better care.

16. The Federal Security Administrator should call a national conference on school health, with adequate representation of the constituent units of the Federal government and of medical, public health, dental, nursing, educational, and other professional and related voluntary and lay groups, to determine goals and recommend procedures for the following purposes:

(a) To clarify the contributions which all related groups can make and determine how they can best work together;
(b) To help insure more systematic, better co-ordinated, and widespread programs;
(c) To promote the integration of school efforts with other community efforts; and
(d) To set an example of co-ordinated action for states and for local communities.

The governors of the respective states and appropriate local officials should be encouraged to call similar state-, county-, and city-wide conferences.

17. Federal and state aid should be provided for the extension and improvement of an integrated program of health instruction. Physical education and health services are indispensable and inherently related parts of an effective program for all children of school age.

18. Advances made in past years toward developing and reaching optimum standards and practices of employment and working conditions of women and minors are of vital importance to the health of our nation's children. Legislation and practices in this regard should be strengthened

rather than be permitted to go backward (as was threatened in many parts of the country and as occurred in some during the stress of the war and post-war periods).

19. To achieve complete health for every child, voluntary and official agencies should develop closer working relations and seek every opportunity for joint effort.

REPORTS OF SUBCOMMITTEES
SUBCOMMITTEE ON THE TRAINING OF PERSONNEL

Physicians

The Section on Maternal and Child Health emphasizes the importance of more training, both undergraduate and postgraduate, for general practitioners, pediatricians, obstetricians, and other specialists in maternal and child care.

Nursing Service

The quality of nursing service given in maternity and pediatric care depends largely on the improvement of basic nursing education and the stressing of the emotional, social, and health aspects of care. Qualified young women should be recruited and directed to schools which meet the standards of institutions of higher learning.

The desirable goal for the next ten years is one public health nurse to every 2,500 people for health teaching and for preventive and bedside care. Within the next five years the goal should be at least one public health nurse to every 5,000 persons. Facilities for postgraduate education in advanced maternity and pediatric nursing should be expanded so that many more teachers, supervisors, and consultants in these fields can be prepared. More specialists in maternal and child-health nursing should be placed in strategic administrative and teaching positions in basic nursing programs.

Special nursing consultants should be placed on the staff of more state and local health agencies, to improve nursing service related to the care of mothers and children.

Direct services of advanced maternity nurses or nurse-midwives should be recognized as a part of a total program for maternity care. Effective methods for the control of untrained midwives giving care to maternity patients should be developed and maintained until the untrained midwife can be replaced by the trained nurse-midwife.

Practical nurses will eventually comprise an important group in the total provision for nursing services. Methods should be explored for the preparation of various types of auxiliary workers in providing complete care for mothers and children.

Social Services

The expansion of health and medical care programs, hospital facilities, convalescent resources, and mental-hygiene services has increased the demand for social services as an integral part of medical care. The present supply of medical and psychiatric social workers is inadequate to meet this demand. This lack is especially significant in the field of maternal and child health.

Plans for training additional qualified medical and psychiatric social workers should be developed. Assistance should be given to graduate schools of social work to enable more of them to offer approved medical and psychiatric social curricula. This will require increased facilities for supervised field-work experience. Funds for more scholarships are needed through Federal, state, and private resources.

During the next ten years, greater emphasis should be placed on the study of social, emotional, and economic factors as contributing causes to the breakdown of health and the failure to profit as fully as possible from medical services. In the daily practice of medical and psychiatric social workers there is cumulative evidence of the effects of such insecurity. Findings of studies of this type would contribute to sound community planning for mothers and children.

Nutrition

The present supply of nutritionists is inadequate to meet the demands, especially in maternal and child health. During the next ten years an adequate number of qualified nutritionists should be provided to work with public health, education, and welfare agencies. They must be trained in the social as well as in the biological sciences, with emphasis on education and psychology, in order to work effectively in a consultant capacity with nurses, practitioners, teachers, social workers, and lay groups concerned with the nutrition problems of the family.

Federal Grants-in-Aid

More adequate funds are needed to support medical and nursing education, especially in those branches related to maternal and child health.

Lacking adequate resources from medical-school budgets or endowment funds of universities, consideration must be given to the proposal to seek new Federal funds, in addition to increasing the Federal funds already being used in special fields of education, in aid of general medical education, or in specific disciplines in medical curricula which deserve the special attention of this Section.

SUBCOMMITTEE ON THE HEALTH OF THE SCHOOL-AGE CHILD

The statement submitted here is not all-inclusive. Additional proposals which have been widely accepted are found in *Suggested School Health Policies*[1] and similar publications. The necessary omission of some subjects does not mean that the committee does not consider them important.

In much that follows there is an implication of the wide need for increased funds, personnel, and facilities. Constructive legislation on Federal and state levels is needed in order to reach the goals in health services and education in community and school set forth in this report. Much can be accomplished by co-operative planning and a better use of existing facilities and personnel. To achieve progress an informed public opinion is essential.

[1] *Suggested School Health Policies* (New York: Health Education Council, 10 Downing St., 1946), 46 pp., 25c.

Need for Co-operative Planning

It is recommended that the Federal Security Administrator call a National Conference on School Health with adequate representation of the units of the Federal government concerned and of educational, public health, medical, dental, nursing, and other professional and related official, voluntary, and lay groups to determine goals and recommend procedures for the following purposes: (a) to clarify the contributions which all related groups can make and determine how they can best work together in the attainment of specified goals; (b) to help insure more systematic, better co-ordinated, and widespread programs; (c) to promote the integration of school efforts with those in the community; and (d) to set an example of co-ordinated action for states and for local communities.

It is recommended that a national committee be formed and charged with the responsibility of implementing the goals in the above recommendation.

The governors of the respective states and designated local officials should be encouraged to call state-, county-, and city-wide conferences, representing all governmental, professional, and voluntary groups with related interests, to implement the objectives of the two recommendations above.

Since community health programs, including organized local health units staffed with an adequate number of full-time personnel, are essential to a health program for school-age children, we believe that all groups interested in the health of the school child should work actively for the organization and development of local public health units.

It is recommended that a critical study be made of Federal, state, and local laws and regulations with a view to developing, where necessary, the legislation needed for the co-operative planning and execution of school health programs.

Training of Health Service and Education Personnel

It is essential that the training of teachers, physicians, dentists, nurses, and others who serve the child of school age include: (a) orientation in the general educational program and philosophy of the school, as well as training in their special professional areas; and (b) basic knowledge of the child's behavior and development and his emotional as well as his physical health.

Principles of co-operation and joint planning should extend to the training of school personnel.

For health service personnel and public health administrators, the orientation and understanding of the educational administration and philosophy should be obtained through the co-operation of schools of public health and schools of education. For health personnel in service, including teachers, such orientation should be obtained by means of in-service institutes, workshops, summer courses, or other jointly sponsored training activities.

For the training of health teachers it is recommended that health education courses be made functional rather than technical; that teachers preparing for the elementary and secondary fields be required to take courses in health and physical education and mental hygiene; that all health teachers and supervisors be adequately trained and certificated; that in-service training be made available to health teachers through summer courses and clinics. Attention should also be given to the selection of health teachers with respect to their physical and emotional adjustment.

Mental Hygiene for School Children

Since health includes mental as well as physical aspects, consideration should be given to the mental-hygiene effects of all school administrative practices, the curriculum, classroom procedures, and the teacher-child, child-child, and parent-child relationships in the school.

Training in mental hygiene should be included in the preparation of school administrators and teachers. Material for training the child in understanding his own development and mental hygiene should also be integrated into the school curriculum.

Health Instruction and Physical Education and School Health Services

Health instruction and physical education and health services are indispensable and inherently related parts of an effective program for all children, including the handicapped child. A proper emphasis on a preventive and educational approach during the strategic child years will greatly insure success in eliminating or reducing many of the needs for corrective and medical procedures.

The school curriculum should include a program of comprehensive instruction in physical education planned progressively for all grades, including a modified program of activities adapted to the abilities of the physically handicapped. In addition, all schools should provide opportunities for year-round recreational programs in which consideration is given to the values of camping and outdoor education.

There should be a program of health instruction, emphasizing personal health, community health, home care of the sick, family relations, first-aid, safety, and nutrition.

The Nutrition Program

The nutritional program, including the school lunch, is a significant part of the total education program both for improving the nutrition of the children and the teachers and for instructing them in regard to the relation of nutrition to health and growth. The following are recommended:

(1) Providing adequate school lunches, or whatever meals are needed during school hours, for all children, teachers, and staff

(2) Discouraging schools from selling any "commodities" which do not contribute to the health and well-being of children

(3) Providing an appropriate environment in which food can be prepared, served, and eaten

(4) Directing nutrition instruction toward children's food habits, the availability of foods, and the ability to procure foods needed for health

(5) Determining food habits of children at appropriate intervals for (a) locating points to emphasize in nutrition instruction and (b) evaluating the nutrition program

(6) Co-ordinating nutrition instruction at both elementary and secondary

school levels with (a) the school lunch program, (b) other phases of the school health program, and (c) appropriate areas of the curriculum

(7) Providing necessary nutrition instruction to school-lunch personnel, parents, and others concerned with child health

Administration of the School Health Service Program

The problem of administrative responsibility for health services for school children is a major stumbling block to progress. Differences of opinion largely reflect an attempt to adhere to the dictum of single-agency administrative responsibility. Compliance with this dictum is impossible because, on the one hand, educational authorities have basic administrative responsibility for all activities taking place in the schools and, on the other hand, health authorities have official responsibility for activities for safeguarding and promoting the health of all the community. The solution lies in the direction of joint program planning and execution which recognizes the responsibilities of each agency in its respective area of competency. For example, the circumstances under which child-health examinations will be carried out are a matter of joint planning; the technical conduct of the examination and plans for corrective care are the responsibility of the health authority, whereas the use of the results of the examination for instruction is the responsibility of the educational authority.

Nursing service. Recognizing that the school child cannot be separated from the family group, it follows that nursing service to the child can best be given by one who has responsibility for the whole family, in accordance with the principle of generalized nursing service.

Your committee recognizes that educational authorities have been compelled to employ school nurses because of inadequate generalized nursing service in the community. Asking that the service of these nurses be integrated into a generalized program and at the same time, because of the legitimate demands of the generalized program, reducing materially the service actually given in the schools would arouse protest. Though it may properly be said that a better-planned generalized program will benefit the child more, both immediately and in the long run, nevertheless it is unrealistic to ask a school official to give up an established service before provision is made for an acceptable program of generalized service.

The first necessity, therefore, is adequate generalized nursing service planned on a community-wide basis. This service may have to be developed by degrees. At all times there should be close co-ordination of all nurses engaged in public health nursing irrespective of the agency by which they are employed. Such an arrangement, by reducing duplication, will be more economical both for the school and for the community.

Functions of the teacher. Because of her close daily contact with the child the teacher occupies a strategic position in the entire health program and should participate in all its phases.

Follow-up and treatment services. It should be recognized that the school health service programs are not complete until the necessary facilities are provided in the community for the medical treatment needs of all children. Plans for the extension of medical treatment services for school-age children should be developed by health authorities in co-operation with medical, dental, nursing, educational, and other professional and lay groups.

Educational Provisions for the Handicapped Child

The handicapped child of school age should have educational opportunities made accessible to him at least to the same degree as they are to non-handicapped children. Toward this end, special provisions should be made when necessary in regard to such matters, among others, as transportation, home or institutional instruction, reduced teacher-pupil ratio, psychological testing, health care, building favorable attitudes toward self help, and modification of class location, program, or day's schedule.

Over and beyond the steps necessary to make the ordinary curriculum accessible to him, the handicapped child of school age may need special measures to help him utilize his full capacities, such as remedial reading, lip reading, hearing aids, intensified health supervision, individualized remedial physical education, vocational planning and aid, mental health counseling, and assistance in building helpful attitudes toward his handicap.

Specially trained personnel may be required in addition to special facilities and programs. All special provisions should point toward the child's participation in the regular school program.

It is recommended that steps be taken by way of legislation or other necessary measures at the Federal, state, or local levels to provide adequate support for the education of handicapped children of school age.

Safety and Sanitation of the School Environment

Every community should provide a safe and sanitary school environment. This is essential not only for the protection of the school child but also as a means of building favorable attitudes toward sanitation; these will encourage the child to work for the gradual improvement of his surroundings wherever he may be.

SUBCOMMITTEE ON PARENT EDUCATION

Parent education is an attempt to communicate to parents the new knowledge and understanding of child growth and the recently developed insights into personality development. It is much more than the teaching of subject matter, since it involves radical changes in the ideas and beliefs and expectations of parents and the replacement of old concepts by newer ones. Parent education should be available to growing boys and girls who will be the future parents, to expectant parents, and to parents of children of all ages.

We believe that all expectant parents should have available to them the fullest knowledge about the life processes involved in childbearing, including the importance of their own feelings and attitudes. They must know the facts about how a baby is conceived, grows, and is born and the relation of this information to the selection of a doctor, a nurse, and a hospital and to the creation of a happy home into which a child is to be born and in which he will grow and thrive and become a well-balanced individual in his own right.

This education for family living begins with conception of the baby and continues through infancy, childhood, adolescence, and adulthood. The attitudes and habits which are created in the growing-up years come into full play when these young people themselves become parents.

The foregoing statement of principles suggests the following recommendations:

1. Parent education should be an integral element of all efforts to promote the physical, mental, and social well-being of children. Opportunity should be provided for parents to have full access to the best that is known in the field of child health and development. This is the joint responsibility of the Federal, state, and local health and education authorities and of private agencies, institutions, and professional workers engaged in family guidance and child rearing.

2. Parent education should embrace knowledge of the principles of physical care which contribute to sound bodily growth as well as of the basic factors which enter into the intellectual, emotional, and social development of the child. As far as possible, therefore, all professional groups involved in counseling with parents (and this includes general practitioners, obstetricians, pediatricians, teachers, nurses, social workers, and others) should have at their command a unified body of information about physical and mental growth and their interrelationships.

3. All professional schools preparing workers for the field of child rearing should incorporate into their curricula an integrated body of knowledge about child growth and development, parent-child relationships, and family life.

An opportunity should be afforded to such workers in training to observe the behavior of normal children and to participate in the application of this integrated knowledge to problems of child rearing and family life. Similar training for the professional personnel on the job in these categories should be provided through extension courses and institutes. Particular attention should be paid to the general practitioner, who has such a large opportunity and responsibility to educate parents.

4. All professional workers should accept responsibility for acquiring and applying a knowledge of principles and methods to be employed in the teaching of these facts in a manner which will insure their fullest use in the lives of children and their families.

A substantial knowledge of the techniques of getting information to people and influencing attitudes and practices now exists. This needs to be clarified and more fully understood by all groups engaged in the child-rearing professions.

Recognizing the importance of parental attitudes, a special study of methods which will stimulate parents to put into practice the facts at their command is much needed and should be undertaken.

5. Although our knowledge in both the physical and the psychological areas has grown rapidly in recent years, much remains to be discovered before parent education can substantially fulfill its responsibility as a social function. Continuous research in both the physical and the psychological areas of child life and in the factors which enter into the shaping of parental attitudes is imperative. Centers of education, whether private or governmental, should furnish

active leadership in guiding basic research activities in child development and family life. More funds and resources should be devoted to this purpose.

6. Parent education is the responsibility of members of many professions and a variety of community agencies, both voluntary and official, but the primary responsibility should rest with the health and education authorities. These agencies should therefore undertake to provide for the development and maintenance of parent-education programs. Parent education should not be limited to parents but needs to be integrated into all forms of education of both children and adults. It begins in the home and in the school and continues in the doctor's office, in the clinic waiting room, in the nurse's home visits, in the minister's interviews, in classes for expectant parents, in counseling and family interviews, in the press, over the radio, and by other means of mass education.

7. All programs of parent education should be planned so as to mobilize the fullest participation by parents in teaching each other as well as their children.

Subcommittee on Program to Raise Standards of Maternity, Newborn, and Pediatric Hospital Care

Standards of hospital care for mothers and children will be raised when the people know the meaning and the value of good care. The following recommendations are offered as indications of the standards that should be established and the means by which they can be achieved:

1. There can be only one standard of hospital care for all mothers and children—that which puts into practice the newest and best medical and nursing knowledge and techniques for each patient and uses every modern facility and service on the basis of medical need rather than on the basis of ability to pay or other barriers. This care must insure the emotional security as well as the personal dignity of each patient and family.

The development or revision of hospital licensing systems is recommended because it is an important force in ensuring a high standard of care. A revised licensing system, placing full authority in the hands of the health department, should aim at achieving standards, not minimum requirements. The enforcement of licensing laws is more effective in raising the level of service in hospitals when educational guidance (rather than mere inspection) is provided by highly qualified hospital consultants.

2. The community facilities for the prevention and treatment of disease should be joined with the facilities for the development of mental and physical health, if the needs of the whole personality of each mother and child are to be met.

The hospital should be the center around which the health-promoting forces of the community revolve. Under this joining of forces every mother and child could receive continuous care and supervision in health and in illness.

3. The use of professional and auxiliary personnel in the hospital care of mothers and children must be carefully studied, and every effort must be made to release doctors and nurses from tasks not requiring professional skills by the addition of technicians, orderlies, messengers, nurses' aides, and so on, wherever this can be safely arranged.

4. Every hospital having maternity and children's service should have out-patient services closely integrated with all phases and departments of care for mothers and children in the hospital.

5. Facilities should be available so that all babies can be born in hospitals. Fewer additional hospital beds will be needed if an annex can be added for the care of normal mothers and babies 24 to 48 hours after delivery. The care in the annex should simulate home care at its best. For mothers who have sufficient housekeeper assistance in their homes, early return from the hospital will be possible if provision is made for necessary medical and nursing super-vision from the hospital.

For areas where good maternity hospital services are not yet available, home services provided by nurse-midwives under direction of an obstetrician, with access to hospital services when necessary, is recommended. Obstetrical con-sultation should also be available to all general practitioners, if and when needed.

6. A program of care for convalescent children, closely affiliated with hospital services for children, should provide for institutional or foster-home care as may best be suited to the individual child and to the community. Adequate service to meet the psychological, nutritional, social, medical, and nursing needs must be provided. Provision must also be made for education for recrea-tional, occupational, and physical therapy when needed.

7. The services of the combined hospital–health center should be made readily available to all mothers and children, no matter where they live. The development of a series of interlocking regional plans is imperative to provide this care according to the economic situation and geography of each region, with special attention to the provision of transportation to and from the hos-pital and to itinerant clinics and health services closely related to the hospital and staffed by skilled personnel.

8. The Children's Bureau and other Federal agencies should, jointly with professional organizations, develop standards of care for *all* maternal and child-health services—these standards to include provision for the total care of each mother and child and take into account the psychological, social, and physical needs of the individual.

9. Every citizen should be made aware of the health needs of himself, his family, and his community and should be taught to select good medical, nurs-ing, and hospital care.

Subcommittee on a Program of Research in Child Life

Enormous advances have been made in recent years in our fund of usable knowledge in the physical sciences. Research has become the people's business, for they have learned its essential importance in their very survival and in the constant quest for a fuller life. The expansion in research, a large proportion of which has been through liberal government spending, has been chiefly in the physical sciences.

Much less spectacular, but no less important, has been the gradual acquisition of knowledge in the growth and development of children, in our cultural patterns, and in the social adjustment of people. Many workers in isolated situations have added to our knowledge of human behavior, but no all-out concerted effort has been made to find answers to many of the problems concerning the health and welfare of our children—a field of research as important to the people as that of nuclear physics.

Ever increasing funds are being spent for services to people, but there has been little or no increase for the investigation of the basic problems which produce the needs for service. More infant deaths are associated with premature birth than with any other factor. The care necessary to save the prematurely born infant is expensive, often running into hundreds or thousands of dollars per individual. Compared to the cost of care, the amount expended on research into the causes of prematurity is insignificant. The situation is the same for other diseases, such as cerebral palsy, rheumatic fever, and congenital defects.

In the social field the same disproportion exists. Effort and money are expended in caring for the end results of a problem—the emotionally ill, the socially maladjusted, the delinquents—but there is a continuing neglect of research into the basic causes underlying these problems.

Just as child health is no longer considered entirely the result of medical care but is recognized as the product of endeavor by many professional and non-professional disciplines, so research in child health has broadened to include many fields which may better be grouped under the term "child life." The interaction of a child and his environment is so complex that research into almost any of his problems must have a multi-disciplined approach. Often a problem which on the surface appears to be a simple physical situation, such as inability or failure of mothers to breast-feed infants, may require an approach from such fields as medicine, psychology, anthropology, economics, or a combination of them.

Knowledge of the basic facts about children is essential to our economic and social well-being. Therefore the Maternal and Child Health Section of the National Health Assembly recommends that a vigorous program of research in child life be stimulated, encouraged, and supported.

Types of Research Needed

A few examples of the types of research urgently needed are listed below. All are national in scope or significance and beyond the planning capacity of any individual or group within a single research organization.

Changing patterns of family life. The family as an institution is undergoing rapid changes. Studies are needed which cut across the fields of health, the social services, mental hygiene, education, and the cultural patterns of child rearing. Consideration should also be given to the economic basis of the family support of children.

Personality and environmental factors behind various kinds of child behavior. There is need for a study of child life which will focus on the "natural history" of various outcomes—delinquent and problem children, impaired and handicapped children. This would throw light on the genesis of these outcomes, now largely studied retrospectively after the child's behavior has been determined.

Attitudes of parents toward healthful living and ways of modifying such attitudes. There is need for study related to the fact that diagnostic clinics and school health programs often fail of their objectives because the professional personnel concerned do not recognize the force of attitudes and because they lack knowledge of how to change these attitudes.

Nursery-school experience. There should be an organized effort to appraise the effect of group experience for the pre-school child.

Accidents. More children over one year of age die as a result of accidents than from any other single cause. Many others are permanently crippled. Much could be learned about the factors, both physical and emotional, which cause accidents, including those from poisoning.

Rheumatic fever. This kills and cripples more children than any other disease. The life history of the disease, the problems of regional differences, and the causative factors all desperately need further investigation. Observations should be made on the kind of community and family where rheumatic fever occurs and the kind of state or community program best able to meet the many problems involved.

Maternity and prematurity. There is urgent need for securing further basic knowledge as to the causes of abortion, premature labor, toxemia, sterility, and fertility. Many critical problems relating to premature birth need to be investigated.

Review and integration of recent and current research programs. The current lack of co-ordination of research projects related to various aspects of child life results in unnecessary duplication. A central clearing house to which research protocols might be submitted without implying any regimentation of research would raise the quality of research and avoid many false steps. At the same time, such a clearing house, as it collects information on research in progress or completed, could point out the desirability of research in uncovered areas.

Many more problems could be added. Early infancy is full of problems for which our answers so far are largely in the form of theory and speculation. Self-regulating schedules, rooming-in and how it may be accomplished in our modern hospital system, and the infant's need for early attachment to one person and how that affects our adoption procedures all need thorough and impartial investigation. Already wide application is being made of theories of child care for which adequate supporting data are not available.

SUBCOMMITTEE ON THE CARE OF HANDICAPPED CHILDREN, INCLUDING THE PREVENTION OF ACCIDENTS

There are at least 300,000 crippled children in the United States, according to the incomplete registers of the various states; undoubtedly the total number greatly exceeds this figure. Because of the recent notable rise in birth rate, the number of handicapped individuals will probably increase in the years to come. Furthermore, with the advances in medical science, many who in the past would have died for want of adequate care will live longer, although they will carry with them through life varying degrees of handicapping conditions. Thus it can be seen that the problems of the handicapped will probably continue in increasing numbers in the decade ahead.

It is therefore the responsibility of the nation to marshal its resources to prevent the production of handicapping conditions and to lessen the severity of each condition physically, mentally, and socially to the end that a large segment of our population will be assured a proper place in an enlightened society. As steps in that direction, your committee makes the following recommendations:

1. All official state programs for handicapped or crippled children should broaden their basic definitions of handicapped children—which are now often limited to those with orthopedic and plastic surgery conditions—to include those with other physical handicaps, such as heart disease, neurological conditions including cerebral palsy and epilepsy, speech, hearing, and visual defects, and other conditions which can be considered as producing handicaps to the individual afflicted or to his family because of definite social, psychological, or economic implications.

2. A national census based on standardized definitions should be taken of such persons, a study which it would seem desirable to include in the 1950 national census and periodically thereafter.

3. In order to obtain the fullest service and to avoid duplication, the efforts of all official, voluntary, and private rehabilitation agencies and personnel participating in giving care should be co-ordinated; also rehabilitation centers should (a) be developed in conjunction with existing or projected medical centers and (b) provide for in-patient and out-patient service to insure accessibility for the severely handicapped and for the individual who resides at a distance.

4. Eligibility requirements for any service should be primarily the need for service rather than the age of the handicapped individual.

5. Educational, recreational, governmental, and other public and semi-public buildings should be designed and equipped to insure greater utility to the handicapped and to set an example for other construction.

6. More adequate provisions should be made for the institutional care of children with severe handicaps, both mental and physical, who cannot receive benefit from the usual therapeutic and educational programs (designed for so-called incurable conditions) in order to improve the physical, mental, and social health of the family as a whole; also institutional care should provide adequate health supervision and should help the child to develop to the best of his limited ability.

7. Accident prevention should be recognized as a major health problem; official responsibility for this field should be vested in health departments; and in each state health department and large metropolitan health department an official should be appointed to develop and co-ordinate community activities in this field.

Departments of preventive medicine and health education in the universities and in the health departments should carry a major responsibility in this program. Other efforts such as those of the police and fire departments, safety councils, American Red Cross, departments of education, and the medical profession need to be enlisted in co-operative programs.

Research needs to be carried on to the end that the nation will be familiar with the real magnitude of the problem, the causes of accidents, and methods to prevent the large numbers of accidents which we know are preventable. Various types of personnel will have to be trained to meet the needs.

Support both in the research and in the community program needs to be given to a major extent by the medical and allied professions in order to carry out most effectually the public educational program. The prevention of accidents is as much a health problem as is the prevention of disease.

GOALS FOR MATERNITY AND CHILD HEALTH: LOOKING AHEAD FOR TEN YEARS

Whenever stock is taken of achievements in any area of effort designed to increase the chances of a good life and to improve the conditions of living, the people turn to examine the status of public and private action in behalf of children and to assess the extent and quality of the care provided. This is natural because the world has long recognized that the strength of any nation lies in its children—in their health and vigor, in their capacity to learn, in their ability to grow as thinking, reasoning human beings and to develop stage by stage from infancy through childhood and youth until they reach adulthood as fully mature persons, secure in their ability to take their place as citizens and as parents of the next generation.

Our task is to assess the status of the health of children today, to point out gaps in the services and programs designed to provide health and medical care, and to lay down lines of advance—during the next ten years—which will bring the nation closer to the attainment of our goal of health for all children. Goals for the health of mothers and children can be and have been stated in terms of the rights of the child and of action which, if implemented in full, would assure a highly desirable degree of health to each and every child in this country—health which as defined by the World Health Organization is "a state of complete physical, mental, and social well-being and not merely the absence of disease." As from time to time we restate such goals for a comprehensive program of maternity care and child health, we appreciate that gradually we are coming nearer to attaining them. We realize that many goals could be attained rapidly if vigorous action were taken. We have the technical knowledge and skills necessary for their attainment, but we discover that we are not putting our knowledge to work because certain barriers to action exist—barriers that are economic, sociological, or psychological.

The following goals are set forth as desirable standards toward which action must be directed. Our existing knowledge and skills make possible the attainment of these goals as rapidly as trained personnel, adequate facilities, and economic resources permit.

Goals for Maternity Care and Child-Health Programs

To assure to every child the experiences in life which will result in his attaining adulthood fully mature and healthy in body and mind, emotionally secure, and able to give more than is asked for, to face success and frustration with equanimity, persistence, and tolerance, to be self-reliant, to co-operate with his fellows, to take his place in our democratic society as a thoughtful, responsible citizen concerned with the common good, and "to live harmoniously in a total changing environment."

To accomplish these ends our goals must include:

1. Good maternity care for all mothers—to assure the safety and well-being of the mother and her infant—adequate in every respect according to advancing knowledge of medical care, nutrition, and social and psychological understanding of the needs of mother and child and of the parent-child relationship.

2. Care of the newborn infant of a kind that will not only preserve his life, protect him from infection, nourish him, and assure a good start in his physical growth but also provide him with an opportunity to experience at once the security of close contact with and care and breast feeding by his mother and start him on the road to a normal emotional development.

3. Care during infancy and the years of early childhood that will assure full opportunity for physical, mental, and emotional growth within the limits of the inherent capacity of each individual child—care that will make it possible for every child to experience in his own home adequate food, play and exercise, sunlight, and sleep; abounding physical health and avoidance of preventable disease; emotional and physical security in the care and affection of his parents and in his relationships with all members of his family; opportunity to grow and develop mentally and socially through exploration of his expanding world, through widening contacts with other children, and through skilled guidance of parents and teachers in his learning process.

4. Opportunity for the child as he reaches school age to move out of the family circle into school life protected against the infectious diseases known to be preventable, free from physical defects and adverse conditions that are remediable, secure and confident in family ties yet increasingly able to take his place with his schoolmates in the activities of school life, eager to learn and with an ever-growing sense of curiosity about things around him.

5. Opportunity throughout the years of school life, including adolescence, for each child to experience to the full those activities which will assure his growth and development according to his individual capacity, will promote his physical and mental health, and will permit him to make best use of his inherent talents and capabilities. By such encouragement of each youth's

capacities and the recognition of his need for experiences that will lead to his healthy sexual adjustment, his ability to live happily and harmoniously as a contributing member of society will be enhanced.

6. Opportunity for parents to have full access to the best that is known in the field of child health and development, and for them to have the support and guidance of professionally qualified leaders in meeting the problems of family life and of their own personal adjustment.

7. Extension of health, medical, nursing, nutrition, social, and other auxiliary types of care and service required to provide the kind and amount of care needed by mothers and children until all have equal opportunity for the best care known to medical and related sciences. Included among the persons providing care must be not only professional personnel who give general care but also specialists in each type of service who are particularly equipped by training and experience to care for children and for mothers in the maternity period.

8. Sufficient opportunities for education and training in the special skills required by physicians, nurses, and all other health workers in the care and education of children or in maternity care, including training and experience in giving positive mental-health guidance as well as physical care.

9. Provision of facilities—such as health centers, diagnostic clinics, hospitals, and convalescent homes—in which child-health and medical services and maternity care can be made available to all families who wish to utilize them; provision of all diagnostic, laboratory, and treatment services and equipment and adequate patient accommodations required by physicians and other health workers to provide care in accordance with advancing scientific knowledge of the physical and psychological needs of children and mothers; provision of transportation facilities to increase the accessibility of diagnostic and treatment facilities and services to families living at a distance from them.

Certain phases of the total program of maternal and child health stand out as most in need of concentrated attack in the immediate future in order to make possible substantial progress toward all goals within the next ten years. These phases have been selected for special recommendation in this report, but such selection should not be interpreted as meaning that action toward all goals must not go forward simultaneously. It is believed that total action toward reaching a state of complete health for every child will be hastened and made more effective if attention is now focused on:

(1) More and better-educated professional and technical personnel
(2) An expanded research program in all areas of child life
(3) Parent education and a positive mental-health program permeating the maternity-care program and affecting every state of the child's development
(4) A program of health service and medical care and health instruction for all children of school age

(5) An expanded service to physically and mentally handicapped children

(6) A program to raise the standards of hospital and clinic care for maternity patients and for children

These six areas of attack are not mutually exclusive; they do not lend themselves to action by separate groups of workers or different professions. In fact, there will necessarily be overlapping in action, and planning will be necessary to assure co-ordination and integration into the over-all maternal and child-health program.

APPENDIX

PLANNING COMMITTEE

Leona Baumgartner, M.D., *Chairman*	Director, Bureau of Child Hygiene New York City Department of Health
John P. Hubbard, M.D.	Director, Study of Child Health Services American Academy of Pediatrics
Herschel Alt	Executive Director Jewish Board of Guardians New York, New York
Miss Hazel Corbin	General Director Maternity Center Association New York, New York
Herbert R. Kobes, M.D.	Director, Division of Services for Crippled Children Illinois State Department of Public Health
Duncan E. Reid, M.D.	Obstetrician-in-Chief Boston Lying-In Hospital Boston, Massachusetts

STAFF ASSISTANT

Katherine Bain, M.D.	Director, Division of Research in Child Development, Children's Bureau Social Security Administration, Federal Security Agency

REGISTRANTS

C. Earl Albrecht, M.D.	Commissioner, Territorial Department of Health of Alaska
Miss Corinne M. Bancroft	Director of Nursing Education Children's Hospital Cincinnati, Ohio
Jessie M. Bierman, M.D.	Professor of Maternal and Child Health School of Public Health University of California

Herbert M. Bosch	Chief, Environmental Sanitation Section Minnesota State Department of Health
Mrs. Westroy B. Boyce	National Society for Crippled Children and Adults, Inc.
Coursen B. Conklin, M.D.	Chairman, Legislative Committee American Academy of Pediatrics
Miss Frances K. Crouch	Director, Nursing Service, North Atlantic Area American National Red Cross
Mrs. Horace Davis	Washington, D. C.
Ethel C. Dunham, M.D.	Washington, D. C.
Miss Claudia Durham	Instructor in Public Health Nursing Meharry Medical College School of Nursing
Miss Theo Floyd	Director of Public Health Nursing Georgia State Department of Health
Miss Margaret Gillam	Dietetics Specialist American Hospital Association
Lee Forest Hill, M.D.	Past President, American Academy of Pediatrics
Horace Hughes	Maternity Center Association New York, New York
Mrs. Lois S. Johnson	Editor, *Junior Red Cross News and Journal* American National Red Cross
Mary K. Johnstone, D.O.	Osteopathic Physicians Association
Althea Kessler, M.D.	Assistant Professor of Pediatrics Howard University School of Medicine
L. E. Kling, M.D.	Acting Medical Director Planned Parenthood Federation of America
Ben W. Miller	Executive Secretary American Association for Health, Physical Education, and Recreation
Miss Mary Blanche Moss	Executive Secretary American Association of Medical Social Workers
Miss Mary Elizabeth Murphy	Director, Elizabeth McCormick Memorial Fund
Ralph H. Ojemann, M.D.	Chairman, Parent Education Committee National Congress of Parents and Teachers
Mrs. Carlos Recker	Education Chairman Washington, D. C., Junior League
Oscar Reiss, M.D.	Chairman, Section on Pediatrics American Medical Association

Hilla Sheriff, M.D.	Maternal and Child Health Director South Carolina State Health Department
Mrs. Hester Stoll	Chairman, Washington Group American Association of Medical Social Workers
Lazare Teper	Director of Research International Ladies' Garment Workers' Union
Hart Van Riper, M.D.	Medical Director National Foundation for Infantile Paralysis
John B. Van Why	Director of Health Education Wittenberg College
Alfred Vignec, M.D.	New York Foundling Hospital New York, New York
Alfred W. Wagner	New York State Chairman Community Services Committee Congress of Industrial Organizations
Joseph S. Wall, M.D.	Past President, American Academy of Pediatrics
Myron H. Wegman, M.D.	Professor of Pediatrics Louisiana State University School of Medicine

(VI)

A National
Program for Rural Health

A NATIONAL program for rural health is not a thing apart; it is inter-woven into every program to raise the health standards of the nation. But because improvement in rural health is a major requirement for raising the levels of the national health, and because a variety of factors makes this difficult to achieve, a special section devoted to rural health was set up at the National Health Assembly.

This Section was confronted with a difficult task. Since rural people have a stake in all health and medical programs that seek to raise the health standards of the nation, every subject considered by the Assembly was of deep concern to the Section on a National Program for Rural Health. A basic requirement, however, for making the benefits of modern medical science available to all rural people is a more equitable distri-bution of health personnel, health facilities, health services, and health financing. The Section, therefore, chose to focus its attention on the special rural characteristics which affect the distribution, organization, and financing of health and medical services. It sought to bring into clearer focus the special measures and the particular emphases in general programs needed to enable rural people to enjoy equal opportunity for health and medical services regardless of distance, economic status, race, or creed. It recognized that any measures to raise the health standards of rural people can be achieved only as an integral part of the health pro-gram for all the people and require the co-operative effort of agriculture, industry, labor, the professions, and all health organizations and agencies.

Where We Are in Rural Health

This Section was opened with a review of the rural health situation. Joseph Fichter, Master of the Ohio State Grange and Chairman of the Section, and Franklin S. Crockett, M.D., Chairman of the Committee on Rural Medical Service of the American Medical Association, reported

encouraging progress in organized effort on the part of the medical profession and of farm organizations and agencies to assist rural people to
improve their health and medical services.

Three years ago the American Medical Association set up a Committee
on Rural Medical Service, composed of physicians representing different
sections of the country. An advisory committee consisting of representatives of four national farm organizations participates in all its deliberations. During the past three years this Committee on Rural Medical
Services has done much to stimulate interest on the part of medical
societies in forty-five states in giving special attention to rural health
problems and in seeking the co-operation of farm organizations and
agencies in their solution. It has sponsored three annual national rural
health conferences. These, in turn, have stimulated medical societies in
several states to sponsor rural health conferences in co-operation with
the farm organizations and the extension services of the colleges of
agriculture, with a view to finding ways of pooling efforts to advance
rural health.

The farm organizations have taken an increasing part in promoting a
wide range of rural health programs. They have been especially interested
in setting up their own prepaid medical and hospital plans or arranging
for the enrollment of their members in existing well-established plans.
Some of them have assisted local people to organize co-operative health
associations. The national farm organizations, in co-operation with the
Farm Foundation, have set up a health committee whose major concern
has been the broadening of areas of common agreement among the farm
organizations so that a co-ordinated approach may be made toward the
attainment of a comprehensive health and medical service for all rural
people.

The extension services of the land-grant colleges have long taken an
active part in developing personal and community health programs
through the 4-H clubs and home economics clubs. In more recent years,
a number of extension services have employed specialists in rural health
organization to assist in state and local planning for the development
of health and medical services to meet rural needs.

Through the leadership of one or another of these organizations, state
rural health committees or councils composed of a representative group
of all concerned with improving rural health have been set up in a
number of states. These state health committees encourage the formation
of county health councils. Their aim is to stimulate and assist rural

people to study, plan for, and develop health programs needed to meet local health needs.

Reports of the work done by farm organizations and agencies and by the medical profession presented encouraging examples of organized efforts to assist rural people to improve their health and medical services. They revealed, however, how vast was the task of education and organization when measured against the need.

The need was reviewed by Frederick D. Mott, M.D., chairman of the Health Services Planning Commission of the Province of Saskatchewan. His paper, based on a comprehensive study of rural health and medical care,[1] provided the basic factual data on which the deliberations of the section were based and is therefore summarized below.

Measured by a variety of indices, improvement in the health of rural people lags far behind that of urban people. One index of unfavorable rural health conditions is the death rate. At the turn of the century the death rate among farmers was about 50 per cent lower than among city people. Today the death rates of the two groups are practically the same. Death rates for infants and mothers are considerably higher in rural areas than in our big cities. The same is true of death rates for most communicable diseases—such as diphtheria, whooping cough, and measles—just those conditions where death can be prevented through the application of measures well known to modern medical science.

Various surveys and special studies indicate that the total burden of illness and disability is greater in rural areas than in the cities. Other studies have shown that rural nutrition is poor, that uncorrected dental caries is more prevalent among rural children, that the incidence of syphilis among rural men from twenty-one to thirty-five years of age throughout the nation is actually higher than among urban men, and that the highest rates for most mental disorders occur in rural communities. A survey by the Farm Security Administration showed that, among low-income farmers, only 4 per cent were free from significant physical impairments. In the draft for the armed forces, farm boys were rejected to a greater extent for physical defects than were the boys of any other major occupational group. Irrespective of what interpretation is given to the Selective Service rejection rates, they present evidence, for rural areas, of a tremendous backlog of current needs for medical care and a continuing volume of medical care in the future.

[1] Frederick D. Mott, M.D., and Milton I. Roemer, M.D., *Rural Health and Medical Care* (New York: McGraw-Hill Book Company, 1948).

Services and facilities to meet these needs have long been lacking in rural areas. The 1,200 rural counties that have no recognized hospitals within their borders have a total population of 15 million people. In many other rural counties existing hospitals have been declared dangerous to the public's health. The Hospital Survey and Construction Act has been the first forward step toward improving this situation.

Organized public health services are underdeveloped and generally inadequate. There are still about 1,400 counties, most of them rural, which lack full-time public health services. Even in those counties with full-time health departments, in 1946 only 3.4 per cent of the population was served by departments with sufficient personnel to meet accepted minimum standards.

Not only is there a lack of doctors, dentists, nurses, and all health workers, but the pull of cities and specialization is making the situation progressively worse. As an example, only 4 per cent of all pediatricians are located in places of less than 10,000 population—where 60 per cent of the nation's children live! The shortage of dentists is even more acute than that of physicians, and there are equally serious shortages of nurses, laboratory technicians, and other health workers. The situation is that the more rural the area the fewer the medical personnel, services, and facilities in proportion to the population.

What are some of the underlying causes for these deficiencies? The very character of rural living presents the handicaps of distance, isolation, and increasing costs of services. Purchasing power for medical care has been lacking in much of rural America. Even in a prosperous year such as 1945 the net per capita income of persons living on farms was $743, whereas for persons not on farms it was $1,259. Other factors which unfavorably affect rural health conditions are the lack of rural electrification, roads, and telephone services, low educational standards, poor housing and sanitation, a failure to arouse in rural children an awareness of good hygiene and of community health, and the individualism of the farmer which makes him inclined to get along with his difficulties in a somewhat stoical manner. Hence such factors as the dispersion of the rural population, the instability of agriculture, the social psychology, and other cultural characteristics of farmers must be taken into consideration before satisfactory solutions can be found.

Rural health is a special and complicated problem which requires complex organization and co-ordinated effort to solve. The co-operative effort of professional and lay groups must be concentrated on five major areas before a comprehensive health program can be developed. These areas and some of the questions which the Section decided to consider are as follows:

1. *Public health services.* There is a lack of concerted demand for the organization of public health services. Yet delay in establishing these means a failure to do the basic and economical job of prevention. It also means the lack of co-ordinating health agencies prepared to take on new tasks. How can effective full-time public health services be brought to all of rural America?

2. *Hospital and health facilities.* The Hospital Survey and Construction Act is a gratifying forward step in planning for and financing hospital construction. But will present legislation do the job? Should appropriations be increased? Should the life of the program be extended? Should the grants be available in accordance with need? Should the basis for priorities be changed? How can rural people be assured of the provision of an integrated hospital system which will bring modern medical science to every rural community?

3. *Health personnel.* Of crucial concern to rural people is reasonable access to the services of an adequate number of competent general medical practitioners, specialists, dentists, nurses, and other health personnel. How can the workers needed for rural areas best be trained? Can undergraduate and graduate training be designed to meet rural needs? How can proper distribution be assured? Must not the economic pull be made exceedingly powerful and real, through measures to increase and spread medical purchasing power, before rural areas will be supplied with medical health personnel?

4. *Improvement in quality of medical services.* Group medical practice can be one of the most important ways of bringing the services of specialists close to rural people and of raising the quality of medical care. What are the farm groups and the medical profession prepared to do to foster the development of group clinics in rural areas?

5. *Paying for medical services.* How should the problem of payment for medical services be solved so that comprehensive services may be available to all, modern hospitals may be adequately maintained, and rural health parity may become a reality? Is there anything in experience here or abroad which indicates that voluntary health insurance will do the job? That it will ever cover many farm and rural people? That it can offer them complete services at a cost they can afford to pay? That it

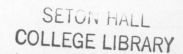

will so mobilize medical purchasing power as to maintain hospitals in needy areas—or attract and hold doctors?

Where We Want To Be—Rural Health Goals

In the light of the rural health needs, this Section decided that ten-year rural health goals should include the following:

1. Every rural family should be enrolled in a comprehensive health insurance plan within the next ten years.

2. Medical education should be expanded to train an adequate number of doctors, nurses, and other health personnel to meet rural needs. Special consideration must be given to provide educational opportunities and facilities for rural Negro physicians and other health personnel.

3. Hospital and health facilities must be available to all rural communities and rural physicians. The Hospital Survey and Construction Act must be extended to make this possible.

4. Ways must be found of developing group practice and interdependence of hospitals so that specialists and other modern services will be available to all rural areas.

5. There should be complete coverage of all rural areas with adequately staffed county and multiple-county health departments.

6. Immediately attainable goals to promote health and prevent disease should be a safe water supply and sanitary privies in every rural home, school, and community.

7. Health councils should be set up in every state and county to plan for and develop rural health programs.

8. A requisite for a healthy rural America is a healthy agriculture with good standards of living, improved education, communication, roads, electrification, and stabilization of farm income.

At later meetings of the Section on a National Program for Rural Health these health goals were greatly expanded. Final recommendations for ten-year rural health goals are listed toward the close of the present chapter.

How to Reach Rural Health Goals—Breaking Bottlenecks, Organizing for Action

The Rural Health Section found that it was one thing to agree on rural health goals, but quite another to agree on how to achieve them. The springboard for that discussion was a consideration of the kind of medical services rural people should expect in the future. In the main, the Section agreed that the rural medical service of the future should center around the general practitioner who has had special training in helping people with their mental and emotional problems as well as with their physical ailments. He must be concerned with people rather than with patients. He should be a health counselor to the families he serves. Some of his greatest healing gifts should be found in the quality of his relationships to those who seek his help.

To render the highest type of service, the modern family doctor must have the support of specialists working in organized groups prepared to serve rural areas. Such medical practice must be centered in or around hospitals, which may increasingly put less emphasis upon the bed patient and more on early diagnosis, health education, and other measures to maintain health. These hospitals, in turn, must be part of an integrated system through which specialist and other services from the large medical centers can be made available to the small rural hospital and diagnostic centers.

Much of the personal preventive health services will be performed by the general physician of the future, while the health officer will be the program planner and organizer of health services for the entire area. A first essential for developing such a rural health program is some financial scheme which will make it possible for medical personnel, hospital facilities, and other services to be maintained and for rural people to make use of all the services available.

With this as a background, the discussion centered primarily on the special rural factors that need to be considered in the development of programs for the training and distribution of medical and other health personnel, in the financing of medical care, and in community organization to improve rural health services.

Medical and other health personnel. The Section's description of the general practitioner of the future made a strong appeal to the rural delegates. They saw in him a modern version of the kind of family doctor they had known in the past. They wanted to know how they might have him again at the center of a modern integrated health system. For many rural people, the family physician of today is a man who does not keep abreast of modern medical science, who sometimes attempts to perform operations beyond his skill in a substandard local hospital, who often feels he functions mainly as a taxi driver to the nearest urban center where a modern hospital and specialists' services are available, and whose total reward for this service is the loss of his patients to the specialists. The problem of having a modern family physician in rural areas was seen to be complex indeed.

Consideration was given first to the kind of training that the family physician of the future should have. Some of the physicians thought that the present type of training offered by the medical colleges was satisfactory. What was needed in many rural areas, they said, was for several general practitioners, each with a leaning toward a different specialty, to work together as a group. This would enhance both the quality and quantity of service rendered. Other physicians took a different point of view. They did not think that a general practitioner could be a good family physician and lean toward a specialty. All his energies should be focused on being a good general practitioner. For this, they said, he needs knowledge of the tools of all the specialties; but his own training should be fundamentally in diagnosis, the usual problems of medical care, public health methods, psychiatry, and other sciences which would help him understand people. As one physician put it, "It is more important for him to know what kind of a man has a disease than what kind of a disease is in a man." Training for such a physician of the future would have to be very different from the present emphasis in medical education on a maze of diseases and a variety of specialties.

Attention was called to the real possibility of the disappearance of the general practitioner and to his lack of interest in keeping abreast of modern medical practice. One suggestion made was that every practitioner of medicine be registered every five years and that, in lieu of adequate evidence of postgraduate training, he should take an examination on the advance in medicine during that period.

Although no agreement was reached among the physicians as to the type of training needed for the general practitioner, the value of the discussion was that it opened for consideration a whole field needing to be fully explored jointly by medical educators and those dependent on general practitioner service.

What special measures, if any, are medical colleges taking to prepare physicians for rural practice, was a question to which the group next turned its attention. Some agreed that, until recently, the only attention given to the rural aspects of medicine in the medical colleges was the advice of professors to their students not to go to rural areas for fear of dry rot. Improvement in rural hospital facilities and the development of regional hospital systems could increase interest in rural practice. As an example, the regional hospital system which serves twenty-five hospitals in eleven counties surrounding Rochester, New York, has resulted in an increase of interest in rural practice. Doctors in outlying areas are now assured of opportunities for postgraduate work and other advantages previously available only to city physicians. The medical school is pointing out that rural areas offer the opportunities of a pleasant living and a reasonably good income. The important thing is to make rural communities more attractive.

A plan recently developed at the Medical School of the University of Colorado to interest physicians in rural practice was described. The three-year course includes two and one-half years of resident training in the university hospital and six months in hospitals in small towns. Much to the surprise of the medical staff, the students are much interested in this course. It is believed that it will result in more medical graduates planning to practice in the communities where they have taken their last six months of residency.

The Section expressed the hope that more medical schools would adopt such a plan and other measures to arouse interest among medical students in the opportunities in rural practice. There are many difficulties in the way of developing such a plan in the rural states that most need it. In Arkansas and Oklahoma, since it is impossible for medical students to secure internship training in their own states because the hospitals are not large enough to be teaching institutions, the young men preparing for medicine are lost to the big urban centers in other states where they take their internship.

The Rural Health Section then discussed what could be done to enable more rural young men and women to take medical and related training and subsequently return to rural areas. Attention was called to the nine states where scholarships and loan funds are offered to rural young men and women interested in medicine or nursing, on condition that they return after training to practice in rural areas for a set period of time. These scholarships and loan funds have usually been made available either through state funds or through the contributions of state medical associations acting by themselves or in co-operation with farm organizations or other groups.

Dr. Lester Evans pointed out the problems involved in these scholarships. He said that to ask a student, before he enters a medical school and really knows what medicine is, to obligate himself to go to a rural area to practice may not be sound. The experience of the Commonwealth Fund in offering scholarships of this nature has not been very satisfactory. Although some of the men who accepted such scholarships are practicing in rural areas, a large number asked to be relieved of their obligation. He suggested that a more constructive approach would be to grant funds for further study to practising rural physicians, rather than, as at present, concentrating on grants to medical students. Such scholarships not only should enable them to take postgraduate work to keep up with the developments in medicine but also should include provisions for protecting their practice while they are studying.

The Section, impressed with this reasoning, hoped nevertheless that the recent development of hospital facilities would make rural areas more attractive and that scholarships for young students might be more successful now than formerly. Therefore it urged that more states provide scholarships for rural young men and women to study medicine, nursing, and dentistry.

Scholarships, it was decided, are not enough. Of more fundamental concern to rural people is the increase in the actual supply of physicians. Many people are under the impression that medical colleges have a definite policy of limiting the number of students. Data showing the very small proportion of medical students entering medical schools from rural areas strengthened the general impression that it is difficult for rural students to enter medical college even though they may have high qualifications.[2]

Representatives of the medical profession pointed out that it is necessary for the medical schools to maintain strict entrance requirements in order to preserve high standards of medical practice. They indicated that one of the reasons why there are fewer rural than urban medical students is that the educational standards of many rural schools are so low that it is impossible for rural students to measure up to the basic requirements for entrance to medical college.

The Section's chairman was not satisfied with this explanation. He called attention to data which showed that the number of medical students graduating in 1946 was approximately the same as the number graduating in 1892, even though both the population of the country and the demand for medical care had greatly increased during that time.[3]

[2] Commission on Hospital Care, *Hospital Care in the United States* (New York: Commonwealth Fund, 1947).

[3] Figures for 1880-1892 from the Report on Medical Education and Medical Colleges in the *Fifteenth Annual Report of the State Board of Health of Illinois* (Springfield, Ill., 1894); for 1900-1935 from R. G. Leland, *Distribution of Physicians in the United States*, rev. ed. (Chicago: American Medical Association, 1936); for 1936-1947 from *Journal of the American Medical Association*, Vol. 134, No. 16 (August 16, 1947).

This was the type of thing, he felt, that gave the general public the impression that the medical profession was deliberately limiting the number of physicians without due consideration for the public's need. He found it difficult to understand why it had not been possible for medical schools to meet the situation in somewhat the same way that colleges and universities had accomplished the heroic task of taking care of the great influx of veterans after the war. If the restricted enrollment in medical schools was due to a lack of facilities and personnel, he thought that the Section on Rural Health should go on record as favoring increased public funds from state and Federal sources to permit the increase of such personnel and facilities and the establishment of new medical schools as necessary. There was not, however, unanimous agreement with this recommendation.

The question next raised was whether any of the proposals to enlarge facilities for medical education or to provide scholarships for rural students would have any real effect on the distribution of physicians in rural areas. Some members of the group considered that rural areas will not receive their share of doctors, nurses, dentists, and other health workers until an adequate financial base is established. The suggestion was made that the methods adopted by the United States Public Health Service to make doctors available in any section of the country to eradicate syphilis might be applied to making general practitioners available to needy rural areas.

In summarizing this discussion, the Section's chairman said that rural people have much at stake in this whole complex matter of medical education. They suffer most from the shortage of doctors. The national farm organizations consider that programs for training physicians for rural practice is basic to the development of any rural health program. At a recent meeting of the Conference Committee on Rural Health Services at the Farm Foundation, the national farm organizations requested that arrangements be made for a meeting of representatives of the farm organizations and members of the medical profession most concerned with medical education, to give a thorough airing to this entire field of medical education as it affects rural practice.

That the Council on Medical Education of the American Medical Association and the Association of American Medical Colleges is planning a comprehensive study of medical education and will welcome hearing from the farm groups about their special problems was gratifying to the Section. Doubt was expressed, however, whether a study conducted by those identified with medical education alone and not by a broadly representative group including the public most concerned would be accepted as definitive.

When, at the last meeting of the Section, the committee which had been appointed to report on health personnel submitted its recommendations, most of the points raised in the discussion had been taken into consideration, so that its major recommendations were accepted by the group. On one point reported on page 158 by the personnel committee, however, agreement was not reached. That was in regard to discrimination and segregation as it affects opportunities for medical education, the use of facilities, and the supply of all health personnel to minority groups. Earlier in the discussions, Dr. Harold H. Whitted called attention to the lack of all types of personnel and facilities to meet the needs of the rural Negro population throughout the nation. The southern states, with 13 million Negroes, he said, do not have one decent institution for the training of Negro nurses and physicians. The committee brought in a recommendation that discrimination and segregation is out of line with democratic principles and should be abolished not only in the institutions of higher learning but also throughout the general education system.

No agreement, however, could be reached on this subject either in general or with special reference to medical education. A suggestion that the Rural Health Section accept a resolution adopted by the President's Commission on Higher Education was rejected as too general and not specific enough in its application to the subject at hand. For a time it seemed that there would be agreement on the point that a first step in solving this problem could be the elimination of discrimination and segregation at professional and postgraduate levels. In the end, however, it was impossible to secure agreement on any aspect of this entire subject.

Paying for medical services. From the very beginning, methods of paying for medical services became the central theme to which the Section returned again and again. All the other topics discussed seemed dependent on the solution of this issue, since it would determine not only the health security possible to rural families but also the financial base for getting and keeping doctors, dentists, nurses, hospitals, and other health services.

Much of the discussion centered on the problem of securing from the medical profession recognition and support of the efforts of consumer groups to organize their own co-operative health associations which could provide them with comprehensive medical services. Because of their long experience with co-operatives, rural people are becoming interested in applying this principle to obtaining medical services. They believe in the co-operatives' emphasis on preventive medicine in medical care. Many obstacles, however, seem to have been put in the way of the movement for co-operative health associations. Instances were cited of medical societies refusing to permit well-qualified physicians interested in serving local co-operatives to join county medical associations, to use local hospitals, or even to secure a license to practice in a state. In twenty-two states, enabling legislation for voluntary prepayment medical service generally prevents organizations not controlled by physicians from establishing prepayment plans to provide medical services. In Minnesota, for example, when the Minnesota Group Health Mutual attempted to introduce a bill in the last legislature to permit citizen groups to establish co-operative health centers, the State Medical Association vigorously opposed the legislation.

A plea was made in the Rural Health Section for more understanding and support from the medical profession for the co-operative movement. Assurance was given the medical profession that co-operatives were the last kind of association that would interfere in any way with the practice of medicine and that they could make an important contribution to the cause of voluntary methods for solving the medical care problem. Endorsement of this movement by the medical profession would serve as a mark of their faith in the fundamentally democratic process of local people voluntarily organizing themselves to obtain needed medical services.

To this plea Dr. Crockett responded that the medical profession is ready to explore the whole medical co-operative movement. The major concern of the profession is not in the management of a non-profit prepayment plan but with safeguards to ensure the highest quality of medical care. The fact was brought out that in Wisconsin enabling legislation for medical co-operatives was passed nearly a year ago with the full support of the State Medical Association. Finally it was agreed that representatives of the co-operative health movement and the American Medical Association should get together to clarify their differences. A resolution in regard to medical co-operatives, presented as a part of the committee report on medical services, was accepted later by the Section. It emphasized the need for greater understanding on both sides. The medical profession needs to appreciate the interest of citizen groups

in enabling legislation to set up medical co-operatives. Co-operative groups need to appreciate the concern of the profession with safeguarding the high quality of medical practice in such plans.

The question then raised was whether enabling legislation for setting up medical-care plans might be broadened to include the right of local people voluntarily to tax themselves for medical services. Dr. Mott described enabling legislation that has existed for years in the prairie provinces of Canada, which permits rural municipalities to tax themselves to secure a general practitioner. If a municipality so votes, a tax is levied which may be either a land tax, personal tax, or a combination of both. Out of this fund a physician is paid a set salary to take care of all the families of the designated area. Similar enabling legislation exists for hospitals. Two or more municipalities, typically eighteen miles square, may unite to tax themselves to build and maintain union hospitals.

Recently one region of the Province of Saskatchewan covering 10,000 square miles, with a population of 54,000, voted to tax itself for comprehensive medical services—general practitioner, specialist, hospitalization. The region is divided into four districts, in each of which there will be a district hospital. In the main community, population 7,000, there will be a regional hospital center of 110 beds. All the physicians in the area are general practitioners. A start has been made to secure a nucleus of specialists at the regional center. A radiologist and pathologist are now available. The president of the district medical society has said that other specialists must be made available on a non-competitive basis, that is, they must be on salary. This medical plan is financed by a combination of a 2.2 mill levy on the land and a personal tax of $15.00 single, up to $35.00 maximum for a family. Everyone must pay the tax, but no one needs to use the services if he does not wish to do so. The program is run by a council elected by the people in each district and by a larger regional council composed of representatives duly elected from each district. It is a compulsory plan that is at the same time fundamentally democratic.

The description of these plans led the Section to agree that in certain instances residents of local administrative units should be free to choose to tax themselves in order to obtain medical services.

Doubt was expressed, however, that any local plans, whether voluntary or tax-supported, could provide comprehensive medical services of high quality to all rural people. A review of rural enrollment in state-wide non-profit voluntary plans was not encouraging. In spite of the outstanding success of the Blue Cross and of medical-surgical plans sponsored by medical societies in industrial states, the enrollment in rural states is either negligible or non-existent.[4]

Mr. George Jacobson, executive secretary of the Minnesota Group Health Mutual, proposed that the best way of meeting the needs of the marginal-income group is for state and Federal funds to be made available to voluntary health associations. Some public agency may have to determine an individual's ability to pay. It may even be necessary to resort to some modified compulsory principle, so that families which show evidence of neglecting the health of their children will have to join a plan. Emotional resistance to the word "compulsory" does not lessen the reality—that certain compulsory measures are necessary to maintain basic freedoms and decent standards of community life.

The Maryland plan for the medically indigent was described as a possibility. There the eligibility of the medically indigent is determined by the county health officer. The advisability of this plan was quickly brushed aside by several people who immediately called attention to the difficulty of determining who are medically indigent. They said that a person may be medically indigent during a part of a year and not during another part. Many people, too, would go without needed medical care rather than face the humiliation of an investigation as to ability to pay.

A suggestion was made that the taxpayers might have less of a burden in taking care of the indigent sick under a system in which everyone contributed to a national plan according to his ability to pay. Such a plan could still assure local administration and free choice on the part of both patients and physicians as to whether they give or receive medical services under the plan.

It soon became clear that opinion was sharply divided on the methods for extending medical care to all people. Some thought the method most congenial to our society was to expand voluntary plans and provide a subsidy for these plans if necessary; others thought the most democratic approach was national health insurance. The committee report on medical care at the last session voiced the opinion of the majority when it recommended that every effort should go into expanding voluntary plans to reach rural areas. Where these plans are inadequate, an increase in public funds for hospital construction might bring the current

[4] Blue Cross Commission, *Special Studies* No. 86-D (February 26, 1948) and No. 87-D (March 11, 1948); Bureau of the Census, *Rural Farm Population.*

cost of medical care within the reach of nearly all families. In all cases local funds should first be exhausted before state funds are utilized. Federal funds should be made available only after these other resources had been tapped.

After these proposals had been made, Dr. Mott electrified the Section by stating that the committee had submitted a defeatist report. He considered it tragic for the welfare of rural America that the organizations represented had not taken cognizance of many countries' experience with voluntary plans and their effect on rural medical services. They strengthen the forces which lead to the concentration of personnel in cities and increase the relative disadvantage of rural sections and rural people. He also thought it tragic for the health of rural America if the recommended policy to exhaust local funds and to delay use of Federal funds were adopted. He considered that any real study of the situation shows that the inequities of rural health services can be resolved only by the concurrent co-operative efforts of all administrative units of government. From his experience in setting up and administering a hospital insurance plan provided by tax funds for all the people of the Province of Saskatchewan, he had learned that a state-wide compulsory insurance plan is democratically sound and relatively simple to set up and administer; it provides a tremendous impetus to the construction and maintenance of hospitals. He considered that rural people stand to benefit by national health insurance more than any other group. He urged that the issue of financing medical care be settled by accepting a nation-wide program of health insurance at the earliest possible date. Then all efforts can be directed to the more constructive task of improving the quality of rural medical services.

Dr. Mulholland, Dr. Crockett, Mr. Slusher, Dr. Graham, and others rose in defense of the committee's report. They said that the possibilities of the voluntary approach to the matter of paying for medical care had been far from exhausted in rural America. If these show limitations, there are still a number of alternatives that may be chosen to provide medical care for all the people. If a national compulsory insurance plan ever did come to pass it would need to assure the continuance of successful voluntary plans. Emphasis in the report was put on local effort before state and Federal effort because of the belief that local administration is the least costly and the most democratic.

In trying to obtain some area of common agreement, the chairman asked if the Rural Health Section would endorse a recommendation that every effort be made to extend voluntary prepayment plans as far as possible but that, if they did not meet the need, some form of taxation or national health insurance would have to be developed. To this, however, all members of the group would not agree. Unanimous assent was won only for the extension of voluntary prepayment plans. At the same time, unanimous assent was won to the immediate enactment of a Federal tax-supported medical-care program for migratory farm workers.

Although high tension marked much of this discussion, the major characteristic was the objective and conciliatory manner in which different points of view were presented. As the chairman pointed out, much gain had been made during the past five years in ironing out differences. There was a deep desire on the part of both organized medicine and organized agriculture to seek common ground on which they might go forward together and find ways to provide comprehensive medical care of high quality for all rural people. The conciliatory atmosphere in which the discussion took place marked a milestone of progress in solving this most controversial and central issue of any rural medical program.

Other health services. Subcommittee reports given at the final session on health facilities, public health services, organization and integration of health and medical services, improvement in rural standards of living, and community health planning were accepted with but little discussion.

In regard to hospital facilities, appreciation of the aims and progress of the Hospital Survey and Construction Act was expressed. At the same time, limitations to the program were recognized. Some communities found that the Federal requirements for construction were so high that they could not meet the costs involved in building according to Federal regulations. It was felt that the program will have to be expanded considerably to meet the long unmet needs of rural areas. It was considered particularly important that specific measures be taken to develop an interdependent hospital system so that specialist and other services might be made available to the small rural centers. To date the only outstanding examples of regional planning to link the isolated rural practitioner and the rural hospital into a network of modern medical services are the Bingham Associates, serving Maine and other New England states, and the Rochester Hospital Council. The question was raised whether the time had not come, now that private organizations had pointed the way to a desirable pattern, for multiplying these demonstrations a hundredfold through public funds.

The report on public health services was accepted. Local health units were considered "a good thing." Concern was shown that, in the setting up of city-county or multiple-county health units, care be taken to provide due representation of rural groups on the county boards and health councils.

The committee on the organization and integration of health services pulled together the various parts of a comprehensive health program into an integrated whole.

The committee on improvement in rural standards of living emphasized the importance of a prosperous agriculture if rural people are to have parity of health services.

Community planning for health services. One theme that was repeated over and over again throughout the deliberations of the Section was the great need for more effective community organization to plan for and obtain needed rural health services.

At the opening session, Dr. Crockett recommended the establishment of state and county health councils as a valuable tool of community organization for health improvement. He suggested that these health councils might concern themselves with such matters as nursing and nurses' aide training for farm women, provision of health facilities, study of prepaid medical and hospital plans, promotion of health education, strengthening of local public health services, improvement in diet, housing, and cultural conditions affecting health.

For a time there was considerable discussion as to who should initiate these councils. Finally it was agreed that it did not make any difference what organization took the leadership. All organizations concerned with the improvement of rural health should be drawn in at an early stage of planning so that the health council would become truly a county or state body.

Attention was called to the difficulty of keeping county health councils anything more than paper organizations unless they could secure continued technical guidance in the development of a program. The Section considered that one important source of such information and guidance should be the land-grant colleges. These colleges should take an important part in developing research and education in health and medical services for the guidance of rural people. To reach rural children, more health education is needed in the schools. Particular attention needs to be given to health education in Negro schools, as well as to programs that provide health educators, nurses, and midwives to rural communities with large Negro populations. Many of the health problems in the South are problems of the Negro population.

As soon as the need for health education was stressed, attention was called to the condition facing rural people when they try to study these problems through health workshops to which Federal workers are invited to provide factual information and technical knowledge. As a result of a Congressional investigation of health workshops, Federal workers may not attend conferences sponsored by lay groups. Rightly or wrongly, many rural people consider that this investigation was instigated by the medical profession. It seemed important to clarify the motives of the medical profession in order to restore a feeling of mutual trust and confidence.

Dr. Crockett interpreted the position of the medical profession. He said that the profession has always supported the United States Public Health Service and recognizes fully its valuable contribution. The medical profession objects only when members of the Service give information that seems tinged with the ideology of a particular administration.

A recommendation to resolve this issue was drafted. As presented and unanimously adopted it reads as follows: "Problems affecting the health of the people can be best solved by local groups meeting together. Government and other agencies at all levels should be free to present to these groups the factual and technical information which, by virtue of their function, they have assembled."

At the close of the Rural Health Section's last session, a final recommendation was made that ways and means be found of holding conferences of this kind over the country as a most valuable means of bringing together all groups concerned with raising health standards. Thus the meeting closed on the note set by the Section's chairman in his opening address, namely, that the health of the people is a matter of public policy. Meetings which would make possible the discussion of difficult issues in as objective and conciliatory a manner as they had been considered at this National Health Assembly should lead to the establishment of a public policy for national health that would protect the best interests of all groups concerned and would assure the highest level of health to all the people.

CONCLUSIONS AND RECOMMENDATIONS

At the close of the Section's third session, when it became evident that time did not permit discussion of many of the important elements in a comprehensive rural health program, seven subcommittees were appointed to bring in reports at the final session. The reports of these subcommittees included many recommendations that were accepted by the Section on a National Program for Rural Health. These recommendations have been merged with others made at earlier sessions so that a composite of rural health goals might be recorded. These goals, culled from committee reports and from general discussion, are listed below according to the topics assigned to the committees.

Ten-year health goals for rural America include the development and expansion of the following programs:

I. *Medical and Other Health Personnel*

The center of a modern rural medical service is the general practitioner. The family physician of the future, however, must practice truly preventive medicine through the evaluation and treatment of mental and emotional stresses as well as common illnesses. He can accomplish this purpose only by working as part of an integrated team which makes available the necessary medical specialists, public health personnel, and community agencies. Among the measures needed to provide the desired type of medical and other health personnel are the following:

1. Medical schools should give special consideration to the type of training needed for general practitioners in rural areas. Medical students should be afforded opportunities to work in situations where they can experience physician-family relationships. The system of rotating interns and residents through small rural hospitals should be extended. Other methods of familiarizing young physicians with the opportunities in rural practice should also be tried.

2. Medical education must be expanded to train an adequate number of doctors, dentists, nurses, and other health personnel to meet rural needs, both white and Negro.

3. Scholarships or loan funds should be available to enable all qualified rural youths to attend medical and other professional schools. This movement is already developing in many rural states. Experience has revealed limitations to some of the current plans. Modifications for the future should be based on a careful study of present arrangements.

4. Scholarships to rural physicians for refresher courses and graduate study should be provided, so that the quality of rural medical practice may be improved.

5. Rural people must have a responsible part in developing plans for

medical education. A first step in this direction is that the farm organizations arrange a meeting with representatives of the American Medical Association and other professional groups most concerned. At this meeting, a joint review should be made of all the factors involved in medical education to meet rural needs.

6. Special measures must be taken to attract and hold a sufficient number of both white and Negro doctors, nurses, dentists, and other health workers in all rural areas.

7. Adequate nursing service, both professional and auxiliary, is essential to the effective functioning of a total health and medical program. This involves improving the quality of nursing schools, licensure for practical nurses, and an integrated system of preventive and bedside nursing services.

II. *Paying for Medical Services*

The over-all goal is to have every rural family enrolled in a comprehensive health insurance plan within the next ten years.

Among immediate steps to achieve this goal are the following:

1. Every effort should be made to extend voluntary prepayment plans to all rural people through the most suitable methods for achieving full coverage.

2. Groups desiring to organize voluntary prepayment plans through co-operative health associations should have full opportunity to do so. To make this possible, the medical profession and medical co-operatives will have to reach an understanding on two points:

(a) The enactment of enabling legislation (such as that recently put upon the statute books of Wisconsin) establishing the right of co-operative health associations to contract with doctors for professional services; and

(b) The desire of the medical profession to ensure that the terms of contracts with doctors in these plans be such as to provide the highest quality of medical care.

3. Aid to communities in the form of an increase in the proportion of the cost of hospital construction might do much to bring the current net cost of medical care within the reach of nearly all rural families.

4. Residents of local political subdivisions should have the right voluntarily to tax themselves in order to obtain comprehensive medical services.

5. A Federal tax-supported program to provide health services and medical care for migratory agricultural workers should be enacted.

III. *Hospital Facilities*

Health facilities should be extended to serve all rural people without discrimination with respect to color or economic status.

The aims and progress to date of the Hospital Survey and Construction Act in providing needed rural hospital, health center, and community clinic facilities and in its policy of local administration are commended. Recommendations for further development of this program include the following:

1. The Hospital Survey and Construction Act should be extended immediately for at least a ten-year period, to provide additional funds to meet the cost of construction for needed facilities in rural areas.

2. Where indicated in rural areas, an appraisal should take place to determine whether an increased percentage of state and/or Federal aid is necessary. Provision should be made to increase appropriations where needed.

3. Hospitals in rural areas should be paid on a realistic, operating, reimbursable basis for the necessary preventive and therapeutic hospital care of patients unable to provide such services from their own resources.

4. In order to avoid duplication of facilities and to encourage the integration of preventive and therapeutic services, health department activities and personnel should be housed within or adjacent to the rural general hospitals.

5. General hospitals in rural areas should be built large enough to ensure efficient and economical operation and the maintenance of a minimum basic medical staff.

6. A co-ordinated hospital program is essential for the equitable distribution to all rural people of health, hospital, medical, and related skills and services.

7. The official public health agency should be responsible for providing mobile facilities where needed (such as dental units, tuberculosis control units, and premature infant and ambulance services).

8. It may be necessary in the most needy rural areas to provide, through tax funds, not only a larger proportion of the construction costs but also funds for maintaining and operating hospital facilities.

IV. *Public Health Services*

Rural areas should be completely covered with adequately financed, well-staffed city-county and/or multi-county health departments. In developing such a program care must be taken to include the following principles:

1. In the development and administration of consolidated health units, rural interests should be adequately represented.

2. The proposed plan for the inclusion of 50,000 people in a public health unit should be sufficiently flexible to meet the needs of sparsely settled areas in many western states.

3. Special attention should be given to making mental-hygiene services and facilities available to all rural areas.

Among immediately attainable goals are the following:

1. There should be a safe water supply in every rural home, school, and community.

2. There should be a sanitary privy for every rural family, and an indoor toilet as soon as possible.

3. Existing knowledge on the control of preventable disease should be applied to every rural area.

4. There should be modern health education in every rural school.

5. There should be a program for the training of all types of health personnel needed to staff adequately the local public health units.

V. *Organization of Rural Health Services*

Rural people, in order to enjoy parity of health services with the urban population, must have access to the specialized services which characterize modern medicine. Effective organization and integration of health service is especially important in rural areas. Bearing that in mind, this Section recommends the following needed measures:

1. Organization of group-practice clinics or units at natural trade centers, so that the services of specialists can be made readily available to the majority of the rural population. The dispersion of the rural population is such that these groups will not be able to serve as a substitute for the general practitioner. If, however, general practitioners will associate themselves with such groups and practice in outlying areas, this tendency toward group practice and specialization can be utilized advantageously for rural people, thus providing a quality and scope of service otherwise difficult to realize. This system allows the general practitioner to remain in his important role of family physician.

2. Co-ordinated hospital planning. This would provide a blueprint for facilities into which co-ordinated health services naturally fit.

3. Co-ordination of medical care and public health services. The

family doctor and the public health nurse, supplemented by technical skills in such fields as health education, dentistry, nutrition, and sanitation, will be the preventive-medicine team of the future.

4. Development of co-operative health associations. This method can improve the organizational structure. It can provide a broader financial base and planned action. All these benefits will aid in the development of an intelligent and integrated pattern of rural medical care. Other and more extensive methods will be necessary in order to achieve adequate programs and patterns for modern rural health services for those areas and families with low incomes.

VI. *Improvement in Rural Living*

A healthy rural America is important to the nation because rural America produces most of the nation's children. Within the next three generations, 80 per cent of the people of America will have come from a farm home. Long-term programs for agriculture that will guarantee the farm family an adequate income are fundamental in making possible a better standard of living. Other essentials are equal opportunities for education and health, improved farm-to-market roads, adequate power electricity, adequate systems of communication, better soil conservation and nutrition, and stabilization of farm income for the purchase of medical care.

VII. *Community Planning for Rural Health Services*

A continuous program of community education and community planning is essential if rural people are to realize their health goals. Toward this end the following recommendations are especially directed:

1. Land-grant colleges should be encouraged to undertake research projects and to organize pilot studies in various types of communities, in order to ascertain the amount and kinds of facilities needed and the personnel required for comprehensive health care, including prepayment medical care. These studies should be the basis for establishing future plans. They should provide some idea of the cost of such care to individual families, the facilities and personnel needed, and the problem areas to be covered.

2. State and local rural health councils should be set up by the people of every state to promote objective study, planning, and organization to improve rural health services.

3. Educational and technical services available in the farm organizations, medical societies, agricultural extension services, public health

agencies, and voluntary health organizations can and should be fully utilized by these health councils.

4. This program, if carried out promptly and effectively, will require more educational and technical personnel than is now available. All agencies and groups involved should take immediate steps to employ and train the personnel needed to do this job.

5. The attainment of comprehensive health care in the future lies in broad health and medical education of today's school child. The applied study of nutrition through a balanced school-lunch program should be a part of school education. School teachers will also have to be trained, if this program is to be properly implemented.

6. Health assemblies patterned after the National Health Assembly should be held in every rural state.

7. One of the greatest problems in rural areas is the obtaining of technical information and guidance for the development of plans and programs to improve health services. Since the Congressional investigation of health workshops, professional health workers from the Federal government have not been available to lay groups to provide technical information. To remedy the situation the Rural Health Section unanimously adopted the following resolution:

Problems affecting the health of the people can best be solved by local groups meeting together. Government and other agencies at all levels should be free to present to these groups the factual and technical information which, by virtue of their function, they have assembled.

APPENDIX

PLANNING COMMITTEE

Joseph W. Fichter, *Chairman*	Master, Ohio State Grange
Franklin S. Crockett, M.D.	Chairman, Committee on Rural Medical Service American Medical Association
Mrs. Gladys T. Edwards	Director of Education National Farmers Union
Harry G. Gould	Acting Director, Extension Service College of Agriculture University of Nebraska
C. Horace Hamilton	Head, Department of Rural Sociology North Carolina State College

Frank W. Peck	Director, Farm Foundation
H. Willis Tobler	Assistant Director, Washington Office American Farm Bureau Federation

STAFF ASSISTANTS

Miss Elin L. Anderson	Specialist, Rural Health Services United States Department of Agriculture
S. J. Axelrod, M.D.	Senior Surgeon (R) States Relations Division Public Health Service, Federal Security Agency

REGISTRANTS

Miss Helen Becker	Extension Service College of Agriculture University of Nebraska
Richard F. Boyd, M.D.	Chief, Division of Local Health Administration Illinois State Department of Public Health
Richard M. Cole	Manager, Community Clinic Williston, North Dakota
Lyman A. Copps, M.D.	Marshfield Clinic Marshfield, Wisconsin
C. H. Crownhart	Secretary, Wisconsin State Medical Society
Reuben F. Erickson, M.D.	Minnesota State Medical Association
Lester J. Evans, M.D.	Medical Associate Commonwealth Fund
Mrs. Jerome Evanson	Director of Education North Dakota Farmers Union
Miss Helen L. Fisk	Chief, Division of Public Health Nursing Maryland State Department of Health
W. E. Garnett	Community Planning Virginia Polytechnic Institute
Msgr. J. J. Healy	Little Rock, Arkansas
Miss Brynhild Hoagland	Minot, North Dakota
Fred A. Humphrey, M.D.	Committee on Rural Medical Service American Medical Association
George W. Jacobson	Executive Secretary Group Health Mutual, Inc.
Albert D. Kaiser, M.D.	Executive Director Council of Rochester, N. Y., Regional Hospitals, Inc.

Rev. Thomas B. Keehn	Chairman, National Citizens Council for Migrant Labor
Mrs. Vivian MacFawn	Northern Great Plains Health Committee Brookings, South Dakota
Miss Ann K. Magnussen	Director, Disaster Nursing and Nurse Enrollment American National Red Cross
Henry B. Makover, M.D.	Hartsdale, New York
Sewall O. Milliken	Rural Health Specialist College of Agriculture Ohio State University
H. L. Mitchell	National Farm Labor Union
Frederick D. Mott, M.D.	Chairman, Health Services Planning Commission Regina, Saskatchewan, Canada
H. B. Mulholland, M.D.	Virginia Council on Health and Medical Care
Carl Neupert, M.D.	State Health Officer Wisconsin State Board of Health
John Newdrop, M.D.	Highlander Folk School
Harry Peterson	Group Health Mutual, Inc.
Mrs. H. W. Peterson	National Cancer Society
H. N. Roberts	Department of Sociology Virginia State College
Miss Elizabeth W. Robinson	Educational Advisor, Junior Red Cross American National Red Cross
Mrs. Charles W. Sewell	Administrative Director Associated Women of the American Farm Bureau Federation
H. Emmett Slusher	President, Missouri Farm Bureau Federation
Carl C. Taylor	American Rural Sociological Society United States Department of Agriculture
May C. Wharton, M.D.	Field Secretary Uplands Cumberland Mountain Sanatorium Pleasant Hill, Tennessee
Harold H. Whitted, M.D.	Howard University Medical School

⟨ VII ⟩

What Is the Nation's Need
for Research in the Service of Health?

*Knowledge acquired through research is the
fundamental resource from which stems all
progress toward general good health.*

THE Research Section of the National Health Assembly was charged
with the responsibility of formulating a plan regarding the function of
governmental agencies in facilitating, by general or specific means, the
solution of public health problems through the medium of research in
the medical and allied fields. The general aim of the program is to
produce and maintain healthy individuals.

Although the importance of emphasizing the disease factor in public
health is duly recognized by prominent men in the medical field, the
more significant purpose in the over-all program is to produce and maintain the healthy individual; for, in the healthy individual, disease may
eventually be extinguished or reduced to an insignificant factor. From
the viewpoint of attracting public attention and assistance in developing
a program for medical research, perhaps it is vital to emphasize the
incidence of important diseases and their related economic factors.[1] But
from the research point of view[2] it would be better to reverse this approach and attempt to determine a means for producing the optimum
functioning of the living organism and maintaining it that way, in this
manner emphasizing some of the more positive, in addition to the nega-
tive, factors of the program.

Immediately, on analyzing the problems concerned with medical research, the question arises as to ways and means of analyzing the field
of public health other than through the medium of data concerned

[1] See Appendix A, Tables 1 and 2, for incidence; Tables 3, 4, and 5 for related
economic factors.
[2] See Appendix A, Table 6.

166

with morbidity, mortality, infringement on the family budget, or social importance, both today and as they will appear in the next fifty years in accordance with the indicated upswing of the longevity curve.

Although the chief approach to most of our problems in connection with medical research leans toward the categories of social importance, morbidity, mortality, and costs, it is hoped that eventually the health of the nation may be measured in other terms, such as its social and biological implications.

In terms of the social usefulness and happiness of individuals and communities, certainly the development and maintenance of a healthy mind is of obvious importance; the term "healthy" in this case may be used in whatever sense it may prove significant.

During the meeting of the Section on the Nation's Need for Research in the Service of Health, Dr. John H. Stokes of the University of Pennsylvania expressed the opinion that there is no clear conception as to what really constitutes a "healthy" individual. It was his opinion that a physically healthy person may in some circumstances be a functionally out-of-place unit; on the other hand, a great deal of the good work of the world has been done by physically unhealthy individuals and, from certain standpoints, by psychoneurotic persons. Therefore, Dr. Stokes maintained, we should be very careful in the use of the term "health"; it is unfortunate to consider morbidity and mortality as exclusive criteria of health and equally unfortunate to consider that a type of healthy individual has ever been defined.

Health is a functional as well as a structural term. Some physically healthy persons are without a degree of conscience or character and should perhaps be rated by all who know them as "unhealthy." Hence, in any program formulated to embrace the ramifications concerned with the public health, perhaps there is still need for a definition of a "healthy" individual in terms other than those of morbidity, mortality, costs, or social importance. Any program of research must be extended to include such aspects as social usefulness, general acceptability, and all-round adjustment to society as a whole in this modern-day living. Certainly medical scientists are beginning to place more and more emphasis upon the mental and psychosomatic aspects of the so-called unhealthy individual in an attempt to resolve the real and pseudo problems surrounding that individual.

The membership of the Research Section of the National Health Assembly was purposely so selected as to bring out all shades of viewpoints as to the role the Federal government should play in medical research. Under the guidance of Dr. Andrew C. Ivy, the Section's chairman, private scientists, heads of foundations, university scientific departments, industrial research laboratories, and officers of learned societies were invited to the Assembly to formulate definite, concrete measures for the solution of the major problems within the broad field of medical research.

In general discussion, the Section raised such questions as the following: "Should the Federal government sponsor only basic or fundamental research?" "Should the support of applied research be funneled through other channels?" "Should governmental agencies be restricted to applied research?" "Should governmental agencies do both basic and applied research?"

Dr. T. Duckett Jones of the Helen Hay Whitney Foundation pointed out that there has been a sharp differentiation between "basic" and "applied" research and a strong disposition to call one group "basic" and another "applied." In the solution of problems, however, Dr. Jones said, it is impossible to tell from which side of the supposed compartment a basic item is going to come. The whole idea of "basic" versus "applied" research can be overemphasized, and it is not considered desirable for government, either Federal or state, to assume the function of applying funds solely to "basic" research and thereby obviously leave some of the "applied" research inadequately supported. There is not, after all, Dr. Jones said, so sharp a line separating "basic" and "applied" as institutionalization tends to insist upon.

In order that the Research Section might agree on a terminology so vital throughout its discussion, the definitions cited by the Steelman Committee in its report to the President were used as a base line for all discussions concerning the types of research:[3]

Basic Research

Fundamental research. Fundamental research is theoretical analysis, exploration, or experimentation directed to the extension of knowledge of the general principles governing natural or social phenomena.

Background research. Background research is the systematic observation, collection, organization, and presentation of facts using known principles to reach objectives that are clearly defined before the research is undertaken to provide a foundation for subsequent research or to provide standard reference data.

[3] *The Nation's Medical Research* (Washington: Government Printing Office, Oct. 18, 1947), Vol. 5, p. 8.

Applied Research

Applied research is the extension of basic research to the determination of the combined effects of physical laws or generally accepted principles with a view to specific application, generally involving the devising of a specified novel product, process, technique, or device.

The campaigns by philanthropic organizations and individuals for raising funds to support problems in connection with poliomyelitis, cancer, tuberculosis, and heart disease and the very fact that the National Health Assembly was called demonstrate to a marked degree the desire of the people to increase the rate of discovery of medical knowledge in the United States. This was a realistic problem which confronted the Research Section of the National Health Assembly. Medical research—not the people—created the problem.

Medical research in the past has suffered serious illnesses from lack of people, lack of funds, lack of facilities, and lack of sufficient interest. Nevertheless, medical research has in a limited way been extraordinarily successful in the past. The general public has tremendous faith in medical research and is constantly clamoring for more and better trained physicians, a better distribution of medical facilities, and a determined effort toward the prevention of disease. A trained mind is not required to perceive that the control and cure of disease has progressed tremendously in the last thirty years, that more and more lives have been saved, and that the problem of the aged, of the degenerative diseases, of the nervous and mental illnesses, and of the chronically ill looms larger and larger on the horizon of public health. It is also obvious that the expenditure of money to learn how to prevent disease will decrease the need of expenditures for the custodial care of the chronically ill in later life.

The people and their representatives in Congress know this. They realize that research is essential for the advancement of humanity and vital for the survival of any nation or group of nations. It is natural that they should desire that knowledge regarding the prevention and cure of disease be increased. It is natural that they should expect great discoveries to be made—too many and too soon—if more money is made available. And it is natural that the people and the Congress, through their agent the Public Health Service of the Federal Security Agency, should seek the advice of the medical scientists in our country—the people who are trained and whose duty it is to know how best to advance medical knowledge.

Approach to the Problem

In approaching the problem it is important to emphasize that money cannot buy knowledge or discoveries as it buys labor and products of labor. It does, however, provide for the physical needs of the investigator, and it gives him a prospect of security. In the long run, money should be so provided as to insure the freedom of the researcher and release those who have the necessary ability from the additional burden of supplementing their incomes by activities outside the field of research.

The freedom of the researcher to investigate the problem of his choice must be rigidly maintained; otherwise independent thinking, which is vital for progress, will be stultified. This does not mean that it should be beneath the dignity of a researcher to devote time, energy, and thought in co-operating in research conceived and directed by others. It means that an investigator in the university or medical school must be free to decline research that is unattractive to him. Indeed, the universities and medical schools have the chief responsibility for maintaining freedom in research, for the performance of fundamental research, and for the training of investigators.

Moreover, no group with money for research—whether it be a governmental agency, the National Research Council, private foundations, commercial concerns, or fund-raising groups—should be permitted to become so powerful that an investigator has no hope for continuing research without its support. Competition and co-operation are both important for progress in research. In addition, it would be fatal for any non-educational group to become so involved with medical research, as a means to an end, that the necessity of educating and holding research educators in the educational institutions would be ignored. If the government, industry, and the people are going to demand more medical investigators and medical research, it is obviously essential to hold more and better research teachers in the medical and allied science schools and to provide facilities for them to train additional medical investigators.

The Research Section felt strongly that what is really needed to augment and to prevent a slowdown in the rate of the production of medical knowledge is more good research men and more fluid money.

The money should be rendered available so as to prevent such recessions in scientific research as occurred prior to the Second World War. In fact, in order to hold good men and to prevent a recession from occurring now, it is necessary that careers in medical research be made more attractive. Fellowships and money for research expenses are not the complete answer to the medical research problem. The career situation is a major factor in the research problem. Financial assistance in buying brains for research is more urgently needed now than at any time in our history. Fluid money must be made available to raise salaries so that zeal for research will not be dampened by the financial appeal of the much larger incomes offered by commercial concerns and by the private practice of medicine. Nothing in this statement should be construed as making salary either a major attraction to research or a substitute for inspiration and opportunity.

In the past, medical research in universities, medical schools, and research institutes has been rendered possible by providing money in two ways. Benefactors have made either an *institutional gift* or a *project gift*. The institutional gift has been made for improving medical research and education in a broad manner. The project gift has been made for increasing knowledge regarding a specific disease, or a special part of the body, or a specified small area of medical science.

In making project grants or in making money available for research on a specified disease, every granting body has emphasized the vital importance of spending an appropriate portion of the money available on fundamental or so-called basic research. This is of the essence; it must be continued and expanded. The history of medical research shows that the discovery of the cause and control of disease has been based on a broad understanding of biology and of disease processes, structurally or functionally, as well as of the nature of the causative agents. It is obvious that so long as the knowledge of a function of a tissue is incomplete the possible relation of a disease to the tissue will be incomplete.

In certain areas of public health it is becoming more and more evident that research is best conducted when specialists in various fields of science direct their attention to a problem as a team. An example of teamwork is the multi-approach to research on child and parental attitudes and behavior, relative to ascertaining the best methods for developing wholesome attitudes and conduct. Similar team research has been conducted in the general field of human reproduction, looking toward the improvement and maintenance of health both from the eugenic and euthenic aspects; another example is shown in connection with the problem of determining the ways and means of best utilizing the productive capacity of individuals who are being retired from their ordinary activities.

Should the Federal Government Assist in Medical Research?

A great majority of scientists believe that the Federal government should support medical research, both because it is unlikely that support of the type needed to solve the problems confronting us today will be forthcoming except from Federal sources and because it is a responsibility of government to support research on problems pertaining to the health of the people. The Federal government has supported research in agriculture for many years, and surely it is just as important to improve the health of our human beings as it is to improve the health and welfare of our cows, pigs, chickens, and horses. It is essential, of course, to distinguish between the problem of how best to foster medical research and how best to foster a better distribution of medical care.

These scientists, however, are even more certain that money given for medical research should be free of so-called dictation and interference by bureaucratic bodies. The conditions under which the money is rendered available should conform to the principles outlined by the Public Health Service, along with non-Federal councils and study sections, and must be justly distributed among the various medical research institutions.[4]

It is believed that the random plan existing for the development of medical research prior to the Second World War must be markedly augmented in order to develop research and make possible its application in a manner that is now necessary to meet the needs of the people.[5] The value of the voluntary small donation as a means of giving the public an active sense of participation in and concern for the support of research is fully recognized, although this source of funds is extremely inadequate today. It seems clear that medical research and the training of research workers cannot depend solely on gifts from private and corporate sources and that everyone should donate, through taxes, on the basis of his ability to contribute.

If Federal money is to be accepted for fostering medical research, the medical and other co-operating scientists, who are the people in the

[4] United States Public Health Service Policy Statement "On Research Grants and Fellowships," March 13, 1948, authorized by Public Law 410, 78th Congress, as amended (58:462).

[5] Prior to the organization of the Office of Scientific Research and Development, Federal government agencies engaged in medical research only as specific problems presented themselves. Private philanthropies, industry, and fund-raising groups are still under a random plan for research.

best position to know, should formulate the conditions under which it is advisable to accept money. The conditions, however, should be such as to manifest no lack of faith in the democratic procedures of government. *In other words, we must look upon our government as "we" and not as "they."*

CONCLUSIONS AND RECOMMENDATIONS[6]

Broad Base of Financial Support

The continued progress of research and development in medicine and public health requires increased resources. Important advances in research frontiers have in the past been successfully made in universities and other research institutions supported by both private and public funds. The basis of all research is the supply of scientists, whose inspiration and development depend upon the continuance of the physical and intellectual integrity of the American university. It is desirable that the support of research spring from as broad a base as possible.

Support by non-governmental funds of research and development in the interests of medicine and public health should be encouraged and stimulated by all means consistent with democratic principles. Such sources of support should include:

(a) Funds collected and disbursed by voluntary agencies;
(b) Funds from philanthropic foundations;
(c) Funds from industrial foundations or individual industries; and
(d) Funds from individual donors and community sources.

Even with such stimulation, Federal support will be necessary for the continuance of strong research departments in most universities and essential for the development of research in those institutions now lacking adequate personnel and facilities.

"Fluid" Funds Necessary

The support of medical and related research during the past several years with funds provided by Federal taxation has been productive of great benefit to the people of the United States and of other countries who have been permitted to participate in the research findings. Regardless of this support, it is recognized that many medical schools and other scientific institutions are having serious financial difficulties and that there are many instances in which fluid financial support will be the only means of insuring research success. Fluid funds should be

[6] The Section on Dental Health (Chapter XI) made recommendations regarding dental research.

provided on a long-term basis from Federal tax sources to foster research in these institutions under the following conditions:

(1) Fluid funds should be used primarily to increase the salaries of permanent investigators, so as to provide the economic security necessary for effective work, and also to increase the number of permanent personnel available for effective long-range research.

(2) Applications for fluid funds should spring spontaneously from the institutions seeking such support. Except in rare instances, the institution to which the funds may be granted should take the initiative. The application of the institution in question should set forth the adequate justification for any grant for fluid support. The amount of fluid grants must lie within reasonable limits. It is suggested that the amount may vary among institutions and from year to year but should not exceed $100,000 annually for each institution.

Increased Facilities

Although it is probable that a moderate increase in the number of scientists in training and of permanent personnel can be accommodated within the space at present available to medical schools and other scientific institutions, expanded research programs will require increased basic facilities, including the construction of buildings, remodeling, and equipment. Scientific buildings have a short span of usefulness and require frequent alteration and new equipment to meet the needs of new studies and research programs. The provision of basic facilities is essential to good scientific work. This is a pressing need of established medical schools and other institutions where research is now being conducted. Excellent research opportunities and special problems worthy of study exist in some areas where no research institutions are present.

Fluid funds should be provided on a long-term basis, when necessary, to supplement funds used to cover basic facility costs commensurate with personnel needs and research programs to be undertaken.

Project Grants-in-Aid

The research grants-in-aid program now in effect is an important part of the larger plan to increase the knowledge necessary for human health. This knowledge, which is so essential for maintaining optimum health, starts with an understanding of all living organisms. Such information depends directly on the fundamental sciences of general biology, chemistry, and physics, as well as on subjects basic to medicine. Although the foundations and industry have successfully supported research grants-in-aid for many years, the present Federal program of research grants-in-aid is relatively new. Necessarily the methods used have been of an exploratory nature, but the program has been successful because of its broad outlook on research, because of its council and study-section system, and because of the complete freedom allowed the investigator.

Great care should be taken in making future grants; for excessive expansion, with the possibility of sudden withdrawal of support, is more dangerous to the economic stability of research progress than limited support, even if the latter means slower immediate attainment of our goal.

In addition to present fields which are now being supported, two additional phases of research should be given immediate consideration:

(a) Funds should be provided to stimulate those fields in which research is not being conducted commensurately with its importance to the health program.

For example, in the development of machines, such as the automobile and the airplane, as much thought should be given to the man that runs the machine as to the mechanical design of the machine. The expenditure of funds to develop machines and devices is enormously greater than the expenditure to render the use of machines and devices by man safe and efficient. In fact, many millions of dollars are spent on the development and production of machines and domestic animals, whereas relatively little is spent on the improvement of man so that he may more effectively cope with his environmental enemies.

Research should also be directed toward decreasing accidents in the home and factory, on the streets and in the air and water, and toward studying people's proneness to accident.

Only four or five of the first twelve diseases of greatest social importance are receiving considerable research attention at present.

As an example of a new area of research, the migration of our citizens to the Arctic calls for research on Arctic health.

(b) Funds should be provided to enhance support in fields where important discoveries appear imminent but have failed to reach solution for one reason or another or need additional critical studies for decisive conclusion.

From time to time each research project should be re-evaluated in order to determine if the grant should be terminated.

All grants should be considered supplementary to the research program of an individual or of an institution; otherwise these grants may interfere with the internal harmony and the fiscal policy of the institution. If the program is bigger than one person can supervise effectively, it should be a joint program with other individuals or departments.

Research Fellowships

The fellowship program is naturally closely integrated with the grants-in-aid program. It is useless to have grants-in-aid unless properly trained investigators are available to do the work. In the specific case of national health, it is necessary not only to train the man to carry on experimental investigations but also to train him to apply the findings and to educate other workers. In other words, selection depends not only upon the mental ability and capacity of the individual but upon his interest in the field.

Every effort should be made to select individuals for the training program as early in life as possible. This places considerable responsibility at the local level for the ultimate success of the fellowship program. After selection, the recipient should be given the broadest possible training, including a limited amount of teaching. Although he will do research work to secure his training, he should not be used to supply additional technical help for a specific project. After fellowship training, scientists should be conserved for research and should not be used merely in technical capacities.

A fellowship program should be carefully correlated with the predicted need for trained investigators. At the present time there is a great shortage of properly trained individuals in certain fields. Since the demand may change rapidly from year to year, the need should be reevaluated annually.

Research Information Center

Basic to the effective distribution of fluid research funds, grants-in-aid, and research fellowships is the collection and classification of information concerning all research that may pertain to the promotion of better health.

An information center on research fellowships—on projects under way, the sources of their support, and facilities and personnel—should be established and maintained. Naturally this information will have to be obtained on a voluntary basis. It is specifically understood that the center would have no control or directing relation to the research project. Such a center, however, would be of assistance in avoiding unnecessary duplication of effort.

Animal Experimentation

Attention should be directed to the fact that the provision of funds for research in medicine and other sciences would be negated if the humane use of animals—such as mice, guinea pigs, monkeys, and dogs—for experimental purposes should be restricted in any way. Medical knowledge is usually gained in three steps: first by experiments with test tubes, second by experiments on animals, and finally by the application of the results to man.

Most of the knowledge we possess today regarding the function of the organs of the body, nutrition, and the prevention and control of disease has resulted from animal experimentation. The control of such diseases as diabetes, pernicious anemia, smallpox, pellagra, scurvy, rickets, beriberi, diphtheria, typhoid, and thyroid disease was derived from experiments with animals. The same is true for the use of penicillin and sulfa drugs.

Practically every surgical operation performed today was perfected on animals before it was used on humans. The new operation for the treatment of "blue babies" was tried on dogs before it was tried on a human child. Untold human suffering has been avoided as the result of experimental research on animals. The average length of life has been extended from thirty-five to sixty-six years, and some fifty million people in our country owe their lives to the application to man of discoveries made on animals during the past century.

As to the future, an increase in knowledge regarding the control or cure of cancer, heart disease, hardening of the arteries, high blood pressure, rheumatism, and peptic ulcer will depend largely on the humane use of animals in university and medical research laboratories.

A national educational program should be conducted to inform the public regarding the accomplishments of animal experimentation and the necessity and humaneness of the use of animals for the discovery of the prevention and cure of disease in both men and animals. The animals now being wastefully destroyed in the city pounds should be made available, as needed, for use in university and medical research laboratories.

Medical Education Survey

A. The Section on the Nation's Need for Research in the Service of Health endorses the survey of medical education to be conducted by the Association of American Medical Colleges and the Council on Medical Education and Hospitals of the American Medical Association for the purpose of determining the current and future needs in medical education and research and *recommends that this survey be completed at the earliest possible date.* Research may profitably be undertaken relative to the cost of educating physicians and allied personnel.

B. This Section recognizes the importance of the professions of dentistry, nursing, social service, pharmacy, psychology, sanitary engineering, and veterinary medicine and of the many other scientific categories in any well-balanced program of health and is aware that, as a consequence, these groups are frequently concerned with research.

Necessary steps should be taken by the appropriate bodies to evaluate the aims of these groups as to educational philosophy, curriculum, research, and service, and steps consistent with these aims should be subsequently taken so that in health matters this nation's educational, research, and service programs may be as well balanced and effective as possible.

As a case in point, the Section recognizes the frequent importance of the nurse as a member of the research team. The report of the Subcommittee on the Needs for Research in the Field of Nursing presented later in this chapter is largely concerned with problems of service and of the education, distribution, and more effective use of nursing personnel. In other words, the report indicates, and the Research Section recognizes, the need of educational and socio-economic research in the field of nursing and believes that this work is largely the concern of nursing educators and of those interested in the broad problems of nursing service.

Need for Federal Support

Federal funds should be allocated in support of essential research in medicine and allied fields when it is evident that the research is not adequately supported by funds from other sources.

It is recognized that duplication of research on fundamental questions of basic importance may be necessary and is often desirable but that uncorrelated duplication of work at the development level is, in general, undesirable and to be avoided.

Although the allocation of Federal funds on the basis of matching dollar for dollar may be desirable in some instances, it is the opinion of this Section that it should not be an absolute requirement. The guiding principle should be to base the allocation of such funds upon the need for research and the ability to carry it through the desired research program.

Research Freedom

Federal funds should be provided through grants-in-aid with a recognition of the principle that the institution and the individual shall have complete freedom in working out the research program so long as the activity remains within the broad field of research designated in the grant.

Federal Funds Are Additive

Federal funds should not be used to substitute for the ordinary teaching, administrative, or research responsibilities of an institution; any such funds which are employed should be employed additively and not substitutively. Appropriate action in this regard should be taken either before or after the research grant is made in order to carry out the intent of this recommendation.

Continuance of Public Health Service Program

The policies relative to governmental allocation of funds for research construction, grants-in-aid, and fellowships should continue in the hands of scientific advisory boards similar to those governing the present program for grants and research fellowships in the Public Health Service which has proved so successful.

Early implementation of the foregoing recommendations will constitute a vigorous approach which not only will prevent a recession in medical science but, of even more significance, will inaugurate a more dynamic program in the search for medical truths and their application to the production and maintenance of healthy individuals.

REPORTS OF SUBCOMMITTEES
SUBCOMMITTEE ON BASIC SUPPORT OF PERSONNEL AND FLUID FUNDS TO SUPPORT GENERAL RESEARCH

Dr. Ward Darley, *Chairman*

Your committee believes that the support of medical and related research during the past several years with the aid of funds provided by Federal taxation has been productive of great benefit to the people of the United States and of other countries who have been permitted to participate in the research findings. Because of this, the following two statements of principle are of fundamental importance:

(a) There is need for additional support of research in medical and allied fields; and

(b) It is desirable that Federal funds be made available to foster research in these fields.

This committee has been assigned the task of providing a statement of principles which would enable institutions interested in medical teaching and research to function with maximum effectiveness. It is recognized that many of our medical schools and other scientific institutions are approaching serious financial difficulties and that there are many instances in which fluid financial support would make possible the initiation and maintenance of research and would encourage its practical application.

Your committee therefore recommends that the Research Section of the National Health Assembly agree in principle to the fostering of research with the aid of fluid funds provided from Federal tax sources. In this connection, the following statements would apply:

1. It should be understood that the training of individuals for research and the teaching of research measures may be reached by more than one route; the Subcommittee believes that the purpose of this type of research support should be the stimulation of research and not the mere accumulation of degrees.

2. Federal research grant funds should not be used to substitute for the ordinary teaching, administrative, or research responsibilities of an institution; any such funds which are employed should be employed additively and not substitutively. Appropriate action in this regard should be taken either before or after the research grant is made in order to carry out the intent of this recommendation.

3. These funds should be used to increase salaries of investigators and to provide the economic security necessary for effective work.

4. These funds, furthermore, should be used to increase the number of permanent personnel available for effective long-range research.

5. These funds also should be available for the initiation and continuation of worthy research problems.

Your committee feels strongly that efforts to secure any type of fluid support should spring spontaneously from the institutions seeking such support. Except in rare instances, the institution to which the funds may be granted should take the initiative. The application of the institution in question should set forth the adequate justification for any grant for fluid support. Your committee recognizes that in principle the size of fluid grants must lie within reasonable limits.

SUBCOMMITTEE ON BASIC FACILITIES

Dr. T. Duckett Jones, *Chairman*

Though it is probable that a small increase in the number of scientists in training and even permanent scientific personnel can be accomplished within the space at present available to medical schools and other scientific institutions, expanded research programs will require increased basic facilities, including the construction of buildings, remodeling, and equipment. Scientific buildings have a short span of usefulness and require frequent alteration and new equipment to meet the needs of new studies and research programs. Provision of basic facilities is essential to good scientific work. This is a pressing need of established medical schools and other institutions where research is now being conducted or where it might be advantageously developed.

In some areas, medical schools and research institutions are non-existent. Excellent research opportunities and problems worthy of special study exist in some of these areas, offering unusual knowledge. Provision of facilities in some such areas might offer great advantages.

In stating that it is desirable that Federal funds be made available for research in medical and allied fields, your committee would strongly urge that basic facility costs commensurate with personnel needs and research programs to be undertaken be included in this support.

SUBCOMMITTEE ON RESEARCH GRANTS AND FELLOWSHIPS

C. A. Elvehjem, *Chairman*

The research grants and fellowships program is part of a larger plan to increase the knowledge necessary for human health. This knowledge, which is so essential for maintaining optimum health, starts with an understanding of all living organisms. Such information depends directly on the fundamental sciences of general biology, chemistry, and physics, as well as on the basic medical sciences. The present program of Federal research grants-in-aid and fellowships has been remarkably successful in the development of a program for increasing our knowledge. Although the foundations and industry have supported research through grants-in-aid for many years, the Federal program has been a pioneering experiment in this field. Necessarily the methods used have been of an exploratory nature and certain changes in procedure may be desirable. The program has been successful because of its broad outlook on research, because of its study-section system, and because of the complete freedom allowed the investigator. Any suggestions made at this time are in no way criticisms of the program but an attempt to bring it into the long-term and expanded plan which has been requested by the National Health Assembly.

Basic to the effective distribution of research fellowships and grants-in-aid is the collection and evaluation of information concerning all research that may pertain to the promulgation of better health. Such a collection of data involves detailed information on research grants regardless of the source from which they are derived, available facilities and personnel, the interest and competence of investigators, problems under immediate investigation, and the needs of institutions engaged in research. As a program increases in a given field, more of this work is necessary and eventually can be done most effectively through an agency such as a National Science Foundation.

Specific suggestions regarding the future research grants-in-aid program are as follows: (a) excessive expansion, with the possibility of sudden withdrawal of support, is more dangerous than limited support, even if the latter means slower immediate attainment of our goal; and (b) many of our research programs are now progressing very well and continued support of these should be encouraged. In addition, two other phases of research should be given consideration: (1) Funds to stimulate a field in which progress in research is not being conducted commensurately with its importance to the health program; in supporting work in this area, care should be taken that funds are not dissipated in projects where possibility of success at the present time appears remote. (2) Funds should be provided to enhance support in fields where important discoveries appear imminent but have failed to reach solution for one reason or another or need added critical studies for successful conclusion.

SUBCOMMITTEE ON FORMULATION OF GENERAL POLICY

Dr. Fred L. Adair, *Chairman*

1. Additional financial support is required from Federal and/or state and local funds and/or from corporate and/or private sources.

2. Although the allocation of Federal funds on the basis of matching dollar for dollar may be desirable in some instances, it should not be an absolute requirement. Rather, the guiding principle in the allocation of funds should be on the basis of need for research education, personnel salaries, equipment, and the like, and the ability to carry through the desired research program.

3. The Federal funds should not be allocated in support of medicine and allied fields until it is quite evident that the research is not adequately supported by funds from other sources. It is recognized that duplication of research on fundamental questions of basic importance may be necessary and is often desirable but that uncorrelated duplication of work at the developmental level is, in general, undesirable and to be avoided.

4. The Federal government, in the allocation of research funds, should be guided by the principle of supporting existing institutions devoted in whole or in part to research, rather than in utilizing its funds to set up competing organizations in its various bureaus and departments. This is especially important at this time in view of the shortage of personnel capable of research in the field of health.

5. We recognize the importance of the use of Federal funds to stimulate and support research programs in the less wealthy areas of the country in order to equalize opportunities for citizens of those areas. On the other hand, we do not favor the allocation of such funds on a political basis where the environment is not favorable to the development of research programs in the service of health for these and other areas.

6. It is recommended that the Federal government study the possibilities of securing greater co-ordination of the research activities, in fields pertaining to health, which are now being carried on in its various departments and bureaus or are contemplated in the future.

7. It is recommended that the Federal government should recognize that research programs are being carried out by other institutions and agencies and that duplication of research programs should be minimized and our personnel and other available resources should be conserved.

8. It is recommended that the allocation of Federal funds be made with the recognition of the principle that the institution and the individual have complete freedom in working out the research program so long as the activity remains within the broad field of research designated in the grant.

SUBCOMMITTEE ON ANIMAL EXPERIMENTATION

Charles M. Carpenter, *Chairman*

The full report of this committee is given above under Conclusions and Recommendations, *Animal Experimentation.*

SUBCOMMITTEE ON THE NEEDS FOR RESEARCH IN THE FIELD
OF NURSING AND SOCIAL SERVICE

Dr. Mary C. Connor, *Chairman*

Your committee has listed five areas in which research is needed:

1. National survey of needs for nurses
   (a) Definition of what should be the functions of professional nurses in relation to physicians, medical social workers, visiting teachers, practical nurses, or other auxiliary workers
   (b) Classification of existing nursing personnel according to function; and redistribution
   (c) Cost, activity, and time studies of nursing service
2. Preparation of personnel to meet the needs of nursing service—validation studies of curriculum content of both basic and student personnel
3. Preparation of personnel to meet the needs of nursing education in clinical areas and in relation to areas of education—vocational and higher education
4. Improvement of nursing techniques and procedures
5. Administration of nursing service in hospitals and special health agencies

APPENDIX A

Table 1

Relative Social Importance (in descending order) of Diseases as Estimated by the Number of Deaths, Days Lost, and Medical, Dental, and Nursing Care

1. Circulatory Diseases
2. Respiratory Diseases
3. Infectious and Parasitic Diseases
4. Accidents
5. Mental Diseases
6. Genito-Urinary Diseases
7. Neoplastic Diseases
8. Digestive Diseases
9. Allergic, Endocrine, and Metabolic Diseases
10. Complications of Childbirth and Pregnancy

Table 2

Relative Social Importance (in descending order) of Chronic Diseases as Estimated by Days Lost, Number of Invalids, Number of Cases, and Number of Deaths

1. Heart Diseases
2. Arteriosclerosis and High Blood Pressure
3. Nervous and Mental Diseases
4. Rheumatism

Table 2—*Continued*

5. Nephritis and Other Kidney Diseases
6. Tuberculosis
7. Cancer and Other Tumors
8. Diabetes Mellitus
9. Hay Fever and Asthma
10. Diseases of Gall Bladder and Liver
11. Diseases of Female Organs
12. Ulcer of Stomach and Duodenum

Table 3

Estimated Annual Costs (Medical, Dental, and Nursing Care) of the Leading
Causes of Illness and Disability, and Research Funds Devoted to the Study of
Those Diseases by the U. S. Public Health Service in 1946-1947[1]

Group	Costs[2]	Research Funds	
		Projects Conducted by Agency[3]	Grants-in-Aid[4]
		(In thousands)	
Teeth and mouth	$700,000	$157	$15
Digestive	449,000	—	41
Respiratory	367,000	96	108
Mental	331,000	52	68
Genito-urinary	267,000	—	41
Infectious and parasitic diseases ...	204,000	4,043	1,248
Circulatory	193,000	159	350
Accidents	188,000	22	8
Bones and organs of movement ...	178,000	—	56
Neoplasms	137,000	891	515
Allergic, endocrine, metabolic	110,000	—	19
Eye and blindness	103,000	—	—
Ear and deafness	88,000	—	—
Complications of pregnancy, childbirth, and puerperium	75,000	—	30
Skin	33,000	26	—
Blood and blood-forming organs ..	16,000	13	52
Congenital malformations and diseases of infancy	10,000	—	—

[1] Figures from the 1937 health survey made by the U. S. Public Health Service, adjusted to 1946-1947.

[2] Medical, dental, and hospital care.

[3] Does not include $2,848,566 for research projects in basic research or of general nature which cannot be allocated to a specific disease group.

[4] Does not include $889,985 granted for research projects in basic research or of general nature which cannot be allocated to a specific disease group.

Table 4

Estimated Man-Years Lost per Year from the Leading Causes of Illness and Disability, and Research Funds Devoted to the Study of Those Diseases by the U. S. Public Health Service in 1946-1947[1]

Group	Man-years Disability	Research Funds Projects Conducted by Agency[2]	Grants-in-Aid[3]
		(In thousands)	
Mental	1,000,000	$52	$68
Respiratory	654,000	96	108
Circulatory	653,000	159	350
Infectious and parasitic diseases ..	587,000	4,043	1,248
Accidents	428,000	22	8
Bones and organs of movement ..	323,000	—	56
Digestive	263,000	—	41
Genito-urinary	170,000	—	41
Allergic, endocrine, metabolic ...	150,000	—	19
Neoplasms	113,000	891	515
Eye and blindness	80,000	—	—
Complications of pregnancy, childbirth, and puerperium	75,000	—	30
Ear and deafness	57,000	—	—
Congenital malformations and diseases of infancy	49,000	—	—
Skin	39,000	26	—
Blood and blood-forming organs ..	26,000	13	52
Teeth and mouth	7,000	157	15

[1] Figures from the 1937 health survey made by the U. S. Public Health Service, adjusted to 1946-1947.

[2] Does not include $2,848,566 for research projects in basic research or of general nature which cannot be allocated to a specific disease group.

[3] Does not include $889,985 granted for research projects in basic research or of general nature which cannot be allocated to a specific disease group.

Table 5

Estimated Annual Costs (Medical, Dental, Nursing Care, Time Lost) of the Leading Causes of Illness and Disability, and Research Funds Devoted to the Study of Those Diseases by the U. S. Public Health Service in 1946-1947[1]

Group	Cost[2]	Research Funds	
		Projects Conducted by Agency[3]	Grants-in-Aid[4]
		(In thousands)	
Mental	$1,331,000	$52	$68
Respiratory	1,021,000	96	108
Circulatory	846,000	159	350
Infectious and parasitic diseases	762,000	4,043	1,248
Digestive	723,000	—	41
Teeth and mouth	707,000	157	15
Accidents	616,000	22	8
Bones and organs of movement	501,000	—	56
Genito-urinary	437,000	—	41
Allergic, endocrine, metabolic	260,000	—	19
Neoplasms	250,000	891	515
Eye and blindness	183,000	—	—
Complications of pregnancy, child-birth, and puerperium	150,000	—	30

[1] Figures from the 1937 health survey made by the U. S. Public Health Service, adjusted to 1946-1947.

[2] Medical, dental, and hospital care; also cost of disability estimated at $1,000 per man-year.

[3] Does not include $2,848,566 for research projects in basic research or of general nature which cannot be allocated to a specific disease group.

[4] Does not include $889,985 granted for research projects in basic research or of general nature which cannot be allocated to a specific disease group.

Table 6

Deaths from Certain Disease Conditions, 1945, Compared with Research Funds
Devoted to the Study of Those Diseases by the U. S. Public Health Service in
1946-1947[1]

Group	Deaths	Research Funds	
		Projects Conducted by Agency[2]	Grants-in-Aid[3]
		(In thousands)	
Circulatory	554,813	$159	$350
Neoplasms	177,464	891	515
Genito-urinary	95,521	—	41
Accidents	95,918	22	8
Infectious and parasitic diseases ..	89,880	4,043	1,248
Respiratory	68,386	96	108
Congenital malformations and diseases of infancy	66,966	—	—
Digestive	46,519	—	41
Allergic, endocrine, metabolic	38,000	—	19
Complications of pregnancy, childbirth, and puerperium	5,668	—	30
Mental	2,293	52	68

[1] Figures from the 1937 health survey made by the U. S. Public Health Service,
adjusted to 1946-1947.

[2] Does not include $2,848,566 for research projects in basic research or of general
nature which cannot be allocated to a specific disease group.

[3] Does not include $889,985 granted for research projects in basic research or of
general nature which cannot be allocated to a specific disease group.

Disease Groups Used in the Study, for Tables 3, 4, 5, and 6, and Some of the
Most Important Diseases in Each Group

Infectious and parasitic diseases:
  Tuberculosis
  Syphilis
  Typhoid, dysenteries, diarrhea
  Communicable diseases of childhood
  Poliomyelitis
Neoplasms:
  Cancer
Allergic, endocrine, metabolic:
  Hay fever and asthma
  Diabetes
  Pellagra
Blood and blood-forming organs:
  Anemia
Mental and nervous:
  Psychosis
  Epilepsy
Circulatory (cardio-vascular):
  Arteriosclerosis
  Hypertension
  Rheumatic fever

Respiratory:
  Pneumonia
  Influenza
  Colds
Digestive and abdominal:
  Appendicitis
  Ulcer
  Hernia
  Diseases of liver and gallbladder
Teeth and mouth:
  Dental caries
Genito-urinary:
  Nephritis
Skin:
  Dermatitis
Bones and organs of movement:
  Arthritis
Congenital malformations and diseases
    of early infancy
Accidents
Complications of pregnancy, child-
    birth, and puerperium

APPENDIX B

PLANNING COMMITTEE

Andrew C. Ivy, M.D., *Chairman*	Vice-President, University of Illinois
H. G. Baity	Professor of Sanitation and Environment University of North Carolina
Ward Darley, M.D.	Director, University of Colorado Medical Center
C. A. Elvehjem	Dean, Graduate School University of Wisconsin
T. Duckett Jones, M.D.	Medical Director Helen Hay Whitney Foundation
Josiah J. Moore, M.D.	Treasurer, American Medical Association
John H. Stokes, M.D.	Syphilologist University of Pennsylvania
S. Bernard Wortis, M.D.	Professor of Psychiatry New York University College of Medicine

C. J. Van Slyke, M.D.   Chief, Division of Research Grants and Fellowships
National Institutes of Health
Public Health Service, Federal Security Agency

Manley W. Kilgore   Special Assistant to the Chief
Division of Research Grants and Fellowships
National Institutes of Health
Public Health Service, Federal Security Agency

REGISTRANTS

Fred Adair, M.D.   Professor Emeritus
University of Chicago

Joseph H. Barach, M.D.   Falk Clinic
University of Pittsburgh

Gilbert W. Beebe   Representative
American Veterans Committee

Miss Ella Best   Executive Secretary
American Nurses Association

Charles M. Carpenter, M.D.   Professor, Infectious Diseases
University of California School of Medicine

Mary C. Connor   Research Associate, Teachers College
Columbia University

E. H. Cushing, M.D.   Veterans Administration

George B. Dowling, M.D.   Deputy Administrator
National Blood Program
American National Red Cross

Per K. Froelich   Merck & Company

A. Baird Hastings   Professor of Biochemistry
Harvard University

L. G. Lederer, M.D.   Medical Director
Capital Airlines

Morris Leikind   Library of Congress

Milan A. Logan   Professor of Biochemistry
University of Cincinnati Medical School

Randolph T. Major   Vice-President and Director of Research
Merck & Company

F. C. Mann, M.D.   Mayo Clinic

George W. Merck   President, Merck & Company

Carl J. Potthoff, M.D.   Associate Medical Director
American National Red Cross

Stanley Rappeport	Research Council on Problems of Alcohol
Raymond M. Rice, M.D.	Research and Control Eli Lilly & Company
Murray Saunders	Associate Professor of Bacteriology College of Physicians and Surgeons Columbia University
Austin Smith, M.D.	Council on Pharmacy and Chemistry American Medical Association
Charles E. Smith, M.D.	Professor, Public Health and Preventive Medicine Stanford University School of Medicine
Miss Emma Spaney	Assistant Director Department of Measurement and Guidance National League of Nursing Education
Y. Subba Row	Lederle Laboratories Division American Cyanamid Company
Walton Van Winkle, M.D.	Therapeutic Trials Committee American Medical Association
John S. Zinsser	Chairman of the Board Sharp & Dohme

⟨ VIII ⟩

What Is the Nation's
Need for Medical Care?

PRIOR to the Assembly, the planning committee of the Section on Medical Care held two meetings. At the first of these the staff was instructed to prepare a draft of a factual statement of the medical care problem. This draft was to be sent to all members of the committee in advance of the second meeting. At the second meeting the committee considered this draft, directed its revision in certain respects, and, subject to such revision, adopted it as an agreed-upon statement of the problem for presentation to the Section as the first item of business. Inasmuch as it provided a point of departure for the discussions of the Section, it is presented in full below:

THE PROBLEM OF MEDICAL CARE

America's medicine is probably the best in the world, but its benefits are not equally available to our people. Judged by the average expectation of life and by the mortality rates, this country is one of the healthiest nations in the world, but millions of our people fail to receive adequate health care. Our health resources are great, but we are not using them as effectively as we could to prevent illness and disability and to save lives.

Our physicians, on the average, are probably better trained and more numerous in relation to the population than those of any other country, but their distribution is such that many parts of our country have insufficient medical personnel. Our hospitals, by and large, are the envy of the world, but here too large areas of the country simply have no such facilities. In medical research—in our contributions to the stream of medical knowledge—this country's position is pre-eminent, but our people are not receiving all the benefits of these scientific advances. The well-to-do in our large cities probably receive medical service which in quality and quantity is unequaled; by contrast, others, particularly in rural areas, frequently receive medical care which is deficient in both quality and quantity.

Contrasts in Medical Care[1] Available

The contrasts between the good and bad in the American medical scene are shown in comparisons among the states and among the various economic levels of the population. Thus the people of New York State receive an average of 1.46 days of care in general hospitals per person per year, whereas those in Mississippi receive less than one-third as much— 0.40 days per person per year. In Massachusetts 95.3 per cent of all births are attended by a physician in a hospital, and virtually all of the remaining 4.7 per cent are attended by a physician outside of a hospital. In South Carolina, however, only 41.2 per cent of all births take place in hospitals, 24.4 per cent are attended by a physician outside of a hospital, and 34.4 per cent are attended by a midwife or some other unspecified attendant. Among the colored population of that state, only 11 per cent of all women in childbirth are attended by a physician in a hospital, another 18.3 per cent are attended by a physician outside of a hospital, and 70.7 per cent of all births receive a midwife's care. These differences in the care received are undoubtedly related to the fact that in Massachusetts the maternal mortality rate is 1.8 deaths per 1,000 live births, whereas in South Carolina it is 3.7—and among the white in that state 2.0 and among the colored 5.8.

The infant mortality rate in the nation as a whole in 1946 was 39.8 per 1,000 live births. In Connecticut it was 30.7, but in New Mexico it was 89.1. Had the Connecticut rate obtained throughout the country, thousands of infants would have been saved in that year alone. Among whites in the country as a whole, the infant death rate in 1944 was 36.9 per 1,000; among Negroes it was 59.3.

Differences in the quantity of health facilities and health service personnel among the various states naturally indicate, in a rough way, differences in the availability of health services to the populations involved. New York State has 5.3 general hospital beds (exclusive of beds in Federal hospitals) per 1,000 population; Mississippi has only 1.8 such beds. New York State in 1940 had one physician for every 597 persons; Mississippi had one for every 1,784. New York State in the same year had one dentist for every 1,321 persons in its population; Mississippi

---

[1] The term medical care is used in a broad sense and includes the services of physicians, dentists, nurses, and hospitals and the provision of drugs, orthopedic appliances, eyeglasses, and so forth.

had one dentist for every 5,250 persons. New York State in 1941 had one active registered nurse for each 698 persons; Mississippi had one such nurse for each 2,143 persons.

Differences in Economic Status

These differences among the states are of course due in the main to differences in average economic well-being. When one ranks the states according to their per capita income, with the state of highest per capita income at the top and the state of lowest per capita income at the bottom, one finds among the well-to-do states relatively abundant hospital facilities, a high number of days of hospitalization per capita, large numbers of physicians, dentists, and nurses in proportion to the population, a high percentage of births occurring in hospitals, and low maternal and infant mortality rates. As the average per capita income declines, there is a decrease in hospital facilities and in days of hospital care, in the supply of health personnel in proportion to the population, and in the percentage of births attended in hospitals, as well as an increase in maternal and infant mortality rates. (See Table 1, in Appendix A, near the end of this chapter.)

Within states and communities there are similar differences in the volume of medical care received by groups of different economic status—those at the top of the income scale receiving the most and those with the lowest incomes (except where public or charitable care is available) the least. This is not because those of low income have less illness and therefore less need—most studies, on the contrary, show that on the average these groups suffer more sickness and disability—but because, in general, they have less money to spend for medical care.[2]

The contrast between the services received by the low- and high-income groups would be greater than it is were it not for the volume of free service given by physicians and hospitals. Indeed in certain large cities which make free hospital care readily available to those with low incomes, the latter frequently receive more days of hospital care than those with higher incomes, who are ineligible for free care.

The Negro population tends, in general, to be at the bottom of the

[2] Thus the studies of the Committee on the Costs of Medical Care showed that in 1928-31 families with incomes of less than $1,200 a year received 1.9 physicians' home, office, and clinic calls per person per year, as against 4.7 such calls per person per year among families with incomes of $10,000 or more. Similarly the proportions of persons having dental care in a year ranged from 117 per 1,000 persons in the lower-income group to 622 per 1,000 in the $10,000-and-over group. The volume of hospital care was 0.9 days per person for the under-$1,200 group; it dropped to 0.7 days in the $1,200-to-$2,000-income group, and rose to 1.2 days per capita in the $10,000-and-over income group.

economic ladder and to receive care which is least adequate in terms of both quality and quantity. This is undoubtedly one of the important causes of the higher mortality rates among this racial group. In 1940 the death rate, corrected for differences in age composition, for the country was 8.2 per 1,000 for whites; for Negroes it was 14.0—a mortality rate 71 per cent higher than the rate for whites. In 1940 the life expectation of Negroes at birth was from 10 to 20 per cent less than that of whites, the expectancy for males being 52 years among Negroes and 63 years among whites and for females 56 years among Negroes and 67 years among whites.

No matter how well the health record of this country compares with that of other nations or with our own past, it is inadequate so long as the potentialities of our medical resources are not available to our people, so long as our people are not getting all the service and care which the medical profession can render. It is evident that if the high standards of health care available to the population of some states were available to the entire population of the country, many lives would be saved. It is estimated, for example, that with our present knowledge at least one-third of the deaths from cancer would have been preventable if those afflicted had received prompt diagnosis and care.

Various studies indicate in certain population groups the presence of neglected illness or conditions impairing health. Thus the New York Academy of Medicine report, *Medicine and the Changing Order*, states:

But mortality statistics tell only part of the story. There is a vast amount of illness which, while it does not lead directly to death, has far-reaching and immeasurable effects on individuals, families, and social groups. No one can gauge the suffering and anxiety caused by sickness. A number of attempts have been made to establish just how much and what kinds of illness and physical disabilities prevail among the population of the United States at any given time. Much of the data yielded by these efforts is of uncertain value. The induction examinations during World War II did reveal, however, that close to a third of those examined were unfit for military service because of physical and mental deficiency and disease. Even granting that the examination standards were high and that some of those unfit for military service may yet be fit for civil life, the residual facts still constitute a serious charge against our national well-being. There are evidently many among our people who are below par and whose condition would be improved by raising their standard of living and by making available to them more and better medical services.[3]

[3] New York Academy of Medicine, *Medicine and the Changing Order* (New York: Commonwealth Fund, 1947), p. 39.

THE GOAL AND THE PROBLEM

The goal which a democratic nation implicitly accepts is that there shall be equal opportunities for health and that all those services which are necessary for the prevention of illness, the cure and relief of sickness, and the promotion of a high level of positive physical and mental health shall be available to all its people. The problem of medical care in the United States, whether this be considered as a single social and economic problem or as a bundle of related problems, is that these services are not now so available and that, given our present medical resources— our physicians, dentists, and other trained health personnel, our hospitals and other facilities, and the total amounts of money currently spent for medical care plus the even larger amounts we could afford to spend—we as a nation are not doing all that could be done in using these resources to bring adequate care to the entire population.

FACTORS INVOLVED

Why is it that some in our population do not receive adequate care? There are various factors involved, among the most important of which are the following: (a) the increased expensiveness of modern medical care; (b) the irregular and unpredictable incidence of medical costs when these costs are paid by the individual on a fee-for-service basis; (c) the low incomes of many in the population; (d) the lack of medical personnel and facilities in various areas; (e) the need for public understanding of the value of medical care, including preventive services; (f) the existence of community discriminatory practices affecting minority groups; and (g) insufficient co-ordination of action among the personnel and facilities providing service.

Increased Expensiveness of Modern Medical Care

There was a time when medical care, to all intents and purposes, consisted of the ministrations of a physician who could carry in a small bag all the equipment he had for diagnosis and treatment. The modern physician is the product of a long and expensive training. His own services are supplemented by those of auxiliaries—the nurse, the technician, the medical social worker. He needs expensive equipment for diagnosis and therapy. The modern, wonderful, but very costly hospital has developed. Modern dentists also require extensive training and costly equipment. All these and other changes resulting from advances in medical knowledge have greatly increased the effectiveness of medical care, but at the same time they have greatly increased the cost of that care.

The report, *Medicine and the Changing Order*, puts the situation well:

But as medicine and surgery progressed the whole situation changed. The increased cost of care made it difficult for the poor to afford the expert attention now available. The public and the profession became enmeshed in a distressing and paradoxical situation. As the competence of the profession increased, and as the public learned to appreciate this and to desire its services, the costs of medical services increased until they were beyond the resources of many.

The mounting costs of medical practice confront the public in the shape of fees charged by physicians, hospitals, laboratories, and the like. But the origins of the costs are essentially those very precise, involved, and expert procedures which made modern medicine so widely desirable and effective. The problem of how to reduce the one and retain the other, how to make medical care widely available without losing its effective qualities, is the core of the current problem in medicine . . .[4]

Uncertainty of Medical Expenses

For the individual, the coming of illness is in general unpredictable. In a given year an individual may have no illness or he may have one or several illnesses of varying degrees of severity, but as to all of this he cannot tell in advance. It follows that the medical needs of the individual are as a rule irregular and unpredictable. Similarly, in the absence of prepayment of the costs of medical attention such costs are unpredictable.

In any given year among any given group of families of a certain income level, a majority of the families will have no really serious or expensive illness and their medical costs will be below the average for the entire group of families. At the other extreme there will be a few families who will have one or more serious illnesses entailing heavy expense for medical care. The medical charges incurred by such families will amount to a considerable fraction of their entire annual income and will constitute a very sizable proportion of the total costs incurred by the entire group of families.[5]

[4] *Ibid.*, p. 25.

[5] For example, the 1928-31 survey of the Committee on the Costs of Medical Care showed that, among families with incomes of $2,000 to $3,000, 70.6 per cent incurred in a single year medical charges of less than $100; another 23.4 per cent of the families had charges of between $100 and $300; and 6 per cent of the families had charges of over $300 (and ranging up to over $1,000). The total charges incurred by this last group of families amounted to 31 per cent of the charges incurred by the entire group. (Bureau of Research and Statistics, Social Security Administration, *Medical Care and Costs in Relation to Family Income*, Bureau Memorandum #51, Washington, D. C., May, 1947, Table 142.)

The cost of necessary medical attention in a severe, prolonged illness may well amount to more than a family's entire annual income. Hospital bills in a single illness of $2,000 or $3,000 are by no means unknown. A severe illness requiring thirty days of hospital care might well result in a hospital bill of, say, $500. Adding to this the charges for the attending physician or surgeon and possible costs for special nursing and drugs, the total bill for a single illness may well amount to $1,000. It is obvious that many families cannot meet costs such as these and that such costs will represent a severe financial blow to all except the very well-to-do.

The situation is bad alike for those receiving and those providing care. To virtually everyone the possibility of heavy expense for medical care is a source of insecurity. The payment of hospital or doctor's bills frequently requires people to draw upon past savings, if they have them, or to go into debt.[6] (Various studies of the small-loan business show that payment of hospital and medical bills is the chief reason why people take out these loans.) Frequently people are unable to pay for service and must either ask for charity care or go without, where they cannot get or will not ask for such care. All of this means that frequently physicians and hospitals are prevented by economic barriers from rendering the necessary services they would like to give and that the economic basis of their services is less broad and stable than it should be.

The situation obviously requires the development of arrangements by which people may prepay the costs of medical attention through some form of advance budgeting. The desire of the population for such arrangements is seen in the avidity with which people have voluntarily enrolled in prepayment plans or taken out commercial insurance against hospital and surgical costs. Fifteen years ago few people were covered by plans or insurance of this kind. Within this space of time over 48,000,000 persons have been enrolled in hospital service prepayment plans or have taken out hospital expense insurance. Of those some 23,000,000 are also covered for physicians' services in surgery and obstetrics, but only about 4,200,000 are also covered for physicians' services in the home and office.

---

[6] Many families have no savings, and some have savings of only a small amount. A study by the Federal Reserve Board showed that, in early 1947, 24 per cent of all spending units (separate individuals and families) had no liquid assets, 26 per cent had from $1 to $500, 28 per cent had from $500 to $2,000, 14 per cent from $2,000 to $5,000, and 8 per cent had $5,000 and over. Among those with incomes under $1,000, 51 per cent had no liquid assets, and an additional 27 per cent had assets of from $1 to $500. (Federal Reserve Bulletin, *Survey of Consumer Finances*, Washington, D. C., July, 1947, p. 797.)

Complete health service, including dental care, drugs, and so on, is not yet available under existing prepayment plans. (See Table 2 in Appendix A.)

Experience even with the existing limited prepayment arrangements shows that they are, or can be, mutually advantageous both to the recipients and to the providers of care. Thus the report of a recent survey of the Blue Cross hospital service plans and of affiliated medical service plans (these plans are generally limited to surgical and obstetrical service or to care of hospitalized illness) states:

> The first conclusion of this survey is that hospital and medical plans are beneficial for the subscribers, the hospitals, the medical profession, and the general public. The plans enable the subscribers to pay for hospital and medical care in a convenient manner. They give protection against the risk of heavy sickness costs. Having this protection, people obtain care who otherwise might go without, and they tend to obtain care more promptly. Some persons, who in the absence of advance provision, would be forced to ask for charity care, are enabled to pay their own way. Knowledge that all or the greater part of the costs of his illness will be taken care of aids recovery of the subscriber-patient. He feels free to stay in the hospital as long as may be necessary. The plans enable subscribers to receive care in better hospital accommodations than they would otherwise be able to afford.[7]

The conclusion is that payment of medical costs by the individual on a fee-for-service basis has many limitations and that virtually the entire population would benefit from group arrangements for spreading the cost of health services.

Low Income of Many in the Population

An important factor in the situation is the low income of part of the population. We have seen that a large proportion of the population who are not indigent will in serious illness be unable to meet—or will find it difficult to meet—the cost of necessary medical care on an individual payment basis. Moreover, there appears to be a certain part of the population with incomes so low that even on a prepayment or insurance basis they would be unable to pay the full cost of adequate care.

In 1946, 12.8 per cent of all single individuals and families in this country had gross cash incomes of less than $1,000, 15.4 per cent had incomes between $1,000 and $2,000, 19.5 per cent had incomes between $2,000 and $3,000, 31.4 per cent had incomes between $3,000 and $5,000, and 20.9 per

---

[7] Louis S. Reed, *Blue Cross and Medical Service Plans* (Washington: U. S. Public Health Service, October, 1947), p. 230.

cent had incomes of $5,000 or more.[8] These figures relate to cash incomes only and do not include the value of an owned home or of food raised and consumed at home. Although incomes have since risen about 10 per cent, the cost of living has risen to at least the same extent.

Families with incomes of $1,000 or $2,000 may have difficulty in paying the full cost of needed care even on a prepayment or insurance basis. Consider the present subscription charges under existing prepayment plans. Under the Blue Cross, monthly subscription charges range from about $0.75 to $1.25 a month for an individual, $1.50 to $2.50 a month for a couple, and $2.00 to $3.00 a month for a family. The charges for surgical and obstetrical or for in-hospital coverage under the Blue Shield plans tend to run at about the same figures. Coverage of hospitalization and complete physicians' services, including home and office visits, would probably entail costs of $2.50 to $3.50 a month for a single individual, $5.00 to $7.00 a month for a couple, and $6.00 to $10.00 a month—or $72.00 to $120.00 a year—for a family. Expenditures for physicians' services and hospitalization amount on the average to between 50 and 60 per cent of family expenditures for medical care, the remaining costs being made up by those for dental care, nursing, drugs, eyeglasses, services of other types of practitioners, and so forth. If the same proportionate relationships were to hold, it might be expected that under prepayment plans providing comprehensive medical care—including dental care, nursing care, and drugs—the subscription charges for a family would be in the neighborhood of $120 to $200 a year.

At the present time people spend for medical care about 4 to 5 per cent of their income, on the average, the percentage being somewhat higher than this for those in the lower-income groups and gradually declining as income rises. It might well be that if, through prepayment, medical care were given a firm and established place in the family budget people could be encouraged to spend a larger proportion of their income than at present for medical care. Yet when one reflects that many families with incomes under $2,000 or $3,000 are unable to afford an adequate diet or adequate housing—things which in the long run are as essential to health as medical care—it appears doubtful that families at this income level can appreciably increase their expenditures for medical care. In short, one may conclude that there is a certain proportion of families—over and above the indigent—with incomes so small that they would be unable to afford the full costs of adequate medical care even on a prepayment

[8] Economic Report of the President to the Congress, Jan. 14, 1948, p. 19.

basis.[9] Obviously if this group is to receive adequate care, part or all of the cost must be borne by those with higher incomes.

Lack of Personnel and Facilities

Another important factor in the problem is the lack or insufficiency of hospital facilities and medical personnel in various rural areas. In large measure this problem is a special evidence of the underlying economic problem; that is to say, these areas lack facilities and personnel not because they are rural but because they are areas of low income and because the population has been unable to support or maintain the necessary facilities and personnel.

There are, however, certain special factors at work. The sparsely settled character of some rural areas makes the provision of medical attendance especially expensive and difficult. Frequently, since rural areas lack hospital facilities, physicians trained in modern methods of diagnosis and care are reluctant or unwilling to locate where they will not have suitable hospital and diagnostic facilities at their command.

Need for Public Understanding of the Value of Medical Care, Including Preventive Service

One reason why some people do not receive adequate care is that they have an insufficient appreciation of the value of good medical care—especially that of preventive service—and therefore do not seek it. Some even refuse to obtain needed hospital or medical attention. A very large share of the population, including some physicians, have an insufficient understanding of the value of preventive service. Lack of appreciation of the value of dental care is particularly widespread. Much needless disability and death could be prevented if people sought care early in illness.

A good deal of the lack of appreciation of the value of medical, hospital, and dental care is, in a sense, a reflection or even a result of the economic problem: people have been unable to afford care and have not

[9] The U. S. Bureau of Labor Statistics has drawn up a list of the commodities and services considered necessary for a minimum but adequate standard of living for a family of four—man, wife, and two children under 15. It has priced these commodities and services in 34 representative cities and found that the total cost as of March, 1946, ranged from $2,573 to $2,985. In 1945, of urban families with two children, 29.1 per cent had total money incomes of less than $2,500, and 45.3 per cent had total money incomes of less than $3,000. From *City Worker's Family Budget, 34 Cities of the United States* (Washington: Bureau of Labor Statistics, U. S. Dept. of Labor, Dec., 1947), and *Current Population Reports, Consumer Income*, Series P-60, No. 2 (Washington: Bureau of the Census, U. S. Dept. of Commerce, March 2, 1948), p. 13.

experienced its value; therefore they do not value it highly. Thus the situation calls for measures in addition to economic ones.

Community Discriminatory Patterns

Still another factor in the situation—and one that is not restricted to the South—is the presence of community discriminatory patterns against minority groups. Community discriminatory patterns work to the disadvantage of all minority groups affected. But they are of particular importance as regards the Negroes. This group is already at a disadvantage because of its generally low economic status, but to the economic barriers are added other barriers which further reduce access to medical care.

Hospitals in many parts of the country will not accept Negro patients— hence such facilities are practically non-existent so far as the Negro population is concerned. Most voluntary and many government hospitals will not accept Negro patients and will not permit Negro physicians to use the hospital facilities. Hence Negro physicians, in effect, lose their patients if they hospitalize them, a factor which acts as a deterrent to hospitalization. The denial of hospital staff appointments to Negro physicians means that these are denied opportunities for professional growth and even for education and training.

In various areas the medical care available to the Negro group is almost non-existent, or is far less than that available to the whites, because white physicians may be unwilling or reluctant to serve Negro patients. The unwillingness or legal inability of some medical schools to accept Negro students is another important factor.

Insufficient Co-ordination among the Personnel and Facilities Providing Care

The quality of service furnished to the public is lower than it should be and the cost of service is higher than it need be because of insufficient co-ordination among the various individuals, groups, and facilities providing care. There is good reason to believe that the cost of hospital care to the public would be reduced and the quality improved if the hospitals in each hospital-service area were more closely co-ordinated. Thus it would be beneficial if rural hospitals were tied in with central teaching institutions which could provide the former with consultant X-ray and pathology service and would aid in the training of personnel, and so on.

In the field of medical service itself there is reason to believe that changes are necessary if the public is to receive the best possible care at the lowest possible cost. The growth in medical knowledge has made it impossible for any one individual to be skilled in all fields of medicine; hence specialization has developed and has reached the point where in certain cities over half of the practicing physicians are specialists. In cities, many families no longer have a family physician but turn to one or another specialist as occasion arises. The situation has disadvantages both for the public and for the profession. The care of the patient by a number of specialists practicing independently not only runs up the cost but may result in the patient's not being dealt with as a "whole." The referral of patients between independent practioners raises the difficult problem of fee splitting.

The answer to present difficulties which are due to the necessary complexity of medical care and the development of specialization probably lies in some form of group practice. Under this type of practice it is possible to obtain close co-ordination of the services of general practitioners and specialists. Frequent consultation is favored. Economies can be gained through the sharing of overhead, of the services of auxiliary personnel, and of equipment. Close association with colleagues proves stimulating to the individual physician and makes for the maintenance of both ethical and technical standards.

Though group practice is still in its experimental stages, experience indicates that its further development, particularly with the hospital as a center, would have marked advantages for the public and the profession.

PROPOSED CONCLUSIONS

The planning committee of the Section on the Nation's Need for Medical Care agreed on three main principles, to serve as a basis for the Section's discussions, which are summarized below.

1. Adequate medical service for the prevention of illness, the care and relief of sickness, and the promotion of a high level of physical and mental health should be available to all.

2. Sound financing of personal health services requires (a) effective application of the principle of prepayment or insurance and (b) the use of public resources for services not covered in the prepayment or insurance program and for persons for whose care public responsibility is acknowledged.

3. High standards and reasonable costs require a close co-ordination of the services of physicians, hospitals, and other health agencies, in all phases of prevention, diagnosis, and treatment.

DIGEST OF PAPERS AND DISCUSSIONS[10]

FIRST SESSION, Afternoon, May 1, 1948

In opening the sessions of the Medical Care Section, the chairman, Dr. Hugh Leavell, drew attention to the objectives of the Assembly as expressed by Federal Security Administrator Oscar R. Ewing. He stated these as, primarily, an effort to map out possible and feasible goals in health for the next ten years. It was particularly important in the discussion, he emphasized, that areas of agreement, or of disagreement, be clearly defined.

The Medical Care Section, Dr. Leavell submitted, should attempt to assess the needs of the public for improved health services, to evaluate the adequacies and potentials of present plans for medical care, and to define what additional steps should be taken to make medical care of high quality available to all people.

He stated that the planning committee of the Section had found it possible to work together in a spirit of community effort and urged that the delegates now work together in a common effort to find areas of agreement on the problems of medical care. He stated further that no votes would be taken on any points under discussion but that the planning committee would attempt to report the sense of the delegates on various issues.

On behalf of the Section's planning committee, Dr. Thomas A. McGoldrick presented a summary of "A Statement of the Problem of Medical Care," prepared and agreed upon by that committee. The text of the full statement was made available to the delegates. At one point, Dr. McGoldrick departed from the text to state that there were enough doctors in the country now and that the chief problem was to assure their equitable distribution. This point was later challenged by one of the delegates.

A formal paper, "Organization of Medical Services; a Goal and a Responsibility," was presented by Dr. C. Rufus Rorem. In summary, Dr. Rorem stated that the most neglected problem in medical services is the organization of professional personnel and facilities with a view to maintaining standards and controlling costs. Several factors in medical service have combined to make the problem of organization especially important at this stage of our national life and scientific knowledge: (1) the development of specialization in medical practice; (2) the supplementation of art with scientific method in prevention, diagnosis, and treatment; and (3) the increasing use of capital investment in medical service. Any form of organization, Dr. Rorem stated, may be measured by the degree to which it facilitates the objectives of medical service, which include the maintenance of a high standard of professional service; accessibility to the greatest possible number of people; provision of complete services for all types of illness and conditions; professional co-operation rather than economic competition; incentive to control costs, not by lowering quality but by conserving time, effort, and materials; and avoidance of exploitation by any

[10] The program of the Medical Care Section's meetings will be found in Appendix B near the end of this chapter.

group—the patients, the professions, or the public. Dr. Rorem also briefly described the organization of individual medical practice and pointed out the advantages of group practice. With regard to payment of medical and hospital bills, Dr. Rorem described the procedure of charging a composite fee for complete service, like that charged by private group clinics, and also the practice of having a controlled maximum physician's fee for hospital cases. The importance of efficient administration to any form of medical service was emphasized, together with the need for work to be done in the field of co-ordinating medical institutions within the same community. Hospitals should be adapted to the needs of the public, and proposals for new capital investment should be appraised in accordance with rigorous standards of public necessity and convenience. In conclusion, Dr. Rorem stated that there has been a cultural lag between the advance in medical knowledge and skill and the organization necessary to utilize this knowledge and this skill most effectively. The task of medical organization is a joint undertaking for medical and lay people.

Dr. Louis T. Wright, Dr. Samuel Proger, and Dr. H. Clifford Loos presented discussions of Dr. Rorem's paper.

Dr. Wright stated his full approval of the paper presented by Dr. Rorem. Most thinking citizens, he said, are agreed that good medical care should be available to the entire population. In his opinion, this can best be done by the Federal government through a tax-supported plan. He pointed out that some cities and states, particularly in the northeastern and midwestern sections of the country, have maintained high-quality medical services for indigent patients needing general hospital care and for the mentally ill, as well as for those afflicted with communicable diseases. But there has been much duplication of effort and unnecessary red tape, resulting in varying degrees in detriment to the patient and in loss of time and energy for medical personnel. He expressed his opinion that group practice is the answer to the problem of making available to patients the skills and aids necessary to diagnose and cure disease. He then pointed out that many local medical societies of the American Medical Association, especially in the South, bar Negroes from membership. The Master Plan for Hospitals and Related Facilities for New York City was cited as a type of plan that could well be adopted by the nation. In addition, Dr. Wright suggested that the President or the Congress of the United States name a National Planning Commission to direct the co-ordination and organization of medical services for proper care of the health needs of the population. Such a commission, he added, should also have the power to co-ordinate government and civilian medical facilities and services to prevent duplication of effort where such exists and to distribute medical services where they are absent.

The leadership in the field of health, stated Dr. Wright, will come from within the medical profession, even if the government is forced to take over.

Dr. Proger, in his discussion of Dr. Rorem's paper, brought out the importance of seeking a middle ground between no organization of medical service and considerable organization and control. While agreeing with Dr. Rorem as to the virtues of group practice as compared with individual practice, Dr. Proger expressed his opinion that each type of practice has its place; the two types should complement each other. In further discussion of this point he stated his belief that, although group practice is necessary for good diagnosis in a complex illness, the care of the patient with a minor illness can be best and most economically performed by the general practitioner. It is probably true that the average physician is not sufficiently well aware of his obligation to the community as a community. However, emphasis on the fact that the community has a stake in the doctor's education and in providing facilities upon which much of his income is dependent will impress many practitioners with their obligation for service to the public.

Dr. Loos also supported Dr. Rorem's viewpoint with regard to the advantages of group practice over individual practice; nevertheless he thought the physician should have the right to choose the type of practice in which he engages. Dr. Loos expressed his fear that the hospitals might assume the practice of medicine. Blame for this possibility as well as for current talk of government supervision of medicine can be laid in the laps of the doctors themselves. According to Dr. Loos, if the physicians fail to supervise, organize, and offer a medical practice that the people want, then the hospitals or government will. He attributed the success of his organization to the fact that his medical staff has complete freedom in the practice of medicine.

Dr. W. Montague Cobb delivered the concluding formal paper of the session, "Discriminatory Patterns in Community Health Services." As stated by Dr. Cobb, discrimination against minorities constitutes a barrier to the availability of adequate medical care to all Americans that is just as real as, and more deeply significant than, inequalities in economic status and inadequacies in health personnel and facilities. Discriminatory practice in health facilities victimizes more than one group and is not confined to any particular region; but it is at its worst in the South, where the bulk of the Negro population is located. The quality of the segregated accommodations is usually inferior. Although voluntary hospitals, on a country-wide basis, are the greatest offenders as to exclusion practices, even the Federal veterans hospitals are guilty. Dr. Cobb went on to say that discriminatory practices against the Negro physician are even more severe, and he repeated the statement made by Dr. Wright that, south of Mason and Dixon's line, the Negro physician is excluded from membership in the official county and state medical societies. The Negro is finding it difficult to join prepayment medical care plans and is often excluded altogether. Various and repeated surveys in some localities have demonstrated that conditions resulting from discriminatory practices are bad and need correction. Usually a community willingness toward corrective efforts through the provision of separate, segregated facilities will be encountered, but there will be a great resistance to abandonment of the segregative policy. The futility of "separate but equal" arrangements as solutions of the problem has been well demonstrated, he said, but where non-segregation of both patients and physicians has been sincerely tried it has proved uniformly successful.

Following the presentation of Dr. Cobb's paper, the Section's chairman threw the meeting open to discussion, which centered chiefly on two main issues: (1) clarification of the conclusions proposed in the statement of "The Problem of Medical Care"; and (2) discrimination, particularly against Negroes. The major criticisms and comments on the contents of the statement were that:

(1) In discussing the provision of medical care on an insurance basis, the text assumed that prepayment or insurance charges would be on a "flat rate" basis and took no account of the possibility that such charges might be fixed as a percentage of income.

(2) The conclusions proposed in the statement should be clarified and amended. It was suggested that Conclusion 1 should contain a statement that services should be available to all without discrimination because of race, creed, color, or national origin. Clarification of Conclusion 2 was requested by a number of the delegates. With regard to the first section of this Conclusion—that "sound financing of personal health services requires (a) effective application of the principle of prepayment or insurance"—it was asked whether prepayment with government subsidy or governmental health insurance would be included in its terms. With regard to its second section—that "sound financing . . . requires (b) the use of public resources for services not covered in the prepayment or insurance program and for persons for whose care public responsibility is acknowledged"—clarification and a better definition of areas of public responsibility were requested.

A suggestion was made that Conclusion 3 should be divided into two parts, the first to deal with high standards in terms of quality, the second with high quality in terms of administration. Efficient administration, it was stated, should include public participation in planning and in carrying out the requirements of administration. A further suggestion with regard to Conclusion 3 was that it should be amended to state that co-ordination, as recommended, should include the full participation of community groups, consumers, and professional representatives.

At this first session there was also considerable discussion of community discriminatory practices which bar members of minority groups, particularly Negroes, from receiving care or prevent members of these groups from receiving medical training or, when trained, from effectively pursuing their profession. It was declared that doctors have responsibilities as citizens and that if they are to command respect and gain financial support for schools and other projects they must live up to the nation's democratic ideals of citizenship. In answer to the statement that local medical societies of the American Medical Association, particularly in the South, bar Negroes from membership, the point was made that the Association is a federation of state associations which in this matter are free to do as they choose. In response to this, it was stated that the American Medical Association could either act against discrimination by changing its rules so as not to permit exclusion of a physician because of color or could set up standards for state compliance against discriminatory practices. The American Nurses Association, it was stated, expected to set up memberships at large so that persons excluded from local or state associations could still belong to the national association.

SECOND SESSION, Morning, May 2, 1948

The second session of the Medical Care Section began with a series of prepared papers on prepayment plans and proposals. The first of these, "Criteria for Evaluating Prepayment Plans," was presented by Dr. Dean A. Clark. He listed seven criteria by which prepayment plans might be evaluated: scope of medical coverage; proportion of population covered; quality of service; degree of freedom and willingness to experiment; economic and professional satisfaction of participating physicians, hospitals, and others; financial soundness, efficiency, and economy; and method of selection and composition of governing boards with adequate representation of consumers and those providing service. These criteria, Dr. Clark stated, are applicable to all types of prepayment plans and to proposed plans, either voluntary or governmental. Although no plan now in existence can fulfill them all, nevertheless they represent an approach to the exceedingly difficult problem of devising objective methods of appraisal for such plans. The criteria were later approved by the Section's planning committee under the title, "Points to be Measured in Determining the Effectiveness of Prepayment Plans in Meeting the Needs of the People," as set forth near the end of this chapter.

The second paper of the session, by Dr. Franz Goldmann, dealt with "Types of Health Insurance Plans." The term "health insurance," Dr. Goldmann said, is widely used to denote either of two fundamentally different types of plans: (1) "medical care insurance" plans, or those organized for the purpose of budgeting and paying the cost of medical care; and (2) "disability insurance" plans, or those organized for the purpose of compensating insured persons for loss of earnings through disability. Only the first type was reviewed in Dr. Goldmann's paper. The numerous medical care insurance plans now in operation differ in form of organization, administration, eligibility requirements, benefits, method of payment, and cost and may be classed in two broad categories—cash indemnity plans and service plans. Cash indemnity plans were described by Dr. Goldmann as those designed to assist participants in paying the costs actually incurred for medical care, whereas service plans provide members with specified professional and institutional services. The limitations of the two types of plan as well as their common elements were briefly described. The distinctive features of the principal types of plans (commercial plans, Blue Cross plans, non-profit prepayment plans for physicians' services, group-practice prepayment plans, and the medical society plans evolved in the states of Oregon and Washington and in Hawaii) were outlined. Dr. Goldmann concluded his paper with the following comments: "Compared to the situation prevailing before the introduction of voluntary medical care insurance, the protection at present provided for the plan members constitutes a marked improvement. Compared with the standards of adequate medical care set and taught by the leaders of the profession, it is deficient. Except for the medical-society plans in Oregon and Washington and some fifty or sixty group-practice prepayment organizations, the existing plans are so limited in scope and so little used for the improvement of the quality of medical care that they afforded only a partial answer to one segment of the total problem: the adjustment of

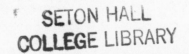

our health services to the rapid progress of medical science and the profound socio-economic changes that have taken place since the nineteenth century."

Dr. Goldmann was followed by Dr. Paul R. Hawley, who presented a paper on "Blue Cross–Blue Shield Plans and Their Ability to Meet National Needs for Prepayment Arrangements." The two types of plans were defined by Dr. Hawley as follows: Blue Cross is the national organization of voluntary associations which provide hospital care, as distinguished from physicians' services, upon a prepayment basis; Blue Shield is the national organization of voluntary associations which provide medical care, i.e., the personal services of physicians and other medical people, as distinguished from hospital care, on a similar prepayment basis. After a brief history of the two types of plans, Dr. Hawley described the plans in terms of the criteria suggested by Dr. Dean Clark. It was emphasized that each of the Blue Cross and Blue Shield plans is a local, autonomous unit and that the national organizations are federations with limited powers, rather than national corporations. The wide variations in medical needs, in available medical facilities, and in the ability of people to pay for their protection make rigid central control and uniform rates and services impracticable if not impossible. Dr. Hawley described the rapid increase in Blue Cross and Blue Shield membership since 1940. Blue Cross, he stated, has grown from a membership of 4,432,000 in 1940 to over 30,000,000 at the present time; Blue Shield, a much younger organization than Blue Cross, has increased from 1,768,000 members in 1940 to approximately 7,500,000 at the present. In concluding his statement, Dr. Hawley stated that he was convinced that Blue Cross and Blue Shield plans more nearly meet the people's needs than any others which are now in operation or have so far been proposed, for the following reasons:

1. They are locally planned and locally controlled, so that they are adjusted to the local level of available services, to local needs, and to the ability of the people to pay.

2. They are the cheapest protection. They are non-profit. More of the dollar collected goes back into direct benefits than in any other plan.

Mr. R. A. Hohaus followed Dr. Hawley with a paper on "The Role of Group Insurance in Financing Personal Health Services." Mr. Hohaus, at the beginning of his paper, reviewed the developments in the group health insurance field. He pointed out not only that great strides in the number of persons insured have been made in a relatively brief period of years but also that much progress has been made in broadening the scope of these coverages in various ways which are increasing their usefulness and effectiveness. This has been accomplished, he stated, by removing limitations which experience has demonstrated are not generally needed to assure reasonable soundness, and by changing the amounts of available protection where experience has shown this to be desirable. Mr. Hohaus emphasized the importance of the part played by the employer in the successful development of the many forms of group insurance. Outstanding contributions of group insurance to the health insurance field are: (1) its flexibility in meeting local problems and conditions and in developing harmonious relationships with other types of health insurance plans; and (2) its potentialities for healthy experimentation and improvement.

The final paper, "Industrial Medical Care Plans," was presented by Dr. J. J. Wittmer. In his opening statement Dr. Wittmer stressed the necessity for employers, either on their own or with the financial co-operation of employees, to provide effective medical care programs for safeguarding employee health and to maintain or improve industrial efficiency. Industrial medical care plans, he stated, at present range from a limited type which provides only first aid and preplacement physical examinations to one which provides comprehensive medical and dental service. As an example of the latter type of program, Dr. Wittmer described the medical care plan of the Consolidated Edison Company of New York. Under this plan, which is financed jointly by the company and the employees, medical services as well as cash sickness benefits are available to "benefit members" of the Employees' Mutual Aid Society. Medical services include preventive care, diagnostic aid, treatment during illness, specialist service, home care by physicians, comprehensive dental care, hospitalization, and convalescent care. Direct supervision of the program is in the hands of three physicians experienced in the field of industrial medicine and thoroughly familiar with personnel and medical department problems. Operation of the Consolidated Edison Program is currently costing about $40 per year per employee. The success of the program, Dr. Wittmer stated, is indicated by a substantial reduction in serious illness among employees, an absenteeism rate which is well below the national average, and a high level of worker efficiency and employee morale. This same type of service, Dr. Wittmer emphasized, can be extended to all workers, regardless of the size of the industrial plant, if employers and employees constructively co-operate in the endeavor.

The discussion which followed tended to revolve mainly around the Blue Cross–Blue Shield plans and, to a lesser extent, commercial insurance. At the beginning of the discussion one delegate listed seven points which he felt were important in planning for prepayment care. These, in brief, were: provision of comprehensive services to everyone; quality of service; high living standards for professional health workers; continued experimentation with various types of insurance; social security provisions, particularly old age and unemployment insurance; public participation in all planning work; and maintenance of trade-union standards in such enterprises. Various criticisms of the Blue Cross–Blue Shield plans and of commercial insurance were made: that the costs were such that large portions of the population could not afford them; that the plans provided only a limited coverage and neglected prevention; that the plans met only part of the cost of the covered services, with the result that the subscriber or policyholder frequently had to make substantial payments out of his own pocket directly to the hospital or physician; that the plans did little or nothing to improve the quality of service and to organize the provision of health services more effectively; that the subscription costs did not vary with the subscriber's income. One labor representative stressed the inability of his union to finance an industry-wide health prepayment program through the Blue Cross because of the variation in subscription charges and benefits from plan to plan.

In response, representatives of the Blue Cross–Blue Shield plans stressed the youth of the plans and stated that in due course they hoped to meet many of these objections.

THIRD SESSION, Afternoon, May 2, 1948

The third session began with a prepared paper on "National Health Insurance" by Dr. Ernst P. Boas. National health insurance, Dr. Boas stated, offers the only solution at the present time for meeting the people's needs for medical care. In answer to claims by opponents of national health insurance that such governmental planning is un-American, he pointed out that the first compulsory health insurance in the world was set up in the United States in 1798 to help finance the costs of medical care for merchant seamen. If voluntary insurance could serve the needs of all the people, Dr. Boas believed it would be welcomed as the solution of the major problem of paying for medical care. But voluntary plans fall far short of meeting the needs, principally because: (1) they do not offer comprehensive coverage; (2) the costs of comprehensive care are higher than persons in the lower income groups and many in the higher income groups can afford to pay; (3) the plans would be unable to fulfill their functions in times of unemployment; and (4) in those voluntary plans which operate with large panels of physicians compensated by the fee-for-service method there is lack of control of the quality of medical care provided. Governmental subsidy for voluntary plans for care of the indigent or medically indigent would result, Dr. Boas said, in the widespread application of the means test—a complete reversal of public policy and of the social security principle. Moreover, it might be that government's stake in the plans would be so great that it would either have to take them over or else regulate them in great detail. National health insurance, Dr. Boas went on to say, would provide complete medical service, making available all needed preventive, diagnostic, and curative services by a family physician of the patient's choice, specialist service, hospital care, laboratory and X-ray service, and unusually expensive medicines and appliances. Dental, home-nursing, and auxiliary services could be added to whatever extent the funds, personnel, and actuarial experience allowed. The Federal government rather than the states should assume responsibility for collecting the necessary funds, and the social security principle of payment of premiums into an insurance fund would be preferable to reliance on tax funds. In conclusion, he stated that national health insurance would attract physicians to regions where at present they cannot make a living, and it would enable communities hitherto unable to support hospitals to maintain institutions suited to their needs.

The second paper of the third session, "The Program of the American Medical Association," was presented by Dr. R. L. Sensenich. At the beginning of his paper Dr. Sensenich presented arguments against governmental administration of a health insurance program. The best social system, Dr. Sensenich said, offers opportunity to each individual to provide for himself and extends aid only in those areas in which he is unable to safeguard himself or to provide for his needs. Governmental administration adds to the cost of the service in question, and taxes—whether direct or indirect—fall upon the small earner as well as the wealthy one. In answer to the argument, often advanced, that those who need insurance most will not voluntarily purchase it, Dr. Sensenich asked why all should be compelled to employ cumbersome, political, bureaucratic machinery and destroy the quality of medical care to compel the contribution of the few who may be negligent. The needy negligent one, he said, must be cared for from tax funds when sick. With regard to governmental subsidy to voluntary plans for care for the indigent and with respect to the use of a "means test," Dr. Sensenich asked why the determination of need is such an offensive matter. And, with regard to the receipt of medical care as a "matter of right" under a compulsory government program, he cited examples of situations wherein benefits are denied persons who have contributed to the present social security programs. The National Health Program of the American Medical Association, Dr. Sensenich stated, recognizes the importance of the individual and his best interests and it assures constant improvement in the health of the American people. This ten-point health program promotes:

(1) Nutrition, housing, clothing, and recreation;
(2) Preventive medicine, health departments;
(3) Prenatal care, childbirth;
(4) Infant welfare, child care;
(5) Hospitals, health and diagnostic centers;
(6) Voluntary prepayment plans for hospital and medical care;
(7) Veterans' needs for hospitals and medical care;
(8) Research for advancement of medical science;
(9) Volunteer health agencies, philanthropic funds; and
(10) Health education in prevention of disease.

Prepared discussions of the foregoing papers on "National Health Insurance" and the "Program of the American Medical Association" were presented by Michael M. Davis and Dr. Walter B. Martin.

Mr. Davis devoted the first part of his discussion to comments on certain phases of the ten-point program of the American Medical Association, in particular those relating to good housing and to the extension of health departments. He asked to what extent the A.M.A. has actively supported measures for providing good housing for the American people. He questioned the degree to which extension of health departments is favored by the A.M.A., stating that this part of its program is restricted by its inclusion of the statement, "The administration of medical care under such auspices tends to a deterioration in the quality of the services rendered." The American Public Health Association, he said, has challenged the ability of the A.M.A. to prove this statement. A number of points appear to have the "dole" as their basic concept. Commercial insurance plans providing only cash indemnities are encouraged by the program, and no mention is made of consumer-sponsored plans. Furthermore, he added, laws enacted in twenty or more states at the instigation of the state medical societies restrict or entirely prevent consumer groups from organizing their own plans, and only those can be organized which are controlled by physicians. He suggested that the American Medical Association could be influential in changing this policy of the state medical societies.

Mr. Davis then turned to the subject of national health insurance and declared as "phony" a number of objections such as the charge that it is socialism and communism, that no free choice of doctor is provided, and that administrative personnel would be required in excessive numbers. The better organization of medical services, especially through group medical practice and its extension, would be stimulated and not set back by a national health insurance scheme. Without national health insurance, he said, the outlook involves two developments: first, some further development of voluntary plans, limited and spotty in their population coverage, restricted in scope of service, costly in operation, and increasingly involved in government control; second, along with the development of voluntary plans, the development of a public or tax-supported medical service which, if it follows the American Medical Association policies, will be a "poor man's system of medical care."

Dr. Martin in his discussion of the two papers emphasized the complex nature of the problem of providing health care for the American people. In addition to environmental factors that may play a part in the provision of medical care, he pointed out that the content of medicine itself plays a part. The components of medical care were listed as: (1) the total quantity of medical care sufficient for the country as a whole; (2) the over-all cost to the nation; (3) the cost to the individual and the distribution of the cost; and (4) the continued advancement of medical science. Dr. Martin then pointed out that if medicine is frozen at its present level, or if any system is adopted that will tend to freeze it, the quality of medical care will deteriorate. As to the cost of medical care, medical costs have decreased considerably since 1940 in comparison with other consumer expenditures. The doctor's part in medical care has decreased from 32 per cent of the total cost in 1940 to 26 per cent at present. The principal cost increase in medical care has been in connection with hospital construction, hospital operation, drugs, and the like. The American Medical Association, he pointed out, believes that medical care is a matter of local community concern and that all factors that tend to disrupt community medical care are harmful to good medical care and to the people. Local control is necessary in order to prevent confusion in medical care, to prevent bureaucracy, and to leave the doctor-patient relationship as it should be. A Federal aid program to build an integrated hospital system, supplemented by a prepayment plan developed on a community basis, would be better for American medicine, for the people themselves, and for the preservation of individual liberty in the communities. In conclusion, Dr. Martin stated that the physician has no vested interest in medicine; that, in activities such as prepayment plans, lay members should have a voice along with the doctors, acting as advisers.

Following the prepared discussion by Dr. Martin, the Section's chairman threw the meeting open to discussion from the floor. One speaker took exception to the tone of Dr. Boas's paper, which, he said, inferred that all voluntary medical organizations were "dollar catchers." The speaker stated that this was not the case, since any organization formed with that intent would not endure.

The same speaker urged that voluntary plans be encouraged and tried out before discarding them for a Federal plan of national compulsory insurance.

It was suggested by one delegate that existing plans be measured against the criteria set forth by Dr. Clark at the morning session. Such a comparison, he believed, would reveal a vast neglected area where improvements should be made.

In response to a question as to the kinds of service provided to low-income groups through voluntary systems of insurance, it was stated that precise statistics were not available but that answers to questionnaires indicated that Blue Cross is enrolling substantial numbers from among the lower-income groups.

There was considerable discussion of the basis of approval of voluntary plans on the part of the American Medical Association, of what types of plans are approved or not approved, of the procedures in approval, and so on. Representatives of various plans not now approved by the A.M.A. wished to know why their plans were not eligible for approval. In one case, it was pointed out that the A.M.A. had not approved a doctor-operated plan although it has been approved for one year by the local and state medical societies. One delegate asked why the A.M.A. and various state societies, in view of their support of voluntary prepayment, had sought and obtained legislation in various states which prevented the establishment of medical service prepayment plans by groups other than the medical profession. It was also stated that in certain instances medical societies had discouraged the operation of consumer-organized prepayment plans through pressures brought upon doctors who participated or were considering participation in such plans. On the other hand, various speakers commented on the aid given by the Wisconsin State Medical Society to the passage in that state of legislation permitting the establishment of co-operative health plans.

The ten-point program of the American Medical Association was criticized on the grounds that it stemmed from a philosophy that would provide only for the needy; that it was based on an archaic philosophy that medical care consisted of a patient-physician relationship alone; and that it overstressed the importance of local control in medical care.

FOURTH SESSION, Evening, May 2, 1948

The fourth session opened with a paper entitled "Unions Move into Health and Welfare Programs," by Mr. Harry Becker. At the beginning of his paper, Mr. Becker reported on the results of a public opinion poll made among UAW-CIO workers in Detroit to determine the kind of insecurity about which workers are most concerned. Next to worry about income maintenance during periods of sickness or accident, the poll showed that the top worry was about payment for doctor and hospital care during illness. Other findings from the poll were with regard to the "felt" need for medical care, the prevalence of illness among the workers and their families, the proportion who incurred doctor or hospital bills during the year, the average size of the bills, and how workers met household expenses during periods of sickness and paid their doctor or hospital bills. The information provided by this study has convinced the UAW-CIO that it must give top priority in its planning to the economic hazards of illness and accident. Today the wage earners in America do not have the minimum social security benefits necessary to meet the social and economic hazards of life. He discussed the inadequacies of existing provisions for benefits during periods of disability and sickness, and pointed out the limitations of commercial insurance and voluntary non-profit prepayment plans. He explained that there is now a movement among unions to organize their own health and medical care plans. Two major problems facing labor unions when assuming more administrative responsibility for the expenditure of health and welfare funds are, first, their inexperience in this area and, second, the great diversity of program which results when many Internationals and many Locals bargain separately with the companies with which they work. An over-all union policy is needed.

The second paper of the session, "Co-operative Health Plans," was presented by Mr. Winslow Carlton. The co-operative approach to the problems of medical care, Mr. Carlton stated, is essentially to mobilize local community resources for the purpose of financing health services. He emphasized early in his paper that co-operative or consumer-sponsored health plans have an essential common denominator in the fact that the recipients of medical care, the consumers, have a substantial voice in determining basic policy with respect to the plan's scope of service and its cost. Out of varied experience in the development of co-operative health plans, one major conclusion has been drawn: the most effective and economical plan is the combination of prepayment with group medical practice. However, Mr. Carlton continued, diversity of approach is basically healthy, and individuals should have the right to choose between different types of plans. Though he recognized that substantial segments of the population lack the means to pay their proportional share of the cost of health services and that many communities and states need Federal help in providing medical care to their residents, he stated his belief that poor-law medicine is no solution to the problem of medical care. Voluntary plans should always have an important place in the national medical care system. Local voluntary developments in energetic communities will serve as yardsticks in the constantly changing and growing social techniques for delivering medical care to people. In conclusion, Mr. Carlton placed emphasis on three points:

(1) Equal opportunity for consumers to set up and operate medical care plans;

(2) Substantial support by Congress for intensive and continuing study of medical care; and

(3) In any program adopted by the Federal government to finance medical care, conformity with the basic principle of encouraging local initiative in, or at least providing opportunity for, development of voluntary medical service organizations.

Mr. Horace R. Hansen presented the session's third paper, "Legislative and Other Restraints Affecting Voluntary Plans." In introducing his subject, Mr. Hansen stated that there was probably general agreement that voluntary plans are in an experimental stage and that no fixed pattern has been set by which such plans should be developed. He found general agreement on the need for further development in this field. But widespread restraint in most of the country, sponsored or imposed by organized medicine, prevents even an attempt at experimentation by lay organizations. Mr. Hansen then outlined the nature of these restraints. In over half the states, enabling acts sponsored by medical associations restrict voluntary prepayment plans to those types which medical associations alone may see fit to offer. Moreover, state medical associations have vigorously opposed bills proposed by lay groups which sought equal privilege to sponsor voluntary plans. In states where there are not yet such legislative restrictions, another type of obstacle is found—restraints imposed by medical societies upon physicians who participate in lay plans. He also stated that the effect of this class legislation and professional restraints is that organized medicine is saying to the public: "You may have prepayment plans, but only upon our terms; you may have a common pool of funds to assist you in a medical crisis, but you shall have nothing to say about the management of the fund or the rates you will be charged." In summary, Mr. Hansen made the following points:

1. Consumer-sponsored prepayment plans have proved successful as an important means toward improving the distribution and availability of modern medical care.

2. Thinking in terms of a program for the nation's health in the next ten years and increased experimentation in the field of voluntary plans, by whatever sponsorship, should be encouraged.

3. Such experimentation should be free and competitive, in order to bring better medicine to more people and at the same time to permit a free demonstration of public acceptability of various types of plans.

4. To assure free experimentation, restrictive legislation and disciplinary restraints should be removed and equal privilege afforded to all types of sponsorship.

The final paper of the fourth session, "Existing Programs of Public Medical Care," was presented by Dr. Dean Roberts. The total volume of care provided by Federal, state, and local governments, Dr. Roberts stated, represents a large portion of the medical care used by the citizens of this country. Government medical care can be divided into three fairly distinct groups:

(1) Medical care for groups for whom government has assumed specific responsibilities, including members of the armed services, veterans, seamen, Indians living on reservations, and prisoners;

(2) Programs dealing with the prevention or treatment of specific types of illness or disability, such as cancer, tuberculosis, mental illness, chronic disease, and crippling conditions; and

(3) Programs of general medical care providing services primarily for the poor.

Dr. Roberts then briefly described the type of service provided under each of the major programs, the approximate number of persons for whom care was provided, and, where the data were available, the volume of service provided. He emphasized the predominant role of government in the provision of hospital care and pointed out that 78 per cent of all hospital beds of all types are in government-operated hospitals. The provision of general medical care for the poor, he stated, is marked by great variation as to services offered, financial criteria of eligibility, and methods of administration. In most areas, he concluded, there is some provision for those on public assistance, but for the medically indigent very little is offered.

At the beginning of the general discussion period, it was declared by one delegate that, in the passage of legislation in Wisconsin which permitted co-operative health plans, the A.M.A. and the state medical association had co-op-erated wholeheartedly. Another delegate declared that in Ohio it was not the doctors who had blocked voluntary plans but a lobby of the insurance companies.

A representative from an industrial insurance plan mentioned that one good point of his plan which had not been brought out was that it allowed medical care insurance to continue after retirement of the employee. A possible program combining prepayment plans and government action, i.e., provision of coverage for persons covered by unemployment compensation by expansion of Blue Cross or some similar plan was suggested by another delegate. Employees not under unemployment compensation, he said, might be covered under state laws possibly with a subsidy for those who earned below a certain figure.

One delegate declared that thousands of physicians who are members of the American Medical Association do not agree with the official position of the A.M.A. and are actually in favor of national health insurance.

Attention was called to some points which were thought to have been overlooked in the discussion: What substitute can be suggested for comprehensive compulsory health insurance? What would comprehensive compulsory health insurance cost? Should compulsory health insurance be an extension of social security or should it be separate? What are the nature and types of various compulsory health insurance plans?

Several delegates called attention to areas of agreement which they thought had been defined, and the suggestion was made that a subcommittee be ap-pointed, including A.M.A., farm, labor, and co-operative representatives, to bring in a draft of areas of agreement. The chairman reminded the delegates that it had been agreed in advance that there would be no voting on any issues and that the Section's planning committee would take the suggestion for a subcommittee under advisement and report back to the section.

Representatives of important labor and consumer organizations expressed their belief that only national health insurance would solve the medical care problem and that their interest in voluntary plans sprang only from a desire to press for whatever was obtainable in the absence of a national health insurance program.

FIFTH SESSION, Afternoon, May 3, 1948

Chairman Hugh R. Leavell, in opening the Medical Care Section's final discussions, presented the points on which the planning committee had been able to reach unanimous agreement. The first was with regard to the conclusions proposed at the end of the statement on "The Problem of Medical Care" read at the first session. Point one, he said, had been amended to read as follows:

That adequate medical service for the prevention of illness, the care and relief of sickness, and the promotion of a high level of physical and mental health should be available to all without regard to race, color, religion, residence, or economic status.

Points two and three of the conclusions, he said, had evaporated in the discussion.

Dr. Leavell next read a group of TENTATIVE CONCLUSIONS OF THE MEDICAL CARE SECTION. The first were:

Points to be Measured in Determining the Effectiveness of Prepayment Plans in Meeting the Medical Care Needs of the People:

(1) The extent to which a prepayment plan makes available to those it serves the whole range of scientific medicine for prevention of disease and for treatment of all types of illness or injury

(2) The proportion of the population of its area—local, state, or national, as the case may be—covered by a plan (cost in relation to ability to pay, restrictions on enrollment imposed by actuarial considerations, income level, age, conditions of employment, means of securing enrollment and collecting premiums)

(3) The degree to which a plan makes use of and encourages the development of a high quality of medical care for its subscribers (standards of personnel and facilities, organization of services, emphasis on prevention of disease, promotion of health, health education)

(4) The degree to which freedom and willingness to experiment with methods of payment and operation are encouraged in a plan

(5) The degree to which a plan succeeds in arranging amounts and methods of payment and conditions of participation that are satisfactory to physicians, hospitals, and others serving the plan's subscribers

(6) The extent to which efficiency and economy in the operation of a plan are achieved and encouraged by its basic policies and its administrative techniques

(7) The extent to which the individuals or board members who carry the ultimate responsibility for a plan represent the interest of those entitled to service and those who are paying the cost, as well as the physicians, hospitals, or others who are providing the services

In the absence of dissent the chairman said he assumed acceptance by the Medical Care Section.

Dr. Leavell next read two of the proposed PRINCIPLES FOR THE IMPROVEMENT OF VOLUNTARY PREPAYMENT PLANS. The first principle was:

1. There should be the freest opportunity for full co-operation among the providers and consumers of service in the establishment and the administration of medical care plans, with the proviso that full control of the practice of medicine in the program must remain with the doctors.

One delegate suggested that the planning committee might wish to change the phrasing. If specific areas of responsibility were assigned to the doctors, he said, there should also be a clear statement of areas of consumer responsibility and authority.

Another delegate suggested that other professional groups should be mentioned.

Dr. Leavell then read the second of these principles:

2. The Medical Care Section strongly urges the importance of joint conferences at the earliest possible date among representatives of the American Medical Association and of groups representing the consumers of medical care and services to study the question of the establishment and administration of medical care plans.

Since there was no discussion, Chairman Leavell stated that he assumed approval.

The question was then raised as to whether or not there should be specific machinery set up to arrange conferences between consumer groups and A.M.A. representatives. A representative of the A.M.A. replied that preliminary steps to arrange such conferences had already been taken.

A delegate then declared that he was heartened by agreement in so many areas but that he thought even wider areas of agreement were possible and suggested that two additional points be added to the list of principles:

3. A high quality of care is essential in all health work, and all efforts should be made to strengthen the quality of medical care.

4. Sound principles of financing are essential to adequate medical care.

High quality of care, he continued, requires the co-operative effort of all professional workers, the integration of hospital work with community work, and co-ordination of all health efforts. Sound financing demands the widest application of the principle of prepayment for medical care, state support for those who cannot afford voluntary prepayment, and health services for other groups for which responsibility is generally accepted.

Another delegate, referring back to the TENTATIVE CONCLUSIONS, suggested that in item 6 the words "sound financing" be inserted after the fourth word, making it read: "The extent to which sound financing, efficiency, and economy . . ."

A representative of one of the major labor organizations, at this point, asked for the floor and stated that there were two ways in which the Section on Medical Care could present its conclusions. One was through adoption of a statement upon which all present could agree; the second was through presentation of a statement upon which a very large group of delegates, though not all, were agreed. He desired to present a statement of the latter sort, which he said had received the concurrence of delegates representing major labor organizations and various farm, public, and professional groups. The statement read:

STATEMENT OF IMMEDIATE GOALS FOR NATIONAL HEALTH SECURITY

1. Adequate medical services for the prevention of illness, the care and relief of sickness, and the promotion of a high level of physical and mental health

should be available to all without regard to race, color, creed, residence, or economic status.

2. The principle of contributory health insurance should be the basic method of financing medical care for a large majority of the American people, in order to remove the burden of unpredictable sickness costs, abolish the economic barrier to adequate medical services, and avoid the indignities of a "means test."

3. Health insurance should be accompanied by such use of tax funds as may be required to:

(a) Furnish services which are public responsibilities; and
(b) Supplement health insurance as necessary to provide adequate services for the whole population.

4. Voluntary prepayment group health plans organized on a community or collective bargaining level, embodying group practice and providing comprehensive service, offer to their members the best of modern medical care. Such plans furthermore are the best available means, at this time, of bringing about improved distribution of medical care, particularly in rural areas. Hence such plans should be encouraged by every means. It is recognized, however, that even under the most favorable circumstances such voluntary plans cannot be expected to cover the health needs of the entire nation.

5. The people have the right to establish voluntary insurance plans on a co-operative basis, and legal restrictions upon such right, now existing in a number of states, should be removed.

6. High standards of service, efficient administration, and reasonable costs require:

(a) Co-ordination of the services of physicians, hospitals, and other health agencies in all phases of prevention, diagnosis, and treatment; and
(b) Efficient co-operation between the providers and the consumers of such services under the general principle that the responsibility for general policies, finances, and administration should rest preponderantly upon the lay group; for professional standards and procedures, upon the professional group; for mutual consultation on all matters of joint interest, upon both groups.

7. A national health insurance plan assuring free choice of doctor, professional freedom for the doctor, and decentralized administration through the maximum utilization of state and local bodies is necessary in order to bring the benefits of health insurance to all who need it.

8. Voluntary insurance plans which provide health services and which meet acceptable standards should continue under a national health insurance plan.

Another labor delegate then read a list of the signatories to the foregoing proposals, as follows:

Channing Frothingham, M.D., Committee for the Nation's Health

Miss Elisabeth Christman, National Women's Trade Union League of America.

Joseph Louchheim, American Association of Social Workers

Miss Josephine Roche, United Mine Workers

Murray Robinson, M.D., American Veterans Committee

Miss Helen Hall, National Federation of Settlements
Miss Elizabeth S. Magee, National Consumers League
Harry J. Becker, United Automobile Workers, CIO
Nelson Cruikshank, American Federation of Labor
Mrs. Abraham Epstein, League for Industrial Democracy
Jerry Voorhis, Co-operative League of America
Ernst P. Boas, M.D., Physicians Forum
Mrs. Gladys Edwards, National Farmers Union
Edward L. Young, M.D., Physician's Committee for the Improvement of
    Medical Care
James Mark, Jr., United Mine Workers
W. Montague Cobb, M.D., National Association for the Advancement of Col-
    ored People

A representative of a farm group declared that his group preferred voluntary plans of prepayment for medical care, and that efforts toward national compulsory health insurance should be delayed until voluntary insurance has had a chance to prove what it can do. It was then pointed out by one of the labor delegates that, regardless of the efficiency of voluntary health plans, there would be many millions in the country who would not receive medical care under such an arrangement. She cited those millions who earn less than 65 cents an hour and the one and one-half million who earn only $30 a week. Only national compulsory health insurance, the speaker continued, would assure such people adequate medical care.

Various suggestions were made from the floor for minor alterations in the text of the proposals presented by the labor delegate. However, the representative from one labor organization protested and pointed out that all of the persons who had signed the document had signed for their organizations and not as individuals. Therefore, he declared, they could not assent to any change in the document.

It was urged by one speaker that the principle of "freedom of choice" for physicians to enter any voluntary association they chose should be expressed in the findings of the planning committee.

A delegate who was a member of the Indiana Medical Association but emphasized that he was speaking as an individual stated that he was happy over the areas of agreement which had been attained and for the opportunity of hearing and presenting views. He proposed a resolution of thanks to the chairman and to Mr. Ewing and to all those who had made this meeting possible. He said that he wanted to express this in the name of all the people of the Medical Care Section. Another delegate expressed the same views and urged that a continuing committee be established to permit such conferences to take place in the future.

In the opinion of another speaker, the National Health Assembly recognized a real relationship between housing and health, and she proposed that the Medical Care Section endorse the principle of public housing on national, state, and local levels.

At the close of the session, a labor representative rose to express the thanks of all labor organizations for the opportunity presented by the Assembly for the exchange of opinions.

Chairman Leavell asked if there was any further discussion or if there was anyone present who felt that he had not had the full opportunity he needed to make his views known. In the absence of any further requests for recognition from the floor, Chairman Leavell declared the meeting adjourned.

CONCLUSIONS

Immediately following the last session, the planning committee of the Section on the Nation's Need for Medical Care met and unanimously agreed upon the conclusions which follow as the main principles. These conclusions, together with the "Points to be Measured in Determining the Effectiveness of Prepayment Plans . . ." and the two "Principles for the Improvement of Voluntary Prepayment Plans," which were approved by the planning committee and discussed by the Section as a whole without dissent, as set forth below, are presented as constituting the conclusions of the meetings of the Section.

Main Principles

1. Adequate medical care[11] for the prevention of illness, the care and relief of sickness, and the promotion of a high level of physical, mental, and social health should be available to all without regard to race, color, creed, residence, or economic status.

2. The principle of contributory health insurance should be the basic method of financing medical care for a large majority of the American people, in order to remove the burden of unpredictable sickness costs, abolish the economic barrier to adequate medical services, and avoid the indignities of a "means test."

3. Health insurance should be accompanied by such use of tax resources as may be necessary to provide additional

   (a) Services to persons or groups for whom special public responsibility is acknowledged; and

   (b) Services not available under prepayment or insurance.

4. Voluntary prepayment group health plans, embodying group practice and providing comprehensive service, offer to their members the best of modern medical care. Such plans furthermore are the best available means at this time of bringing about improved distribution of medical

---

[11] Medical care, as used here, aims at the organization of all the facilities and personal services necessary to attain the highest level of health, prevent disease, cure or mitigate illness, and reduce if not prevent disability, economic insecurity, and dependency associated with illness.

care, particularly in rural areas. Hence such plans should be encouraged by every means.

5. The people have the right to establish voluntary insurance plans on a co-operative basis, and legal restrictions upon such right (other than those necessary to assure proper standards and qualifications), now existing in a number of states, should be removed.

6. High standards of service, efficient administration, and reasonable costs require:

(a) Co-ordination of the services of physicians, hospitals, and other health agencies in all phases of prevention, diagnosis, and treatment; and

(b) Effective co-operation between the providers and the consumers of such services.

7. A medical care program by itself will not solve the health problems of the nation. It must be co-ordinated with all efforts directed toward providing the people with adequate housing, a living wage, continuous productive and creative employment under safe working conditions, satisfying recreation, and such other measures as will correct conditions that adversely affect the physical, mental, and social health of the people.

8. There are areas on which the planning committee of the Medical Care Section is not yet prepared to report. In the Section's meetings differing views were expressed as to the method of effectuating the principle of prepayment or insurance. Some believe it can be achieved through voluntary plans. Others believe that a national health insurance plan is necessary.

Points to be Measured in Determining the Effectiveness of Prepayment Plans in Meeting the Medical Care Needs of the People

(1) The extent to which a prepayment plan makes available to those it serves the whole range of scientific medicine for prevention of disease and for treatment of all types of illness or injury

(2) The proportion of the population of its area—local, state, or national, as the case may be—covered by a plan (cost in relation to ability to pay, restrictions on enrollment imposed by actuarial considerations, income level, age, conditions of employment, means of securing enrollment and collecting premiums)

(3) The degree to which a plan makes use of and encourages the development of a high quality of medical care for its subscribers (standards of personnel and facilities, organization of services,

emphasis on prevention of disease, promotion of health, health education)

(4) The degree to which freedom and willingness to experiment with methods of payment and operation are encouraged in a plan

(5) The degree to which a plan succeeds in arranging amounts and methods of payment and conditions of participation that are satisfactory to physicians, hospitals, and others serving the plan's subscribers

(6) The extent to which sound financing, efficiency, and economy in the operation of a plan are achieved and encouraged by its basic policies and its administrative techniques

(7) The extent to which the individuals or board members who carry the ultimate responsibility for a plan represent the interest of those entitled to service and those who are paying the cost, as well as of the physicians, hospitals, or others who are providing the services

Principles for the Improvement of Voluntary Plans

1. There should be the freest opportunity for full co-operation among the providers and consumers of service in the establishment and the administration of medical care plans, with the proviso that full control of the practice of medicine in the program must remain with the doctors.

2. The Medical Care Section strongly urges the importance of joint conferences at the earliest possible date among representatives of the American Medical Association and of groups representing the consumers of medical care and services to study the question of the establishment and administration of medical care plans.

Table 1

Hospital Facilities, Days of General Hospital Care, Supply of Physicians and Dentists, Percentages of Births Occurring in Hospitals, and Infant and Maternal Mortality Rates, by States Arranged According to Per Capita Income

State	Per Capita Income 1945	General Hospital Beds per 1000 pop. (Excl. Federal Beds) 1945	Days of Gen. Hospital Care per Capita (Excl. Federal Hospitals) 1945	No. of Persons per Physician 1940	No. of Persons per Dentist 1940	Percentage of Births Occurring in Hospitals 1944	Infant Mortality Rate—1944 (Deaths per 1000 live births)	Maternal Mortality Rate—1944 (Deaths per 1000 live births)
United States	$1150	3.8	1.01	935	1878	75.6	39.8	2.3
New York	1595	5.3	1.47	597	1321	95.0	32.8	1.9
California	1480	4.0	1.11	747	1279	95.2	34.5	1.7
Connecticut	1449	4.3	1.17	780	1577	97.9	30.7	1.5
Washington	1407	4.1	1.15	1017	1383	97.1	33.8	1.6
Delaware	1381	4.4	1.05	913	2538	83.6	48.7	1.5
New Jersey	1373	3.9	1.02	842	1555	92.5	34.0	1.6
District of Columbia	1361	5.3	1.44	411	1345	95.0	44.8	2.1
Illinois	1360	4.4	1.24	789	1330	90.0	32.4	1.8
Massachusetts	1321	5.7	1.47	696	1537	95.3	33.1	1.8
Ohio	1289	3.3	.94	927	1837	84.0	38.5	1.9
Rhode Island	1268	4.2	1.18	913	1892	91.9	35.3	1.8
Oregon	1266	3.9	1.06	927	1313	96.8	30.5	1.8
Nevada	1243	4.5	1.14	755	2042	94.6	50.2	2.3
Maryland	1212	4.1	1.10	801	2093	73.8	41.5	1.9
Michigan	1212	4.4	1.03	1017	1986	88.2	37.9	1.7
Pennsylvania	1199	4.4	1.20	891	1675	81.5	40.0	2.5
Montana	1172	6.4	1.64	1203	2020	93.4	36.1	1.5
Wisconsin	1161	4.1	1.14	1113	1489	87.9	32.0	1.8
Indiana	1152	3.0	.83	1039	1896	80.9	34.5	2.0
North Dakota	1123	4.9	1.29	1439	2450	86.2	35.4	1.8

State								
Nebraska	1117	4.2	1.13	992	1433	84.4	33.0	1.7
Kansas	1113	3.7	1.02	1126	1776	83.9	33.3	1.8
Iowa	1109	3.3	.92	1037	1567	85.3	33.1	1.8
Colorado	1100	5.2	1.32	861	1692	82.1	49.4	2.5
Wyoming	1096	3.5	.82	1076	2022	89.7	41.2	.9
South Dakota	1083	3.8	1.03	1657	2136	82.3	34.9	1.8
Missouri	1063	3.8	1.04	1001	1655	68.5	37.6	2.2
Minnesota	1061	5.0	1.42	903	1348	90.0	31.3	1.4
Idaho	1054	3.7	.85	1422	2441	92.3	34.0	2.5
Maine	1051	3.8	1.04	1136	2247	81.2	46.7	2.3
Utah	1023	3.6	.89	1119	1798	90.3	33.9	1.4
Vermont	1023	4.2	1.20	845	2363	81.4	40.6	1.9
Florida	996	2.9	.71	1012	2657	66.8	45.5	3.3
New Hampshire	971	5.0	1.20	975	2194	93.1	37.7	2.8
Arizona	918	3.7	.82	949	3263	79.6	68.8	3.0
Texas	917	2.6	.65	1245	3184	65.9	50.4	2.5
Virginia	903	2.9	.78	1171	3173	55.7	47.1	2.6
Oklahoma	889	2.5	.59	1306	3145	68.1	41.2	2.4
West Virginia	839	3.4	.88	1226	3186	42.7	52.0	2.2
Tennessee	813	2.2	.60	1257	3459	47.1	45.5	2.8
New Mexico	812	2.8	.64	1422	4665	55.9	89.1	4.0
Louisiana	785	3.5	.84	1220	3004	61.7	46.3	3.4
Georgia	745	2.2	.55	1388	3796	50.7	44.5	3.6
Kentucky	735	2.3	.59	1324	3579	38.6	46.7	2.5
North Carolina	732	2.8	.76	1504	4544	51.1	45.4	2.9
Alabama	700	1.9	.45	1684	4683	39.3	45.5	3.7
South Carolina	663	2.5	.60	1565	5263	41.2	54.9	3.7
Arkansas	654	1.9	.48	1392	5077	41.9	34.7	2.8
Mississippi	556	1.8	.40	1784	5250	31.2	44.1	3.8

Table 2

Persons Covered Under Hospital and Medical Insurance,
Continental United States, January 1, 1948

	Number of Persons Eligible for Service Benefits and/or Cash Allowances against the Cost of Service			
		Physicians' Services		
Type of Plan	*Hospitalization*	*Surgical and Obstetrical Care*	*Non-surgical Care in Hospitals*	*Office and Home Visits*
	I	II	III	IV
Blue Cross–Blue Shield Prepayment Plans[1]	28,100,000	7,000,000	3,000,000	800,000
Insurance Companies:				
Group Policies[2]	13,500,000	10,700,000	800,000	500,000
Individual Policies[3]	4,000,000	3,000,000	600,000	400,000
Industrial Medical Plans[4]	1,400,000	1,400,000	1,350,000	1,400,000
Private Group Clinics[5]	375,000	400,000	400,000	330,000
Others[6]	730,000	650,000	650,000	750,000

Note: Because of overlapping and the varying nature of the type of plan covered in this table, no summation is provided in each column. A summation of columns I to IV would be invalid since in general the same persons are included in each column.

[1] Persons enrolled for hospitalization benefits represent total continental United States Blue Cross enrollment plus the estimated number of persons covered for hospitalization under contracts of medical plans (mainly Oregon, Washington, and northern California) not affiliated with Blue Cross plans. Persons covered for surgical and obstetrical benefits represent the total number of persons enrolled in medical-surgical plans affiliated with Blue Cross plans or sponsored by medical societies or both. Figures in columns III and IV are estimates based on total enrollment in plans providing these coverages in combination with coverage of surgical and obstetrical service. All data are from the Jan. 1, 1948, enrollment reports of the Blue Cross Commission, Special Studies 86-D and 87-D.

[2] Figures are based on coverages reported by the Life Insurance Association of America as of Dec. 31, 1946 (Group Insurance and Group Annuity Coverage—United States Business—1946; All Life and Casualty Insurance Companies), increased by the estimated growth in coverage during 1947. The estimated growth in coverage during 1947 was based on reports from four companies doing approximately half of the total group business in these fields.

[3] No reliable figures as to the number of persons having individual policies for hospitalization, surgical benefits, etc., are available. The figures presented are based on estimates for Jan., 1947 (see L. S. Reed, *Blue Cross and Medical Service Plans*, U. S. Public Health Service, Washington, D. C., October 1947, p. 2), with allowances for 1947 growth.

[4] Figures based on data in *Prepayment Medical Care Organizations*, by Margaret C. Klem, Social Security Administration, Washington, D. C., June 1945. Miss Klem's figures show no growth (rather, a small decrease) in the number of persons covered by

APPENDIX B

PROGRAM OF THE MEDICAL CARE SECTION
NATIONAL HEALTH ASSEMBLY

FIRST SESSION, Saturday Afternoon, May 1

Plan for the Section Meetings...................Dr. Hugh Leavell, Chairman

"The Problem of Medical Care" (presentation of a factual statement agreed upon by the Section's planning committee)

Dr. Thomas A. McGoldrick, Member, Council on Medical Service, American Medical Association

"The Organization of Medical Services"

Dr. C. Rufus Rorem, Executive Secretary, Philadelphia Hospital Council

Discussion:

Dr. Louis T. Wright, Chief of Surgery, Harlem Hospital, New York City

Dr. Samuel Proger, Medical Director, Joseph H. Pratt Diagnostic Hospital, Boston, Massachusetts

Dr. H. Clifford Loos, Ross–Loos Medical Group, Los Angeles, California

"Discriminatory Patterns in Community Health Services"

Dr. W. Montague Cobb, Professor of Anatomy, Howard University Medical School

Discussion

SECOND SESSION, Sunday Morning, May 2

"Criteria for Evaluating Prepayment Plans"

Dr. Dean A. Clark, Medical Director, Health Insurance Plan of Greater New York

"Types of Health Insurance Plans"

Dr. Franz Goldmann, Professor, Harvard School of Public Health

"Blue Cross–Blue Shield Plans and Their Ability to Meet National Needs for Prepayment Arrangements"

Dr. Paul R. Hawley, Executive Officer, Blue Cross Commission and Associated Medical Care Plans

"The Role of Group Insurance in Financing Personal Health Services"

Mr. Reinhard A. Hohaus, Actuary, Metropolitan Life Insurance Company

"Industrial Medical Care Plans"

---

industrial medical service plans between 1943 and 1945, and it has been assumed that the 1945 figures still hold good.

[5] Figures based on data in *Prepayment Medical Care Organizations* (see footnote 4).

[6] Includes co-operative plans. Farmers Home Administration plans, non-profit plan not associated with Blue Cross–Blue Shield, university health service prepayment plans, commercial hospital associations. Figures are based largely on data in *Prepayment Medical Care Organizations*, supplemented by recent enrollment data for various leading plans included in this group.

Dr. J. J. Wittmer, Assistant Vice-President, Consolidated Edison Company of New York
Discussion

THIRD SESSION, Sunday Afternoon, May 2
"National Health Insurance"
 Dr. Ernst P. Boas, Chairman, Physicians Forum
"The Program of the American Medical Association"
 Dr. R. L. Sensenich, President-Elect, American Medical Association
Discussion (of both subjects):
 Mr. Michael M. Davis, Chairman, Committee for the Nation's Health
 Dr. Walter B. Martin, Member, Council on Medical Service, American Medical Association
Discussion

FOURTH SESSION, Sunday Evening, May 2
"Unions Move Into Health and Welfare Programs"
 Mr. Harry T. Becker, Director of Social Security Department, United Automobile Workers
"Co-operative Health Plans"
 Mr. Winslow Carlton, Chairman of the Board, Group Health Insurance, Inc., New York
"Legislative and Other Restraints Affecting Voluntary Plans"
 Mr. Horace R. Hansen, General Counsel, National Co-operative Health Federation
"Existing Programs of Public Medical Services"
 Dr. Dean W. Roberts, Chief of the Bureau of Medical Services, Maryland State Department of Health
Discussion

FIFTH SESSION, Monday Afternoon, May 3
Discussion: Points of Agreement and Issues of Disagreement

APPENDIX C

PLANNING COMMITTEE

Hugh Leavell, M.D., *Chairman*	Professor of Public Health Practice Harvard University School of Public Health
Harry J. Becker[1]	Director, Social Security Department United Automobile Workers Congress of Industrial Organizations

[1] Mr. Becker replaced Harry Read, Executive Assistant to the Secretary-Treasurer, Congress of Industrial Organizations, who had served on the Planning Committee up to May 1, 1948.

Ernst P. Boas, M.D.	Chairman, The Physicians Forum
Nelson Cruikshank	Director, Social Insurance Activities American Federation of Labor
Horace R. Hansen	General Counsel National Co-operative Health Federation
Thomas A. McGoldrick, M.D.	Council on Medical Service American Medical Association
James R. McVay, M.D.	Chairman, Council on Medical Service American Medical Association
C. Rufus Rorem	Executive Secretary Philadelphia Hospital Council
Louis Wright, M.D.	Chief of Surgery Harlem Hospital New York, New York

STAFF ASSISTANTS

Harry N. Rosenfield	Assistant to the Administrator Federal Security Agency
Louis S. Reed	Health Economist Division of Public Health Methods Public Health Service, Federal Security Agency
Lorin Kerr, M.D.	Industrial Hygiene Division Public Health Service, Federal Security Agency

REGISTRANTS

Harold Aaron, M.D.	Consumers Union of United States
Miss Sylvia Altman	Manager, Labor Participation Department Community Chest Federation Washington, D. C.
A. J. Asgis, D.D.S.	Professor of Public Health Dentistry New York University
Edward Ayash	Treasurer–Welfare Director, Local 1199 Retail Drug Store Employees Union Congress of Industrial Organizations
E. S. Bagnall, M.D.	Chairman, Legislative Committee Massachusetts Medical Society
Albert W. Bailey, D.O.	Chairman, Committee on Health Insurance American Osteopathic Society
E. Dwight Barnett, M.D.	Director, Harper Hospital Detroit, Michigan
Miss Pearl Bierman	Medical Assistance Consultant Illinois Public Aid Commission

Mrs. Myrna Bordelon	Secretary, Community Services Committee Chicago Industrial Union Council Congress of Industrial Organizations
Mrs. Ruth M. Bronson	Executive Secretary National Congress of American Indians, Inc.
Rev. Robert Brown	Assistant Executive Secretary National Conference of Catholic Charities
Otis Brubaker	United Steelworkers of America Congress of Industrial Organizations
Winslow Carlton	Co-operative Health Federation of America
Dean A. Clark, M.D.	Medical Director Health Insurance Plan of Greater New York
W. Montague Cobb, M.D.	National Association for the Advancement of Colored People; Professor of Anatomy Howard University
J. D. Colman	Executive Director Maryland Hospital Service, Inc.
Morris L. Cooke	Committee for the Nation's Health
Henry C. Daniels	Denver Council on Interracial Relations
Michael M. Davis	Chairman, Executive Committee Committee for the Nation's Health
Leigh C. Douglass	Group Health Association of Denver
Judge Henry Ellenbogen	Court of Common Pleas Pittsburgh, Pennsylvania
V. L. Ellicott, M.D.	County Health Officer Montgomery County Health Department Maryland
Mrs. Abraham Epstein	League for Industrial Democracy
F. L. Feirabend, M.D.	Commissioner, Blue Shield Kansas City, Missouri
Miss Molly Flynn	Washington, D.C.
Maurice Friedman, M.D.	American Medical Association
Oliver A. Friedman	Executive Secretary Goodwill Industries of America
Channing Frothingham, M.D.	Chairman, Committee for the Nation's Health
H. J. Gibbons	Chairman, Labor Committee Co-operative Health Federation of America
D. G. Gill, M.D.	State Health Officer Alabama State Department of Health
Franz Goldmann, M.D.	Associate Professor of Medical Care Harvard University School of Public Health

Miss Gwendolyn Goodrich	Assistant Secretary Co-operative Health Federation of America
Harold Gordon	Managing Director Health and Accident Underwriters Conference
Sidney Greenburg, M.D.	Physicians Forum
Gunnar Gunderson, M.D.	Wisconsin State Medical Society
Miss Helen Hall	National Federation of Settlements
Lloyd Halvorson	Economist, National Grange
William A. Hanscom	Washington Representative Oil Workers International Union Congress of Industrial Organizations
Augustus P. Hauss, M.D.	President-Elect, Indiana State Medical Association
Charles G. Hayden, M.D.	Medical Director Massachusetts Medical Service
John H. Hays	Superintendent, Lenox Hill Hospital New York, New York
Elmer Hess, M.D.	Council on Medical Services American Medical Association
Rev. George Higgins	Assistant Director National Catholic Welfare Conference
R. A. Hohaus	Actuary, Metropolitan Life Insurance Company
Mrs. Charlotte Holtz	Member, State Board Montana Farmers Union
Robert A. Hornby	Vice-President, Pacific Lighting Company
Samuel Householder	Welfare and Retirement Fund United Mine Workers of America
Benjamin B. Kendrick	Social Security Analyst United States Chamber of Commerce
Louis R. Kent, M.D.	Merck & Company, Inc.
Jay C. Ketcham	Executive Vice-President Michigan Medical Service
Howard E. Knuckles	Field Representative United Mine Workers of America
C. A. Kulp	Professor of Insurance University of Pennsylvania
John R. Kumpel	United Rubber Workers of America Congress of Industrial Organizations
D. B. Layton, M.D.	Director, Health Insurance Studies Department of National Health and Welfare Ottawa, Canada

Henry D. Locke	Research Director Liberty Mutual Insurance Company
H. Clifford Loos, M.D.	Ross-Loos Medical Group Los Angeles, California
Joseph H. Louchheim	American Association of Social Workers
Edward J. McCormick, M.D.	American Medical Association
Arthur J. McDowell	American Veterans Committee
Rev. Raymond A. McGowan	Director, Department of Social Action National Catholic Welfare Conference
Miss Elizabeth S. Magee	General Secretary National Consumers League
Mrs. Benjamin Margolin	Executive Secretary National Council of Jewish Women
James Mark, Jr.	United Mine Workers of America
Walter B. Martin, M.D.	Council on Medical Services American Medical Association
Harold J. Mayers	Welfare and Retirement Fund United Mine Workers of America
Fred Mayes, M.D.	Assistant State Health Officer Kansas State Health Department
J. W. Myers	Manager, Insurance and Social Security Department Standard Oil Company of New Jersey
George R. Nelson	Grand Lodge Representative International Association of Machinists
Miss Agnes O'Leary	Director, Public Health Nursing Catholic Hospital Association
Abraham Oseroff	Secretary, Hospital Council of Western Pennsylvania
T. R. Owens	Legislative Representative United Rubber Workers of America Congress of Industrial Organizations
John P. Peters, M.D.	Secretary, Committee of Physicians for the Improvement of Medical Care
Mrs. Esther Peterson	Amalgamated Clothing Workers of America Congress of Industrial Organizations
Harry J. Peterson	Vice-President, Board of Directors Group Health Mutual
Kenneth Pohlman	Health Services Division Welfare and Retirement Fund United Mine Workers of America
Miss Eleanor Poland	American Pharmaceutical Association

Frederic J. Quigley, M.D.	American Medical Association
Herbert P. Ramsey, M.D.	American Medical Association
Miss Marian Randall	Executive Director Visiting Nurse Service of New York
Elmer Richman, M.D.	Medical Director Labor Health Institute St. Louis, Missouri
Miss Marian Rickert	Supervisor of Medical Social Service New York State Department of Social Welfare
Dean W. Roberts, M.D.	Chief, Bureau of Medical Services Maryland State Health Department
Murray Robinson, M.D.	American Veterans Committee
Miss Josephine Roche	Director, Welfare and Retirement Fund United Mine Workers of America
Daniel I. Rosen	Medical Services Committee Washington, D.C.
Miss Emilie S. Sargent	Chairman, Committee on Health Insurance American Nursing Association
L. Howard Schriver, M.D.	President, Associated Medical Care Plans
T. F. Sellers, M.D.	Director Georgia State Health Department
C. A. Siegfried	Assistant Actuary Metropolitan Life Insurance Company
Konstantin Sparkitt	Administrative Health Officer Eastern Health District Baltimore, Maryland
Bernhard J. Stern	Professor of Sociology Columbia University
James Stevenson, M.D.	Oklahoma State Medical Association
Lazare Teper	Director of Research International Ladies' Garment Workers' Union
Arthur S. Thornbury	General Motors Corporation
Patrick A. Tompkins	Commissioner, Massachusetts Department of Public Welfare
John W. Truitt, M.D.	Wisconsin State Medical Society
E. A. Van Steenwyk	Executive Director Associated Hospital Services of Philadelphia
Ralph J. Walker	Associate Actuary Aetna Life Insurance Company

George L. Weaver	Director, Committee to Abolish Discrimination
	Congress of Industrial Organizations
Myron Weiss	New York, New York
Mrs. Mildred W. Wells	General Federation of Women's Clubs
Mrs. Elizabeth Wickendon	Washington Representative
	American Public Welfare Association
Lucius R. Wilson, M.D.	Superintendent, Episcopal Hospital
	Philadelphia, Pennsylvania
Stephen Wilson	College of Pharmacy
	University of Pittsburgh
J. J. Wittmer, M.D.	Assistant Vice-President
	Consolidated Edison Company
Phillip W. Woods, D.D.S.	Welfare and Retirement Fund
	United Mine Workers of America
Edward L. Young, M.D.	Chairman, Committee of Physicians for the Improvement of Medical Care, Inc.

State and
Community Planning for Health

THE Section on State and Community Planning for Health studied the work of thirteen widely scattered, successful civic planning groups to find the principles underlying their results. These groups were as follows:

Committee on Health, Governor's Post-War Planning Commission, Colorado
Illinois State-wide Public Health Committee
New Mexico Health Council
Puerto Rico Island-wide Health Education Program
Virginia Council on Health and Medical Care
Georgia Citizens Council
Committee for Kentucky
Back of the Yards Council, Chicago, Illinois
Flanner House, Indianapolis, Indiana
Miami County Mental Hygiene Association, Ohio
Association for the Handicapped and Health Services of Buncombe County, North Carolina
Public Health Federation, Cincinnati, Ohio
Great Plains Committee on Rural Health and Welfare.

In seeking to find these principles, the Section found it useful to analyze the data on the basis of the following ten analytical questions:

1. How do successful planning groups get started?
2. How do they work out intergroup relationships?
3. How do they discover facts, needs, and resources?
4. How do they spread interest and participation?
5. How and when do they form permanent organizations?
6. How are they financed?
7. How do they interpret their work to the public?
8. How do they meet hindrances to planning?
9. How much do they accomplish?
10. How long may they expect to operate usefully?

From these studies, representing the pooled experience of the participants, it was possible (1) to deduce certain basic assumptions on which dynamic civic planning for health rests; (2) to set forth in some detail the data behind the guiding principles, including a general discussion of the techniques of health councils; (3) to develop broad major recommendations; and (4) to name the ten-year goals set by this Section.

Basic Assumptions Underlying Dynamic Planning for Health

1. Health is defined as a state of complete physical, mental, and social well-being, not merely the absence of disease or infirmity.[1]

2. The promotion of optimal health is a community responsibility. The development and maintenance of *full-time official public health units* and other essential health services are basic to community planning for health.

3. Health is a function of the community's total way of life, and planning for health should be correlated with planning for economic and social well-being.

4. Citizens can act most effectively when there is proper machinery for planning and action at local and state levels. Local autonomy should be safeguarded. Special skills and interests should be fully utilized. These might include, for example, medicine, teaching, organizing, newspaper writing, radio broadcasting, and so on.

5. In matters affecting health, it is often impossible for a community to operate alone. The community planning body needs opportunity to contribute to the plans of state and national groups as well as to receive help locally from such groups. Joint planning is a two-way process.

6. The effective furtherance of health is dependent upon local initiative, interest, aggressive support, and participation of the entire community—professional workers and laymen, individuals and groups. This has been demonstrated in several communities which have developed strong agencies for co-ordinating health activities.

7. Citizens undertaking the plan for the improvement of public health cannot profitably do less than:

(a) Gather the factual data which will establish the existing health needs;
(b) Bring together lay and professional groups for the joint study and solution of the problems and for the correlation of all programs and services (preventive, therapeutic, environmental, etc.) affecting health;
(c) Combine the broad activities of public interpretation and health education with constant efforts to increase the people's participation in, and responsibility for, planning; and
(d) Develop methods for effective implementation of the plans.

[1] Definition promulgated by the World Health Organization.

Inception of Civic Planning for Health

The first requisite to health planning by citizens is that there be room for improvement in the health conditions of their society.

Next, something about the imperfect conditions has to move some person or some group to look for a remedy. The sparks that serve to set off citizens' programs vary. Examples have been the draft rejection rates; the need for co-ordination of civic efforts; problems of economics, politics, labor, medical care, and sanitation; and the basic problem of the lack of full-time local health units. In no instance studied was successful planning by state or local people motivated by *national* recommendations, prescriptions, exhortations, or directives. However, state planning *in which local groups actively participate* may in turn give rise to local planning.

Usually a single individual is in the last analysis responsible for taking the initiative in bringing people together to talk about the conditions that seem to need improvement. This individual may become the public leader in the planning group, or he or she may remain in the background, serving quietly but steadfastly as a sort of catalytic agent. Examples of dynamic personalities who took responsibility on a volunteer basis to get planning started are a woman physician in Colorado and a business man in Kentucky. In other projects studied the initiative was taken, variously, in a governor's office, by a state legislature, by a state medical society, by a university's director of inter-American affairs, by a rural sociologist, by a medical health officer, and by a trained health educator.

The person who takes the responsibility of bringing people together to consider the problems of their society needs to remain in a position to work with all conflicting forces, for it is almost inevitable that the problems will involve controversial issues. In other words, civic planning groups need leaders who are in the true sense, whether by natural gifts or by formal training, adult educators. The discussions are so conducted as to draw out all the people present, to clear away fears and suspicions, and to find areas of agreement. The leaders have confidence in the group decisions of an informed people, but they do not expect people to support what they do not understand. Generous use is made of the technique of asking penetrating questions both of those people who might be called experts and of laymen.

The group which comes together to begin democratic health planning needs to be truly representative of all the people whose social problems are under consideration, and it needs to represent all interested organizations and all economic levels. It should include some individuals who have special knowledge of the medical and public health sciences and of existing health and medical services and programs in the community, the state, and the nation.

There is no blueprint for the planning group in beginning its work. No person or organization, whether from within the population group involved or from the outside, dominates. The "shock treatment" may successfully be used to point up the known needs. But only the problems which the people decide to be worth their effort are the problems about which plans are made. The methods, of course, are the same, whether the group chooses to plan exclusively for child health or inclusively for all public health, and whether the group plans specifically for health betterment or broadly for over-all social betterment. But each group must take its first steps in whatever way seems best to answer its own requirements.

Intergroup Relationships

So far as practical democratic planning is concerned, the boundaries of a community need not be contiguous with state or county lines or with the corporate limits of a city or town. The planning body may effectively represent any "natural community," rural or urban. This may be a particular section of a large city, a special population group, or an interrelated group of towns, of counties, or even of states. It is an association of people sharing closely an important common interest.

When social planning is contemplated, good working relationships are needed among the groups concerned throughout the entire natural community. It is the social problem itself that determines the extent of the community and indicates what groups are concerned. Successful civic planning, whether local, state, or regional, needs to be problem-centered. Community health promotion has many facets. If it is not to be left on a catch-as-catch-can or piecemeal basis, there is need for teamwork among many groups. The key groups are the trained full-time local public health officials and the medical societies, but these do not comprise an oligarchy able to do the job alone. The team requires, in addition, representatives of voluntary health agencies, other professional groups, organizations concerned with fields related to health, and all those groups which might be called the consumers of health services. Each group has a hand in the civic planning and action, but no group forfeits its own identity. If enough of the affected people are actively participating in the planning, the problem of adapting the plans to the normal customs or folkways of the community gives no trouble.

Public health is closely related to many other problems. For instance, social health cannot be achieved without adequate homes in good neighborhoods, income sufficient to maintain healthful standards of living, proper facilities for recreation, satisfactory educational opportunities, and a suitable measure of social security. This means that the maintenance of community health is not an isolated activity; it means that planning for health needs to be part and parcel of broad social and economic planning.

Not until the civic planning team for a natural community is enlarged to include broad representation from all the suggested groups can full co-ordination be expected. Integration of action for health is needed at local, state, regional, and national levels. The process of recruiting and organizing the team at each level has to be worked out by the groups concerned at that level. But, even when such co-ordination is achieved on the horizontal plane, the job is found to be one which no local, state, regional, or national system can complete by itself.

When state and national plans are to be made, they have their roots in the experience and needs of local areas. Whether state and national plans are comprehensive or fractional, service at the local level is their goal; therefore, advice from the communities where the affected people live is essential. Conversely, advice from state and national planning bodies to local groups is important. So long as this advice takes the form of stimulation and guidance, rather than of directives and blueprints, it produces dividends. To achieve this kind of reciprocal relationship between local, state, regional, and national planning bodies, the team that is working in unison at one level needs to enlist the groups involved at the other levels into its own active membership. If the planning is to be really effective, those involved at all levels should take part in it, not simply be brought into the program after the plans are made.

A good workable method by which state and national groups can assist with local health planning is to make trained consultants available. These consultants are usually community-wise adult educators with special knowledge in such fields as sociology, community organization, and public health. They can apparently make their best contributions if their presence is well accepted by the local people. As a rule this means either that they need to live in the community for a time, as did the consultant in Puerto Rico, or that they need to enter the community at the specific request of the local groups, as did the consultant in Buncombe County. As for the contributions of local areas to state planning, these appear to be most fruitful when the state group operates to a considerable degree as a league of local planning bodies banded together for mutual advantage. This is the case in the Georgia, New Mexico, and Virginia groups.

It is rarely feasible to have every geographic subdivision of a state directly represented in the state-level planning body. However, many of the local civic and religious organizations, professional groups, clubs, and so on are represented in the state planning by their own state-level officers. In this way the state planning body makes use of already existing social machinery to reach more areas and to enrich its plans.

Not only do community health planners often make good use of outside consultants; they also need to be alert to the value of their own area's skilled people who have special knowledge or who hold key positions. A typical example is the support given by the health planning group to a new Governor for Colorado and to a new Mayor for Denver, both of whom campaigned for strong health departments. Another example is the use of lawyers by the Miami County group.

Where social planning is truly democratic and problem-centered, relationships between the groups concerned can usually be worked out satisfactorily. For those special cases where serious opposition arises, two methods of meeting the opposition have been found most commonly successful. One is the method of involving so large a majority in the civic planning and action that the opposition gives way. This method was used by the Illinois counties when non-resident taxpayers opposed a health tax.

The other method is that of patient interpretation and education. In such circumstances as those of the Flanner House group this may mean interpretation of the needs of the minority to the majority. Under conditions like the Kentucky group's, it may mean seeking areas of agreement between the majority and the conservative business interests. In situations like the one between the Colorado health planners and the live-stock groups, it may mean educating a leading industry to assume certain responsibilities for the public good. At all events, the aim of this method is to get the opposition to join in the planning.

Facts and Resources

In order to decide how to plan for better state and community health, people must have definite information about their health conditions. They have to know rather concretely the existing needs, the national-regional-state-local resources available, and the possible ways of meeting the needs.

But successful methods of estimating health needs and resources do not adhere to a uniform pattern.

Sometimes a small group of people in high places decides to have the pertinent health facts gathered for the citizenry by an imported expert. This works well if the project is localized and not too academic, and if the resident leadership is able to get enough people to study the findings, accept the criticisms, and go to work on improving the conditions. In some cases in the past, however, the people have failed to be roused to action by expert-surveys. The findings may be wasted if the people do not understand them or do not hear much about them, or if no one can get the people to care, or if the people react too defensively. What is perhaps equally important, any findings printed in an expert's report are static: the printed page does not change with the changing conditions of the state or community concerned.

The self-survey is less likely to run into such difficulties. Under this technique the successful civic planning group begins its work not with a survey report but directly with its own recognition of its social problems. The members pool their first-hand experience, observation, and knowledge. They seek further information and guidance, both written and oral, from national-regional-state-local agencies and individuals. If they decide to make further studies of their health needs and resources, they invite representatives of a variety of social sectors and of resource agencies to participate in the studies. In this way their very resource groups become parties to the fact finding even before the planning is well under way. Various sample survey questionnaires and so-called yardsticks may be consulted, but usually the check lists and yardsticks finally adopted are custom-built in terms of the area and its problems.

Under the following ten questions which health planners might ask themselves about *resources* and fact finding, the Section on State and Community Planning for Health lists some of the kinds of agencies and groups that might be helpful:

1. Have you obtained all pertinent factual data, consultations, and other assistance in planning that are available to you from reliable public and private organizations doing public health work?
   Examples: Bureau of the Census; *Federal, state,* and *local* public health agencies; departments of agriculture, of education, and of welfare; American National Red Cross; American Public Health Association; National Health Council; recognized organizations concerned with special health problems (like cancer, crippled children, heart, infantile paralysis, safety, tuberculosis).

2. Have you posed your planning problems about the people's mental, physical, and social well-being to whatever special or over-all citizens planning groups are already organized for civic improvement of your community, county, state, region, nation?

> *Examples:* National-regional-state-local planning committees, community councils, councils of social agencies, community chests, national-state-regional-local health councils, continuing adult education programs.

3. Have you also taken your problems and questions to agencies and professional associations in fields allied to public health and to public health education?

> *Examples:* National-state-local medical societies (and such other groups concerned with the healing arts as dentists, nurses, etc.), hospitals, universities, schools, teachers' associations, welfare and social service organizations, housing authorities, recreation groups, agriculture groups.

4. Have you discussed existing community health problems with organized civic, professional, religious, fraternal, educational, cultural, and service groups and with prominent individual civic leaders?

> *Examples:* Lawyers, physicians, clergymen, social workers, teachers, parent-teacher groups, Home Bureau, women's clubs, men's clubs, youth groups, veterans' groups.

5. Have you in the consultations included organizations peculiar to your own locality and those serving special population groups?

> *Examples:* Turnverein, Urban League, etc.

6. Have you asked for help and suggestions from business and industrial establishments and associations, advertisers, labor groups, and farm groups?

> *Examples:* Chamber of Commerce, large employers, unions, Farm Bureau Federation, etc.

7. Have you consulted representatives of your newspapers, your radio stations, your motion-picture theaters, your local arts clubs and drama groups (both in the community and in its schools, vocational schools, and colleges)?

> *Examples:* Daily and weekly papers, university radio stations, etc.

8. Have you thought of seeking written and audio-visual educational materials or aid in preparing your own from a variety of sources?

> *Examples:* Health departments, universities, schools, museums, libraries, insurance companies, educational departments of pharmaceutical and food-supply associations.

9. Have you invited all groups having contributions to make in any of the fields mentioned in the above questions to help in the planning itself? If the consultations and discussions should lead to the formation of a permanent council or committee of some kind, would the participants so far be truly representative of all the population?

> For example, if your council or committee is going to plan for the health of all the people, does the group now represent democratically various age groups, all economic levels, religions, political parties,

geographical areas, minority groups, both rural and urban groups, etc.? Do you have both men and women actively interested?

10. What other agencies and groups can you add to these suggested kinds of resources?

Consider the spread of participation in your planning project, the development of your educational program, the need of joint activity, of funds, of personnel, of legislation, of avenues and materials for mass education, etc.

By the time the representative study groups have enough data to formulate plans, widespread interest in carrying them out will already exist. Nor do the studies cease when civic action is launched. Resident study groups re-evaluate the situation continuously, and new or revised plans for better community health are developed from time to time.

There is no hard-and-fast rule as to how this type of fact finding should be done. Self-survey methods to suit the people concerned were worked out variously, for instance, in Chicago's Back of the Yards community, in Buncombe County, in Georgia, and in the Great Plains region.

No matter what process of assembling data is used, a number of basic principles common to all effective methods may be discerned. The essential thread seems to be that fact finding is viewed as the means and not the end of civic enterprise. Facts do not bestir themselves. Citizens, excited about facts, do.

Full use is made of state and local resources, including individual talents and knowledge. The health situation is studied with regard to gaps in the existing programs, to overlapping in available service, to health needs in general, and to practical ways of correcting the problems and meeting the needs. Whatever the facts accumulated and whatever the yardsticks cited in interpreting them, the findings and recommendations are carefully localized. Special attention is given to rural health difficulties because of their special nature. If the people as a whole seem apathetic, the initiators and leaders of the project try to present the facts in a manner that may shock them out of their lethargy without breeding resentment.

As corollaries to its *major recommendations* with reference to fact finding in citizen programs, this Section *further recommends:*

(a) The self-survey of state and community health conditions by resident planning groups, and the subsequent continuous self-evaluation of progress and of changing health conditions; and

(b) Published reports—from each state and local public health department—of a type which clearly shows what still needs to be done to improve the health levels of the area of its jurisdiction.

Spread of Participation

Successful civic enterprise of this kind depends on strengthening the group by broadening the base rather than by concentrating power at the top. To achieve this, the initial planners need to demonstrate in their operations that they really do want widespread leadership and a pooling of many ideas. They need to make clear that their planning and action will follow the principles of majority rule and of "home rule." In other words, they spread interest in the project by the sound method of making it, in actual practice, the people's project.

Another common practice is that of getting local, state, regional, and national groups to join the discussions and the work. Flanner House, for instance, got help from the United States Children's Bureau; the Miami County group got help from the State University, the State Welfare Department, and the United States Public Health Service; and Buncombe County got help from the State Health Department. Local groups also look to state, regional, and national groups for help in working out the kinds of local problems that require state or national action. Examples include the enabling legislation for local health units sought in Colorado and Illinois, and the endorsement of this type of legislation in principle by such national organizations as the American Medical Association and the American Public Health Association.

To build functional programs of this kind, successful planning bodies at state and regional levels, in turn, depend heavily on both national and local participation.

The essential ingredients for success in spreading participation vertically would seem to be: a willingness to seek, as well as to give, advice; and a profound respect for the autonomy of each natural community.

Specific methods which planning groups have found effective in involving more and more people have varied. Each planning project needs at least one person who can remain in a position to work objectively with all groups which might help or hinder the program, as well as with those which might benefit from it. This person may fill the roles of stimulator, catalytic agent, educator, conciliator, and even mediator. Sometimes the resident natural leaders themselves effectively assume all, or most, of this responsibility. Often it is taken, at least for a time, by those who initiated the enterprise. The most commonly reliable way to nurture democratic growth of health planning is to have the *continuous* services of a specially qualified professional person. Examples include the experienced organizational workers in the over-all planning councils of Georgia and the Great

Plains; Virginia's rural sociologist; the social workers at Flanner House and Back of the Yards; and the health educators in Buncombe County, Cincinnati, Illinois, and Puerto Rico.

One procedure that all successful health planning bodies seem to have in common is a diligent search for the less conspicuous of the natural leaders. These are the behind-the-scenes leaders whose opinions often carry greater weight within their groups than those of people in more prominent positions. If they can be ferreted out and made interested in health planning, participation is apt to spread a good deal more naturally and more rapidly than otherwise. In Buncombe County four student health educators went into the highways and byways, talking with people, and trying to find their natural leaders. In the neighborhood Back of the Yards much the same sort of hunt was carried on in barroom conversations, at poker games, and so on.

Planning bodies first try to get leaders concerned about the seriousness of the existing health problems, and then try to interest them and their groups in joint planning and civic action. Some of the things that may move people to take part in such a civic project are: (1) recognition that serious problems exist; (2) certainty that they can be alleviated by an adequate health program; (3) evidence that the problems cost more than the solution; (4) confidence that the project is not a "lost cause"; (5) acceptance of individual responsibility to make democracy work; (6) feelings of religious obligation; (7) desire to render humanitarian service; (8) anticipation that the project will bring greater health security for the individual and his family; and (9) assurance that the help and the skills of the individual or group solicited are needed in the project and will be appreciated by the fellow workers.

Experience has shown that participation spreads on the basis of such motivations if the planning body operates democratically and if the planning body can effectively reach enough people and groups—whether by written invitation, by publication and broadcast, or by word of mouth.

Forming a Health Council

Discussion at the meetings of this Section of the National Health Assembly revealed a number of important points about when and how a permanent community planning organization may best be formed. Heroic national-level efforts to chart blueprints for community councils after the First World War proved of little avail. Thousands of councils, built to nation-wide specifications, were actually organized; but within two years nearly all of them had expired, for they did not really conform to the needs, desires, attitudes, prejudices, and population make-up of the individual communities on which they were imposed.

When and How to Set Up a Health Council

The best time to set up a permanent citizens' council is not when the only stimulus is a national-level directive or recommendation—and not when public interest extends only to members of the medical, health, and welfare professions—but rather when widely inclusive representatives of the area's lay and professional people have gone through the process of learning that they can work together creatively for the public good and have decided that the work requires a permanent organization.

Successful health councils may be called committees, boards, federations, associations, or any other name the people choose. They evolve naturally, through a process of group thinking, and their shape and form are based on the functions that the people expect them to fulfill.

In the long run, health councils do need to be integrated with broader social and economic planning bodies. Overspecialization in such fields as housing, family life, rural life, education, recreation, delinquency, welfare, health, nutrition, and medical care has led to an unrealistic separation of services. Piecemeal planning perpetuates this. What is needed is comprehensive planning, with all the special-interest groups joining forces. Thus the health planning in Georgia and in the neighborhood Back of the Yards is part of the over-all civic planning. The establishment of a health council, however, need not await the creation of a larger planning body. In fact, when an effective health council comes first, it may eventually serve as a springboard for the development of a broader citizens' council.

Functions of a Health Council

Meanwhile, it is with the actual functions of the health council that the organizers are occupied. Sooner or later each successful citizens' planning group finds that its health activities need to include all the following functions:

(1) The working together of representatives of the health and medical professions with representatives of the consumers of health services;

(2) The bringing together of all kinds of conflicting interests, since all have a common stake in the civic betterment of the state or community;

(3) The joint study, by broadly inclusive representatives of all the affected groups, of the prevailing health conditions and the ways in which these conditions affect each group;

(4) The determination of the health needs of the entire area, with continuous re-appraisals;

(5) The interpretation of the health needs, and of the work of the planning groups, to all who can be reached in the natural community;

(6) The education in pertinent public health matters of all who can be reached in the area;

(7) The promotion of widespread interest, participation, and leadership;

(8) The integration of health planning-and-action with over-all civic planning-and-action for the total program of social betterment;

(9) The integration of civic planning-and-action between the community, the state, the region, and the nation;

(10) The correlation, to avoid gaps and duplications, of all programs and services that affect health, whether they be environmental, preventive, or therapeutic;

(11) The promotion (a) of satisfactory health and medical services; (b) of good administration in public health departments, public hospitals, and other public medical facilities; and (c) of the recruitment and maintenance of adequate staffs of well-qualified people in such public agencies; and

(12) The development of various effective methods for carrying out the plans of the citizens' health council.

Structure of a Health Council

The actual structure of the organization is best determined by the people who are building it. Successful health councils are built for the direct advantage of all the citizens, not for the glorification of a few council members.

The planning group needs to consider carefully whether the major decisions are to remain with the entire group as a whole. If not, it must decide to whom it is giving the power and the responsibility for determining policy.

It is desirable that the chairman be a person acceptable to all groups in the area, a person vitally interested, a person of broad vision, and a person who is not employed by the official health department. The Virginia health planning group feels that its chairman must be a member of the medical profession; many other groups prefer non-medical chairmen. Whether the chairman is to be appointed or elected, and exactly what his duties should be, are matters for local decision.

Responsibility and leadership in the health planning project need to be widely spread. New Mexico's plan of dividing the duties of the health council's president among five persons is an example. The common practice of setting up divisional councils, standing committees, study sections, and so on is another example. This device helps solve the problem of how a large and seemingly unwieldy council may effectively draw on the talents and knowledge of its many participants.

Whether or not the health council has a health educator's help from the very beginning, the examples studied show over and over again the need for such a secretariat in the ultimate structure of the organization. The planning groups that specifically mentioned making provisions for hiring trained experts of this kind included those in Buncombe County, Cincinnati, Colorado, Georgia, Illinois, Miami County, New Mexico, and Virginia.

To summarize, a health council should be truly representative, democratic, functional, autonomous, and flexible. It should also allow for expansion and for ultimate affiliation with a more comprehensive citizens' council.

Financing a Health Council

Programs for citizens' planning and action necessarily involve reaching a great many people, whether in conferences, by letter, or through mass methods. As this work piles up it is going to cost money. A full-time person will ultimately have to be employed to travel up and down the area.

Successful state and local health councils have obtained financial support from a variety of sources, among them the following: the Federal allotments of state health departments; the state appropriations of state health departments or of state planning boards; direct state appropriations to the councils; charitable foundations; voluntary health agencies; community chests; contributions of interested individuals, committees, civic organizations, industries, and business firms; fund-raising campaigns, bazaars, and carnivals; and membership fees.

Sometimes the contributions appear as cash, sometimes as services and goods. The services of one trained employee, for example, were given to the Cincinnati health planners by the Anti-Tuberculosis League. The Illinois group was granted the loan of a full-time staff member and the use of virtually all the facilities of the State Health Department. Services and programs benefiting the common project were informally contributed to the Colorado group on the initiative of various civic organizations. In New Mexico and more notably in Kentucky, the planning councils received direct cash gifts from individuals, associations, and other groups. Flanner House received grants from the United States Children's Bureau. The Cincinnati group received moneys from the Community Chest.

However the funds are raised, the health council need not expect to achieve stability and continuity until it can have reasonable assurance of a permanent budget. In accepting contributions the health council will do well to see that there are "no strings attached," regardless of the source.

The need of self-government, or home rule, is shared by the entire natural community. For this reason it seems generally best for citizens' councils to be financed by contributions that come from within their own territory. Whenever a local group feels undue pressure from a state or national group there is apt to be some resentment. Even if the pressure is merely from the national offices of a single voluntary health agency to its own local unit, this resentment may spread through the local health council and possibly through the entire community. This is a problem which may need to be solved at the national level rather than in the states or communities.

Some citizens' councils feel, as did the Committee for Kentucky, that their autonomy is surer if they do not tie themselves to any governmental agency by accepting grants of public funds. Others feel that the tax funds and the government agencies belong to the people and that using them so far as they are available is a right of the people, a right which places the council under no obligation.

These are questions about which each health council will have to reach its own decisions in accordance with the democratic process.

Interpretation to the Public

Health councils undertake programs of publicity, education, and interpretation in order to increase public understanding, enlist wider participation and support, mobilize public opinion, and bring about in a democratic manner more satisfactory health conditions for the entire population.

Councils use the same communication lines that are employed by all who seek to reach masses of people. It does not follow, however, that health councils always rely on the particular methods which other groups find satisfactory. In the interests of clarity, brief working definitions of some of the common methods of disseminating ideas are here offered. Without attempting to give the full meaning of each term, these definitions point up the differences between them.

As used here, to *propagandize* is to spread particular systematized doctrines; to *advertise* is to proclaim desirable qualities in order to arouse a desire to purchase or invest; to *campaign* is to conduct a series of operations to bring about a desired result; to work at *public relations* is to seek to win public good will for an organization; to *inform* is to give news or factual data; to *publicize* is to spread information designed, or "slanted," to advance special interest; to *interpret* is to bring out the real meaning; to *teach* or to *educate* is to cause, or facilitate, learning; and to *learn* is to find out about and to gain knowledge and understanding.

Continuous programs of publicity and public relations are carried forward, both on a mass basis and on a more quiet person-to-person basis. Since it has usually been found unwise to make blatant appeals or exaggerated claims, the publicity is often geared to take advantage of the force of understatement.

When the time seems ripe for an intensive public appeal toward some immediate objective, a campaign is started. Care needs to be taken in the *timing* of such a campaign, so that it will reach its peak at a date when the desired results have a reasonable chance of attainment and so that the whole project will fit into the over-all pattern of civic affairs. For example, it is usually not wise to have many different area-wide citizens' campaigns going on at once. Nor would there be much use in launching a drive without sufficient backing or in bringing public interest to fever pitch months before the thing the people were interested in could happen.

In short campaigns of considerable urgency—voting a local tax levy, promoting legislation, or raising funds for the health council—planners sometimes use the high-pressure methods of the advertiser or the propagandist. Taking the long view, however, it is felt that lasting social benefits need to be built upon a solid foundation of public understanding. For this reason successful health councils prefer to rely at most times on the slower and more democratic methods of informing, interpreting, and educating. They try to adapt what they have to say about public health needs and plans to the level of each group of people they hope to interest in the work. They try to get all kinds of existing organizations—rural and urban, industrial and social, professional and lay—to help disseminate information. This is illustrated in the Virginia, Colorado, and Back of the Yards programs.

For the sake of a sound educational program, successful health councils often emphasize their efforts to get the guidance of full-time community health educators, to arrange for the further training of schoolteachers in health subjects, and to provide leadership training for their own volunteer workers.

The tools and communication lines that health councils use in publicity, education, and interpretation involve the usual written, spoken, and exhibit materials. They include newspaper articles, informational letters, contests, pamphlets, radio broadcasts, speakers' bureaus, public meetings, educational motion pictures, exhibits, and posters.

Studies by educators reveal that it is often difficult to find ready-made educational materials which are actually suited to the groups that use them. Some health educators question further the *educational* value of radio and the public press. Apparently there is need for a good deal of research on the efficacy and relative merits of all the known methods and tools of health education.

Difficulties and Hazards

Experience suggests that hindrances to democratic health planning are threefold: (1) complacency, (2) undemocratic methods, and (3) operational problems or mistakes.

Complacency. The first and foremost obstacle, the one which prevents civic planning from getting started at all, is an attitude of complacency, smugness, indifference, or apathy. One of the basic assumptions of this report is that the promotion of optimal health is a community responsibility. It is the duty of those who are already aware of the possibilities of health betterment to bring the need to the attention of their fellow citizens and to interest them in working together to improve the situation.

Undemocratic methods. The next impediment to dynamic planning for health is failure to build the citizens' project on a truly democratic basis. No matter how much lip service the planners give to the idea of a "people's program," they cannot really develop one, or win broad public understanding and support, unless they demonstrate in actual practice a sincere confidence in the judgment of an informed and truly representative citizens' group.

For example, this report has already cited the ineffectiveness of nation-wide blueprints for health councils. No preconceived and inflexible organizational structure for a citizens' group can be wholly democratic, even if it be designed locally. The successful planning council needs to take shape in accordance with the wishes of the people affected, the social problems which interest them most, and the functions they choose to have the council perform.

The appointment of leaders in the council on the basis of their social prestige rather than on the basis of widespread public confidence in their opinions about public affairs is another of the common deterrents to democratic planning. Key positions in the citizens' council need to be filled by leaders who are chosen for their interest and concern and not simply for the prominence they have achieved on unrelated grounds.

Also detrimental to the achievement of a broadly based people's movement for health betterment is the kind of health council that has a highly selective and largely professional membership, rather than a membership fully representative of all the groups whose health is concerned.

It is in restraint of civic planning, too, to fail to spread widely leadership, responsibility, and credit. To allow one person or group to "hog the credit" is to remove a valuable incentive to participation.

Domination of a citizens' planning body by any individual or group, regardless of the reasons, is a further obstruction of democratic participation. What is needed for a successful health council is the creative blending of group thought. Each time a powerful or dominant group manages to impose predetermined objectives and a ready-made program on the health council, the people whose lives will be affected are debarred from taking a hand in the planning. Such a program has little chance for active public interest, understanding, and support.

In addition to these hazards, there is always the possibility that a health council may retard its own progress through a hasty decision committing the council to a limited and inflexible program for some time to come. Any loss of flexibility may prove crippling.

Undemocratic planning will result in inability to win broad public confidence, to obtain all needed co-operation, and to gain full use of the various state or community resources that might otherwise have been available.

Operational problems. At the operational level, the success of the civic project may be threatened, or at least delayed, by making plans for action without adequate study and preparation. Failure to obtain correct facts and competent professional guidance is in itself perhaps the most calamitous single mistake a citizens' health council might make. Without accurate information and reliable advice, citizens' health plans build mostly air castles.

Air castles are not very functional in a health program. What is more, they tend to tantalize in a way that frustrates civic planning. For this reason, citizens find that planning over-ambitiously for unattainable objectives checks progress. After a few reasonable short-term objectives have been achieved, there is more likelihood of public interest and confidence in the slow pursuit of long-range goals.

One of the besetting problems that many health councils view as a block to planning is the universal shortage of funds and trained personnel for both public and private services in medicine and public health. Some groups, however, meet this problem by finding ways to get personnel trained while plans for the later use of the personnel move forward.

Failure to arrive at a satisfactory way of handling the problem of opposition to the health council is another handicap to civic planning. Sometimes the opposition can rather readily be won over. Sometimes it simply gives way because of the strength of the majority opinion that favors the council. More often, it requires constant and patient efforts to reach areas of agreement, a slow process of sympathetic interpretations.

Overappeasement of enthusiastic people who are uninformed and unwilling to be informed is also a hazard, for it may lead the health council to plan unwisely. Successful civic planning has to be based on the demonstrable needs of the state or community.

Citizens' planning may be fettered, too, by inadequate attention to timing. Much ground may be lost through disregard for the dates of the various scheduled governmental and civic activities into which the health council wants to fit its undertakings.

It is also dangerous to the planning project to "oversell" the work of the council or the benefits expected from it. Discreet understatement of the council's aims and position is likely to carry more weight in the long run.

One further way to put a curb on civic planning is to proceed without making due provision to circumvent any physical or psychological barriers that separate or isolate various segments of the population. If the council is to be truly representative it needs people from both sides of the mountain as well as from both "sides of the tracks."

Accomplishments of Health Councils

All successful health planning projects seem to have the following important achievements in common: (1) improved intergroup understanding; (2) broad lay and professional participation; (3) effective vertical co-operation; and (4) horizontal co-operation leading to (a) better use of resources, (b) correction of gaps and duplications in services and facilities, and (c) co-ordination.

What any particular citizens' health council can accomplish depends upon the problems it faces, how long it has been working, and what its members have chosen to undertake. The council is wise to define its over-all purposes in terms broad enough (1) to allow it to steer a course toward all the people's complete physical, mental, and social well-being; (2) to permit it to move on to new objectives as it fulfills earlier ones; and (3) to make possible its ultimate integration into a broader social and economic council, where it is not already formed in this manner.

If the health council operates in accordance with the principles set forth in this chapter, it may safely look forward to the attainment of each reasonable step-by-step objective pursued. Along the road, however, it will do well to keep the broad goals and purposes always in view.

Steps that successful groups have taken include, for example, the provision of rural health specialists for each of five Great Plains States, the training program in Puerto Rico, the institution of local recreation programs and youth councils in Georgia, the passage of Illinois legislation to make county health departments possible, the arrangement of a teachers' institute on mental hygiene in Miami County, and the development of a cancer control program in Cincinnati.

All successful health councils seem to share as a major accomplishment, in addition to the improving of the health situation, the reawakening of confidence in the democratic process. This confidence may be the most important contribution of the citizens' council to American society today. Where health experts may first have seen nothing but indifference and lethargy, the council helps people find ways to work together for the common good and leads them to accept and cherish their responsibility for government.

Life Expectancy of Health Councils

The successful civic council for health should—and does—continue to function as long as it is able to serve democratically the useful purposes that the people require of it.

How long this may be depends first of all upon what those purposes are. If they are of very limited scope and if the goals are fairly easy to attain, the council soon goes out of existence and with it the painstakingly constructed social machinery for civic action.

To ensure more lasting value for the machinery of the council, it is desirable to give early consideration to five major questions:

1. What unmet needs in the community or region still stand between the people and their complete physical, mental, and social well-being?
2. Does the council have sufficient scope and flexibility to build its long-range goals around meeting all of these needs; if not, how might this be arranged?

3. Is the health council part of a more inclusive social planning body; if not, how might such a co-ordinating over-all council be developed?

4. What further steps might be taken to guarantee that the program of the health council will at all times seek the help, and reflect the needs and wishes, of all groups in the affected population?

5. How can provision be made for the continuous services of full-time personnel specially trained in health education and community organization?

MAJOR RECOMMENDATIONS[2] CONCERNING DYNAMIC PLANNING FOR HEALTH

The Section on State and Community Planning for Health specifically recommends:

1. Development of regional, state, and local meetings along the lines of the National Health Assembly, with broadly inclusive lay and professional representation, and preferably with the addition of sections on school health, industrial health, and the prevention of farm and home accidents.

2. Encouraging the early formation of local and state health councils, where they do not now exist, for co-ordination of efforts. The pattern should be developed democratically and in accordance with the demonstrable needs of the area—rural as well as urban.

3. Making each health council a part of a broader social planning body. The council should be made up of individual civic leaders and of representatives of all agencies concerned with health. It should be truly representative of the entire state or community and should make full use of natural leaders.

4. Financing of health councils at the level at which they function, through contributions of funds or personnel from either governmental or voluntary sources, or both, but with the understanding that acceptance of the contributions will not in any way limit the councils as to program or action. With the occasional exception of certain rural counties or small communities, the provision of a permanent budget and the employment of a director trained in community organization and in public health are essential.

5. Co-ordination and co-operation of governmental and voluntary agencies at national, state, and local levels, with open channels of communication.

6. Dramatization of health needs by national governmental and voluntary agencies (a) through the use of all possible channels of in-

[2] See corollary recommendations in the section on "Facts and Resources" near the beginning of this chapter.

formation and (b) through locating and making available qualified persons to stimulate and advise local and state groups.

7. Stimulation of the recruitment and both pre-service and in-service training, by governmental and voluntary agencies, of professional personnel qualified to serve health departments and health councils in the work of community organization and health education; also stimulation of leadership training programs for volunteers in civic planning.

8. Assistance from national and state agencies, both governmental and voluntary, in the local development of demonstration areas or demonstration projects involving various types of social and health planning bodies, and in the local development of evaluation procedures to measure and perhaps compare the progress in health achieved through various types of civic planning and action.

The Section on State and Community Planning for Health recognizes that extension of preventive service and improvement of its quality necessarily involve increased costs. These costs, however, would amount to a mere fraction of today's economic losses from preventable illness. It believes that relative to other expenditures in the national economy too little is now expended in the preservation and maintenance of health. It recognizes that the necessity for increased expenditures must be understood and accepted by citizens as essential to the achievement of optimal health for all. It believes that state and community planning groups, councils, or committees, organized and financed on a permanent basis, offer a useful if not an indispensable means of accomplishing public recognition and acceptance of the soundness and value of expenditures for public health. In so far as this is accomplished it believes that funds will be forthcoming in the following ways: in an increased volume of tax funds at national, state, and local levels; in increased direct expenditures by individuals and families for preventive services of practicing physicians and health centers; in increased expenditures by employers; and from other sources.

TEN-YEAR GOALS IN DYNAMIC
PLANNING FOR HEALTH

The goals set by the Section on State and Community Planning for Health are:

1. Noteworthy progress by 1958 toward a widespread, well-informed public opinion leading to the establishment of habits, practices, facilities, laws, and services that make for the state of complete physical, mental, and social well-being.

2. Realization by 1958 of effective and functioning co-ordination among all governmental and voluntary organizations concerned with

health at the national level, and similar realization in many states and communities.

3. Development by 1958 of social and economic planning bodies, integrating health in its broader sense with their other planning functions, in each of the states and territories and in local communities.

4. Achievement by 1958, through civic planning and action, of essential public instrumentalities toward the specific ten-year health goals set up by each of the sections of the 1948 National Health Assembly.

APPENDIX

PLANNING COMMITTEE

Florence R. Sabin, M.D., *Chairman*	Chairman of the Committee on Health Governor's Post-War Planning Commission of Colorado
Mrs. Jean Ogden, *Vice-Chairman*	Associate in Adult Education Extension Division University of Virginia
Miss Rose Cologne	Specialist in Community Organization Central Extension Service Pennsylvania State College
John F. Conlin, M.D.	Director of Medical Information and Education Massachusetts Medical Society
Miss Ruth Freeman	Administrator, Nursing Service American National Red Cross
Charles S. Johnson	President Fisk University
Herschel W. Nisonger	Director Bureau of Special and Adult Education Ohio State University

STAFF ASSISTANTS

Mrs. Leona M. Culp	Special Consultant Office of Health Education Public Health Service, Federal Security Agency
Mayhew Derryberry	Chief, Office of Health Education Public Health Service, Federal Security Agency

Dean Snyder   Deputy Commissioner
                                             Office of Special Services
                                             Federal Security Agency

REGISTRANTS

Ernest R. Alexander, M.D.   National Association for the Advancement
                                                 of Colored People
Saul D. Alinsky   Executive Director
                                             Industrial Areas Foundation
Mrs. S. J. Axelrod   Health Chairman
                                             League of Women Voters
                                             Alexandria, Virginia
Cleo Blackburn   Superintendent, Flanner House
                                             Indianapolis, Indiana
Gordon Blackwell   Director, Institute for Research in Social
                                                 Science
                                             University of North Carolina
Andrew W. L. Brown   Congress of Industrial Organizations
                                                 Representative
                                             Detroit Council of Social Agencies
Bailey B. Burritt   Executive Director
                                             National Health Council
Mrs. Everett Butler   Health Chairman
                                             Illinois Congress of Parents and Teachers
Roland R. Cross, M.D.   Director, Illinois Department of Public
                                                 Health
Mrs. Anne Martin Crowell   Assistant Administrator, Volunteer Service
                                             American National Red Cross
Harold C. Fleming   Director of Information
                                             Southern Regional Council
Franklin Foote, M.D.   Executive Director
                                             National Society for Prevention of Blindness
W. E. Garnett   Rural Sociologist
                                             Virginia Agricultural Experiment Station
Mrs. William Goby   Illinois Home Bureau Federation
Miss Julia L. Groscop   Chief Consultant, Health Division
                                             Health and Welfare Council
                                             Philadelphia, Pennsylvania
Miss Hazel Halloran   Chief Social Worker
                                             St. Vincent's Hospital
                                             New York, New York
Randall B. Hamrick   Director, Community Advisory Service Center
                                             Bridgeport, Connecticut

Harry E. Handley, M.D.	Assistant Director Division of Public Health The Commonwealth Fund
Miss Anna Harrison	Chief Medical Social Worker Louisiana State Health Department
Marion Hotopp, M.D.	Director, Division of Maternal and Child Health New Mexico Department of Public Health
Hugh R. Jackson	Executive Director Public Charities Association of Pennsylvania
Mrs. Augusta Firth Jarman	Director, Service Program Virginia Division American Cancer Society, Inc.
Mrs. Eleanor H. Kerby	St. Louis, Missouri
Judge Paul T. Klapp	President, Western Ohio Mental Hygiene Council
Granville W. Larimore, M.D.	Director, Office of Public Health Education New York State Department of Health
Miss Elizabeth Lovell	Health Educator District Health Department Chapel Hill, North Carolina
Miss Catalina Lube	Supervisor of Health Education Santurce, Puerto Rico
Edward Mack	Acting Chairman of Health Committee American Veterans Committee
Mrs. Marion Lerrigo McWilliams	National Board Young Women's Christian Association
Arch Mandel	Program Director Community Chests and Councils, Inc.
Bleecker Marquette	Executive Secretary Public Health Federation Cincinnati, Ohio
Malcolm A. Mason	Rural Health Specialist Agricultural Extension Division Purdue University
Aubre de L. Maynard, M.D.	National Association for the Advancement of Colored People
William S. Meacham	Director, Virginia Council on Health and Medical Care
John Miller	Assistant Director National Planning Association
Miss Grace Mooney	Executive Assistant Connecticut State Medical Society

Miss Lucy S. Morgan	Professor of Public Health Education School of Public Health University of North Carolina
Miss Juanita H. Neely	State Home Demonstration Leader South Carolina State Extension Service
Mrs. H. B. Ritchie	National Deputy Commander, Field Army American Cancer Society, Inc.
Carl Sebelius, D.D.S.	Dental Division Tennessee State Department of Health
T. F. Sellers, M.D.	Director, Georgia Department of Public Health
Donald C. Smelzer, M.D.	Managing Director Germantown (Pa.) Dispensary and Hospital
Dean F. Smiley, M.D.	Consultant in Health and Physical Fitness American Medical Association
Elmer Starch	Executive Secretary Great Plains Agricultural Council
Miss Katherine Steinbecker	State Supervisor West Virginia Department of Education
Lon Sullivan	Director, Georgia Citizens Council
Robert B. Thomas, D.O.	President, National Osteopathic Association
Miss Margaret Tracy	Boston Health League
Clair E. Turner	Assistant to the President National Foundation for Infantile Paralysis
John Whitney, M.D.	Superintendent of Public Health Parish and City of New Orleans
Harvey Zorbaugh	Professor of Education School of Education New York University

《 X 》

Physical
Medicine and Rehabilitation

REHABILITATION is rapidly becoming an accepted part of our way of life. Originally identified with the needs of the war disabled, it has been gradually extended so that its benefits are now available for the larger requirements of the civilian handicapped. It has evolved from the idea of isolated and fragmentary activity on behalf of the crippled and the disabled to the modern concept of integrated and continuous service.

One of the deep disappointments of the Second World War was the discovery of the low state of physical fitness in the United States. It came as a distinct shock to the nation to learn that despite its high standard of living, between 35 to 40 per cent of its selectees for military service were rejected because they could not meet the standard physical requirements. In a pragmatic way, we met this problem by selecting and assigning the so-called physically unfit to man the defense factories and carry on the battle of production. The records of production achieved by that group of our population demonstrated most strikingly the tremendous potentialities of those with physical and mental limitations.

In spite of this overwhelming demonstration, "social prejudice" remains the greatest obstacle to the attainment of economic security and independence for our handicapped men and women. We know, from attempts to remove prejudices by philanthropy and voluntary means, that results remained comparatively limited until the Federal government instituted a broad Federal-and-state comprehensive program of special services to the handicapped. Until 1943 this program attempted to achieve its objective through education and training. With the passage of the Vocational Rehabilitation Act Amendments in 1943, physical restoration services were incorporated, thus broadening markedly the opportunities for handicapped individuals to make the most satisfactory adjustments of which they are capable.

The number of those with physical and mental disabilities who were rehabilitated during the past four years, 166,000, was both a triumph and a failure. In developing public recognition of the potentialities of the disabled, in developing public measures for removing and reducing the effects of disablement, and in the individual services which made this group income-producing instead of tax-consuming, our achievements were most gratifying. On the other hand, it was a failure in terms of the large segment of our population who are urgently in need of these services. Even accepting the minimum goal of 2 million disabled who require these special services, the ultimate aspirations and hopes of the disabled are far from being realized. These urgent needs point to the necessity for expanding our present programs for educating the public to a full realization of its responsibilities and of the infinite potentialities of our human resources and the contributions these men and women can make to the welfare of the nation.

This Section has been charged with the responsibility of exploring the rehabilitation measures and services available to disabled persons and to formulate certain principles which can be presented to the Assembly as a whole and, if accepted, may be broadcasted and brought to the attention of the entire nation.

Definition of Rehabilitation

As a means of entering into the first stage of developing program goals, it is fundamental to arrive at a common and uniform understanding of the term rehabilitation. The commonly accepted definition used by the National Council of Rehabilitation is:

Rehabilitation is the restoration of the handicapped to the fullest physical, mental, social, vocational, and economic usefulness of which they are capable.

It has become apparent that certain limitations are inherent in this definition. Briefly, the definition places emphasis on the process rather than on the individual, stigmatizes the individual as handicapped regardless of his accomplishments, and fails to stress the prevention of becoming handicapped as a result of a physical or mental disability. It should be pointed out that the element of prevention was confined to the serious problems of adjustment which might arise subsequent to disablement rather than to the prevention of disablement. The status of a disabled person is never static. If appropriate services are made available and satisfactory adjustment is attained, his disability no longer remains a handicap but becomes merely an inconvenience.

The following alternative definitions are presented in an effort to incorporate these basic principles and concepts:

Rehabilitation is a process helping the individual to recognize his limitations and assets and to make full use of the latter to attain the fullest physical, mental, social, vocational, and economic usefulness of which he is capable.

Rehabilitation is the process by which individuals faced with physical, mental, or social limitations may be assisted to develop to the fullest extent their physical, mental, social, vocational, and economic capacities.

Rehabilitation is assistance to those individuals who have a physical defect, obvious or hidden, which limits their physical capacity to work or evokes an unfavorable social attitude.

Rehabilitation is the process of overcoming any physical or mental limitation so that the handicapped person may attain the fullest physical, mental, social, vocational, and economic usefulness of which he is capable.

Rehabilitation is the process by which physical or mental handicaps are prevented or overcome.

Rehabilitation is the physical or mental restoration, or both, of an individual to the fullest economic usefulness of which he is capable.

Rehabilitation should be broadly conceived; it should be available to the mentally as well as the physically handicapped; it should not be confined solely to restoring individuals to employment but should be extended to include those who might achieve a more useful and purposeful life.

Need for Rehabilitation

Closely allied to this basic concept is the necessity for a wider understanding of the need for rehabilitation. The public is not yet aware of the fact that the so-called disabled person can be restored through the application of medicine, guidance, training, and related services. A process of education not only is necessary for the lay public but must be similarly directed to the medical, nursing, therapy, and allied professional groups. Some results might be achieved through more active participation of these professional groups and workers in the rehabilitation process. Nevertheless, our one great need is for increased facilities for information. Possibly some independent central agency at the national level might best be able to direct this needed process of education.

Approximately 50,000 persons a year are being rehabilitated through the Federal-and-state program. This is about one-fifth the number that are disabled each year either as a result of injury or disease or from congenital causes. The present program, in order to meet anything like the existing need, has to be increased about five times in size.

PROBLEMS OF THE DISABLED

Since frequent references are made to the numbers of disabled persons, it seems appropriate to give some consideration to the size of the problem. The prevalence of disability and the approximate magnitude of the size of our disabled population has been evidenced through several major sources. Careful analysis of data secured from the National Health Survey, Selective Service, and similar sources indicate that upwards of 23 million persons have some type of defect. If we consider disablement in relation solely to employability, then possibly at least 2 million persons are in need of such service.

General Census

Ways and means of attaining more accurate information about the number of disabled persons in our population must be developed. Any attempt to arrive at an accurate census would necessitate that every American be subjected to a physical and psychiatric examination. The impracticability of this approach is obvious. A second long-term approach might be legislation requiring physicians to report all disease and disabilities in a manner similar to that used at present in reporting communicable diseases. Such provision with regard to the blind has already been made in several states, but without achieving the results that were expected.

Although accurate and reliable figures are not now available for all types of disabilities, nevertheless sufficient information is available to conclude that:

(a) The number is staggering;

(b) The needs of only a small portion of the disabled are being met; and

(c) The needs of those already known could be better met if the nation would concentrate on more and better rehabilitation services and facilities to meet the known need.

The Physically Handicapped
A. Social Groups
(1) The Child

There still remains throughout the United States the tendency to define the crippled child as the orthopedically disabled. The need to broaden this concept is apparent. The scope of the term crippled child should be expanded to include children with all types of disability.

The almost complete absence of physical restoration, educational, and other services for children with disabilities other than orthopedic is emphasized. Reports indicate that only in a relatively few states have the programs for crippled children been extended to those other than the orthopedically disabled such as the visually handicapped, cardiac, and hard-of-hearing. Much latitude is left to the states as to the services to be made available and the types of children to be served by the state programs for crippled children. In this respect the Children's Bureau of the Federal Security Agency encourages the states to broaden their programs of services.

In spite of these efforts, physical restoration services are not available to all types of disabled children in many states. This Section of the National Health Assembly believes that physical restoration services should be extended into areas not now specifically identified in the Federal legislation to assure Federal financial participation in providing physical restoration services to school and pre-school children.

It is further suggested that the Children's Bureau be urged to define what can and what cannot be done for these groups under the provisions of the existing legislation and to keep the states fully informed. In other words, the scope of services and the types of disabled children to be served should be broadened to the fullest extent possible in the present program and re-defined for the state crippled children's programs.

In summarizing this the Section on Physical Medicine and Rehabilitation agrees that:

1. The use of the term crippled child should be discouraged because of its orthopedic, social, and other connotations.

2. In its stead we should think in terms of "children with disabilities," an all-inclusive term embracing children with all types of defects.

3. This concept should be incorporated into both public and voluntary plans and programs which are developed in the future.

(2) The Adult

(a) *The injured worker.* The subject of the injured worker was presented in the Section meetings in the form of a brief outline of the history and development of workmen's compensation programs. The chairman suggested that the group might wish to consider:

1. That a subsection on rehabilitation be established in each industrial accident commission, or

2. That a rehabilitation officer either be assigned or be made a member of the staff of each industrial accident commission.

3. That such methods be adopted as would insure closer co-operation between state rehabilitation agencies and state industrial accident commissions.

It is recognized that the industrial compensation programs cannot be completely revised and changed overnight. Perhaps no other type of legislation is so frequently revised and amended as that of workmen's compensation. There should be a shift in emphasis from compensation and litigation to rehabilitation.

Much progress has been made by industry in developing an interest and concern in the health of the worker. This is evidenced by industry's assumption of greater responsibility for the health of the worker through the provision of medical and rehabilitation services. In a few instances rehabilitation centers have been established to provide rehabilitation which assures a continuity of treatment from injury through convalescence, with more comprehensive placement services and opportunities for return to a suitable job.

Much remains to be done, however, to insure complete and adequate rehabilitation services to the injured worker. His problems demand much more information, study, recognition, and awareness on the part of industry, the medical profession, rehabilitation workers, and compensation officials. For example, some would say that compensation payments do not stimulate the worker to promote his own recovery. Others are of the opinion that the basic problem is one of emphasis and that if the major emphasis were directed by state industrial commissions toward rehabilitation of the injured worker such problems as the relation of compensation to recovery would be markedly reduced.

Three things which would tend greatly to improve the status of the injured worker are:

1. More clinical diagnostic services of the highest possible perfection to avoid errors of diagnosis.

2. Physical restoration—which is the largest missing link in the treatment of the industrially injured.

3. More comprehensive placement in safe, productive jobs suited to any residual temporary or permanent disabilities.

Physical restoration services have been insufficiently considered in the care of the injured worker. It is recommended, therefore, that all state workmen's compensation commissions consider the establishment of rehabilitation as one of their top-level divisions and that they accept responsibility for seeing that such services are made available to all injured workers.

(b) *The disabled veteran.* It is recommended that careful study be given to the programs of rehabilitation and the facilities and achievements of the Veterans Administration, the Army, and the Navy, in order that the body of knowledge, methods, techniques, and practices developed in these programs may be made available to disabled persons in the civilian population.

(c) *The chronically disabled.* Human beings are not fixed entities. They change, depending upon the treatment they receive and their own natural powers to get well. A hopeless picture of chronic disability can be changed into one of ability, but that does not change the original clinical concept of a chronically disabled person. These are the people who must receive treatment. All too frequently we hear, "Nothing further can be done; train around the disability," or, "One hundred per cent, total, permanent disability," and finally, through adequate services, such an erroneously classified, chronically disabled person can and is changed into an economic asset to himself and the community.

(d) *Other civilian disabled.* This category represents those who do not naturally fall into any of the previous categories and is included for the purpose of classification only. Therefore, it is felt advisable to formulate a broad topical grouping as follows:

B. Clinical Groups
  (1) Mentally and Emotionally Disabled
  (2) Orthopedic Disabilities
  (3) Neurological Disabilities
  (4) Other Medical and Surgical Disabilities
  (5) The Blind
  (6) The Partially Seeing
  (7) The Hard of Hearing
  (8) The Deaf
  (9) The Cardiac
  (10) The Tuberculous
  (11) The Epileptic
  (12) Cerebral Palsy
  (13) Other

REHABILITATION IN PRACTICE

This comprises the practical problem of providing the various services necessary for rehabilitation and the sources from which such services should be secured.

Physical Restoration

The scope of physical restoration should be broad rather than specific. Consideration must be given to integrating the services now available and determining what services need to be added to make rehabilitation complete. Although occupational and physical therapy departments have been available in many hospitals for years, there still remains an urgent need to integrate these services in the thinking and administration of the medical services. Where such services are available they should be administered by a physiatrist. In university hospitals provision should not be confined to the operating program but should be extended toward education and training, with major emphasis on rehabilitation as a total program for the patient's complete needs. Rehabilitation must function as a total program and not become a series of compartmentalized services.

A. Services: Hospitals, Rehabilitation Centers, Vocational Guidance, Training, Placement

At the present time too few hospitals have adequate departments of physical medicine. We look forward to the time when every hospital will provide facilities for physical medicine services.

Rehabilitation must start at the time of disablement and continue until such time as the individual is rehabilitated. It must be continuing and must embody a teamwork approach. This Section of the National Health Assembly emphasized that the entire range of rehabilitation services should be available to every individual. Whether or not these total services should be integrated into a single facility would depend primarily upon the way they are organized within the community.

The absence of physical medicine in our hospitals is due in part to the medical profession itself. There is an urgent need to raise the standards of physical medicine in the eyes of the medical profession. It should be recognized that physical medicine is not confined to the disabled but should be a part of all medical care.

Services	*Facilities*
What	Where

1. Physical and mental restoration
   Diagnosis, including consultation
   Dentistry
   Hospital care and treatment
   Nursing, institution and visiting
   Physical therapy
   Occupational therapy
   Speech therapy
   Appliances and mechanical aids
2. Social services
3. Education
4. Vocational counseling and training
5. Employment
   Placement services
   Regular industry
   Special employment
     Shops
     Home industries

1. Hospitals
2. Out-patient departments
3. Convalescent and nursing homes
4. Schools—Regular
         Special schools or classes
5. Special centers
   Curative
   Special shops
   Rehabilitation centers

All rehabilitation facilities must have medical supervision.

B. Personnel

In attempting to describe the various types of services it is strikingly apparent that one of our major needs is that of personnel. Without sufficient trained personnel the services cannot be provided nor the facilities manned. We can have buildings and equipment, but these do not mean a thing unless we also have adequate numbers of trained personnel for the teams.

In terms of the size of the problem, it has been estimated that 50,000 physical therapists will be needed by 1960. On the other hand, the capacity of our training institutions does not exceed 600 students, and less than 500 are graduated each year.

A similar deficiency exists in facilities for training occupational therapists. Approximately 1,500 persons are enrolled in existing facilities, and about 400 are graduated annually.

The need for personnel is by no means confined to these two fields. Instead it is equally applicable to all the professional fields that make up the rehabilitation team. The major handicap to providing rehabilitation to our handicapped men and women and children at this time is insufficient personnel and inadequately trained personnel. The Section on

Physical Medicine and Rehabilitation recommends that all institutions of learning assume responsibility for meeting these needs.

The question has been raised as to whether the scarcity of personnel is due primarily to the lack of training facilities or to the low salaries and unattractiveness of the various types of jobs. Both are factors. Low salaries have been one of the basic problems, particularly in attracting persons in the various therapies and counseling. On the other hand, we find a tremendous interest on the part of the students in these fields; as a result, with more applicants than training facilities, those who cannot enroll soon lose interest and enter other fields. More training facilities would be established if financial aid were available. These facilities cannot be financed solely from tuition.

There also remains the need for educating and orienting our entire medical and hospital personnel to recognize the values of these various services, thus creating a sufficient demand to warrant the payment of adequate salaries.

It is recommended that:

(1) All medical schools include a department of physical medicine;
(2) Universities and colleges accept the responsibility of training teachers, counselors, social workers, and other non-medical personnel;
(3) Non-medical personnel be given essentially professional recognition and independence; and
(4) Salaries be adjusted to make these fields sufficiently attractive to recruit competent personnel.

NATIONAL PROGRAM

Public and Private Agencies; Community and Professional Responsibility

This Section has been asked to think about the role of public and private agencies in the rehabilitation field, and of community and professional responsibility for the rehabilitation of the disabled.

The program of the Office of Vocational Rehabilitation of the Federal Security Agency and the state programs of vocational rehabilitation are not the only rehabilitation agencies in the public field. Other public programs must be noted, such as the crippled children's program of the Children's Bureau and the program for disabled veterans in the Veterans Administration.

Great strides have been made during past years in bringing together public and voluntary agencies and utilizing to the fullest the facilities of both for complete and adequate rehabilitation of the disabled. There still are lapses in the facilities available. Much needs to be done to increase and co-ordinate co-operation between both types of agencies. Co-ordination on national, state, and local levels is indispensable. Co-ordination should extend into all fields—it should exist, for example, for disabled children as well as for adults.

The co-operative agreements or working relationships developed between public and voluntary agencies have spearheaded a unique development in rehabilitation. One of the outstanding lacks in the public rehabilitation program is the dearth of facilities operated by government for providing all necessary services. Through the co-operative agreements this lack is met to some degree.

The attitude toward the severely disabled has undergone a radical change. Whereas in the past they were almost entirely neglected, now they are getting greater consideration. Rehabilitation of the severely disabled will always be difficult. On the other hand, their rehabilitation presents a real challenge to the individual himself and to the rehabilitation worker, the agency, and the community. As we perfect our techniques in each phase of rehabilitation this Section hopes we can extend them to the severely disabled.

The role of the voluntary agency in publicizing the need for adequate state expenditures for rehabilitation was emphasized. Voluntary agencies should take this leadership because of the difficulties faced by public agencies in attempting to do so. The need for adequate state as well as Federal finances must be emphasized.

Every community has employers, manufacturers, and industries that are and should be vitally interested in rehabilitation. The interest of these elements in the community should be enlisted. This includes financial interest as well as personal interest. During the war many industries were forced to employ disabled individuals. To the surprise of their employers, they were often found to be as capable as the non-disabled when properly placed. Responsibility for selling industry on the capacities and abilities of the disabled should be borne by all public and private groups.

The President's Committee on National Employ-the-Handicapped Week also will make the effort to find ways and means to influence employers to employ the disabled. The importance of selecting the right job for the disabled individual who has been adequately trained cannot be too strongly urged. It is necessary to bring the proper employee to the right employer.

Another aspect of co-operation between the public and voluntary agencies involves the matter of research in the development of prosthetic appliances. Questionable practices with respect to charges for prosthetic appliances have been noted and the principle has been expressed that any practice which increases the cost of rehabilitation for the individual should be denounced.

The rehabilitation centers, community facilities, and rehabilitation services should be made available to all the disabled in the state. The question as to whether rehabilitation centers should be operated on a government or a voluntary basis has been raised, and the opinion has been expressed that there should be Federal government financial support but not government direction.

The importance of physical medicine and rehabilitation cannot be overemphasized—it offers a tremendous field for conserving the industrial and occupational man power of the nation. Beyond this lies the recognition of the *inherent* value of the individual, regardless of whether he is ever going to be able to earn money.

RECOMMENDATIONS

The Section on Physical Medicine and Rehabilitation makes the following recommendations:

1. Rehabilitation should be broadly conceived, should be available to the mentally and physically handicapped, and should not be confined solely to the restoration of persons to employment but be extended to include those who might achieve a more useful and purposeful life.

2. A program of Federal assistance through grants-in-aid should be extended to:

    (a) Assist universities and colleges to develop and strengthen opportunities for the professional training of rehabilitation personnel.

    (b) Assist states to:

        (1) Inventory their existing rehabilitation, physical medicine, and workshop facilities;

        (2) Survey the need for the establishment of rehabilitation, physical medicine, and workshop facilities; and

        (3) Develop programs for the establishment of needed public and nonprofit facilities.

    (c) Assist states to provide a broader financial basis for the establishment and maintenance of needed rehabilitation, physical medicine, and workshop facilities. Federal financial assistance should be available not only to establish new facilities when needed but also to enlarge or expand those few which now exist.

(d) Assist universities, non-profit research institutions, and governmental agencies to develop and encourage research in rehabilitation methods, techniques, and prosthetic devices that will contribute to the rehabilitation of all types of disabled persons.

(e) Assist each state to conduct a study to determine the size, nature, and characteristics of its disabled population and determine those who need rehabilitation.

3. Educational standards for training and employment of rehabilitation personnel should be those of the professional groups concerned and the appropriate accrediting agencies.

4. A general program of education and information should be carried on to encourage young persons to select some one of the professions in the field of physical medicine and rehabilitation.

5. Each disabled child should receive adequate diagnosis, treatment, and after-care in accordance with his rehabilitation needs to insure him the opportunity for optimum development.

6. National, state, and local organizations and agencies—both public and private—engaged in various aspects of rehabilitation should exchange information, co-ordinate their activities, and work co-operatively to the end that the individual who is disabled may receive the kind and quantity of attention, care, and training necessary to rehabilitate him to the limit of his capacity.

7. A program of public education and information including all media should be developed to its fullest extent in order to educate workers and the general public with respect to what is being done and what should be done in the field of rehabilitation.

8. All hospitals should provide services of physical medicine.

9. All medical schools should include instruction in physical medicine.

10. The idea of isolated and fragmentary activity on behalf of the physically handicapped should be developed into a dynamic concept of integrated and continuous service.

APPENDIX

Planning Committee

Henry H. Kessler, M.D., *Chairman*	President, National Council on Rehabilitation
Miss Bell Greve	Secretary, International Society for the Welfare of Cripples

William H. Bayne, Jr.   Editor, *Handicap* Magazine

Dudley A. Britton   Director of Medical Relations
                                         American Mutual Insurance Company

Josephine Buchanon, M.D.   Physiatrist, Woodrow Wilson Rehabilitation
                                                Center

Charles Carll   Director, Public Relations
                                         Ford Motor Company

Miss Mildred Elson   Executive Secretary
                                         American Physical Therapy Association

N. W. Faxon, M.D.   Director, Massachusetts General Hospital

Mrs. Margaret Pope Hovey   Pope Foundation

STAFF ASSISTANTS

A. William Reggio, M.D.   Chief, Physical Medicine and Rehabilitation
                                                Section, Hospital Division
                                         Public Health Service
                                         Federal Security Agency

Donald H. Dabelstein   Assistant Director
                                         Office of Vocational Rehabilitation
                                         Federal Security Agency

REGISTRANTS

Lt. Ralph Anslow   Gwynedd, Pennsylvania

Miss Alice O. Booth   Supervisor, Prevention of Blindness
                                         Commission for the Blind
                                         New York State Department of
                                                Social Welfare

Mrs. Virginia Smith Boyce   Administrative Assistant
                                         National Society for Prevention of Blindness

Carroll L. Bryant   Director, Water Safety
                                         American National Red Cross

William McGill Burns, D.D.S.   Trustee, American Dental Association

John W. Chenault, M.D.   Director of Orthopedic Surgery
                                         Tuskegee Institute

Miss Tracy Copp   Member of Board of Directors
                                         Rehabilitation Center
                                         Green Bay, Wisconsin

John J. Corson   Manager in Charge of Circulation
                                         Washington *Post*

Donald A. Covalt, M.D.   Clinical Director, Institute of Physical
                                                Medicine and Rehabilitation
                                         New York University

Mrs. Caroline Elledge	Medical Social Faculty Montreal School of Social Work McGill University
Oliver A. Friedman	Executive Director Goodwill Industries of America
Ben H. Gray	National Director American Epilepsy League, Inc.
Stanwood L. Hanson	Assistant Vice-President Liberty Mutual Insurance Company
Miss Thedine Hedges	Editor, *Spastic Review*
Miss Susan Hendricks	Welfare Board Prince Georges County, Maryland
Holland Hudson	Director, Rehabilitation Service National Tuberculosis Association
Glenn E. Jackson	Executive Director, Orthopedic Appliance and Limb Manufacturers Association
H. Worley Kendell, M.D.	President, American Congress of Physical Medicine
Robert H. Kennedy, M.D.	Chairman, Committee on Fractures and Other Trauma American College of Surgeons
Mary E. Kent, M.D.	Assistant Director Employee Health Section American Red Cross
Berthold Lowenfeld	Director of Research American Foundation for the Blind, Inc.
Robert L. Maynard, M.D.	Surgeon in Chief Fracture Service Mary Fletcher Hospital Burlington, Vermont
Carl M. Peterson, M.D.	Executive Secretary Council on Industrial Health American Medical Association
Rev. Carl R. Plack	Institutional Chaplaincy Consultant Division of Welfare National Lutheran Council
F. Ray Power	Director of Vocational Rehabilitation States Rehabilitation Council Charleston, West Virginia
Jerry C. Price, M.D.	Secretary, National Association to Control Epilepsy, Inc.

Philip G. Rettig   Director, Research and Legislative Service
                            National Society for Crippled Children and
                                Adults, Inc.

Peter J. Salmon   Chairman, Legislative Committee
                            American Association of Workers for the
                                Blind

R. R. Sayers, M.D.   Chairman, Medical Advisory Board
                            Welfare and Retirement Fund
                            United Mine Workers of America

Col. John N. Smith   Director, Institute for the Crippled and Dis-
                                abled

Miss Louise M. Suchomel   Assistant Consultant
                            Joint Orthopedic Nursing Advisory Service

Miss Margaret Taylor   Director, Public Health Nursing
                            School of Public Health
                            University of Minnesota

R. C. Thompson   Director, Vocational Rehabilitation in Mary-
                                land

William B. Tollen   American Veterans Committee

Miss Hedwig B. Trauba   Supervisor Nursing Services
                            Division of Services for Crippled Children
                            University of Illinois

James Weer   Personnel Manager
                            Koppers Company, Inc.

Miss Catherine Worthingham Director of Technical Education
                            National Foundation for Infantile Paralysis

Miss Betty C. Wright   Director, Field Service
                            American Hearing Society

❨ XI ❩

What Can Be Done
to Improve Dental Health?

IN a discussion of the dental health of the American people at the time
of the National Health Assembly, consideration was given to the nature
and prevalence of dental diseases, as well as to the resources available
for the control of these conditions. The various oral conditions which
must be dealt with as a part of the dental health problem are diseases
of the teeth (mainly dental caries), malocclusion and other anomalies
and deformities, traumatic injuries, periodontal diseases and other oral
pathoses. Dental diseases afflict more than 90 per cent of the people; the
need for dental health service begins early in life and accumulates into
a backlog of unmet needs as children become adults.

NATURE AND PREVALENCE
OF DENTAL DISEASES

Dental Caries

Dental caries is the greatest cause of loss of teeth during the early part
of life, and carious lesions accumulate many times faster than they are
corrected. As high as 50 per cent of two-year-old children have one or
more carious teeth. By the time children reach school age they usually
have three or more primary teeth which have been attacked by dental
caries. When the average person is sixteen, he has seven decayed, missing,
or filled teeth, involving fourteen tooth surfaces. The percentage of
children with decayed, missing, and filled teeth increases up to fifteen
years of age. O'Rourke[1] has predicted that, because of the high incidence
of dental diseases, particularly dental caries, it is highly probable that
unless adequate preventive or control measures are provided today's
children will lose half of their natural dentition before they reach the

[1] J. T. O'Rourke, "Dental Care for Children in Relation to Geriatrics," *Journal
of the American Dental Association,* 34:595-604 (May 1, 1947).

age of forty, and about 40 to 50 per cent of them will have no natural means of mastication by the time they are 60. A child of today, with average life expectancy, will need his dentition 42 years longer than the average child of the sixteenth century.

The average white adult has more than 0.4 of a tooth extracted or indicated for extraction per year between the ages of eighteen and seventy, or approximately one tooth for each 2½ years of adult life. It is noteworthy, as Klein[2] has pointed out, that the rate at which the teeth are extracted or indicated for extraction is related to the socio-economic status. For instance, the average white person at age eighteen has 29.8 serviceable teeth. A tooth in serviceable condition at age eighteen in a person of the $3,000-or-more income group may be expected to remain in serviceable condition, on the average, approximately 34 years longer. However, at the same age, a comparable tooth in a person at the less-than-$2,000-a-year income level may be expected to give on the average only about 31 additional years of service.

Malocclusion and Malformations

Facial deformities resulting from abnormal arrangement of the teeth, accidents to the teeth, and such anomalies as cleft lip and palate and impacted teeth also are evident in a large number of children and adults. Such malformations have been shown to influence the incidence of dental caries. For instance, in a study by Bruckner,[3] 19 per cent of 1,668 children had true malocclusion (malocclusion of either the primary or permanent teeth), and in them 29 per cent of the total number of cavities was recorded.

In a recent article, Brandhorst[4] reported that, of 119,000 students between the ages of five and twenty-nine years, 52 per cent were recorded as having some type of dental anomaly. Seventeen per cent of children five to six years of age had teeth which showed some deviation from normal, whereas 71 per cent of those in the twelfth grade (seventeen to eighteen years) had malocclusions.

Messner and associates[5] reported that a study in twenty-six states

[2] Henry Klein, "Tooth Mortality and Socio-Economic Status—Life Tables for Teeth," *Journal of the American Dental Association*, 30:80-95 (January 1, 1943).

[3] Marcu Bruckner, "Studies on the Incidence and Cause of Dental Defects in Children; IV: Malocclusion," *Journal of Dental Research*, 22:315-321 (August, 1943).

[4] O. W. Brandhorst, "Will Orthodontics Become a Part of Contemplated Government Health Programs for Children?" *Journal of Dental Education*, 10:138-143 (February, 1946).

[5] C. T. Messner, W. M. Gafafer, F. C. Cady, and H. T. Dean, *Dental Survey of School Children, Ages 6-14 Years, Made in 1933-34 in 26 States*, Public Health Bulletin 226, May, 1936.

indicated that approximately 9 per cent of children between the ages of six and eight years were in need of orthodontic treatment and that approximately 11 per cent of children between the ages of twelve and fourteen were in need of such treatment. Approximately 24 per cent of children had slight malocclusion, and approximately 11 per cent had severe malocclusion.

The most reasonable data indicate that a cleft (or clefts) appears in one of every 800 births and that the condition is more common in males than in females.[6]

Other Oral Pathoses

Diseases of the gums and supporting structures of the teeth are mainly responsible for the loss of teeth in later years.

Vincent's infection has been found to occur in approximately 31 per cent of persons up to the age of seventy years.[7] Tuberculous oral lesions are observed infrequently and occur, as a rule, in far advanced pulmonary tuberculosis.[8] In a study of ten areas in the United States, according to a Public Health Service report, the incidence of buccal cancer (primary site) was 22 per 100,000 in white males and 5 per 100,000 in white females.[9] The deaths per 100,000 white population from cancer of the buccal cavity were 9.0 in males and 1.5 in females.

CONTROL OF THE DENTAL HEALTH PROBLEM

The resources for the control of dental health may be considered in relation to the four basic problems in this field: (1) the causes and treatment of dental disease; (2) the low level of dental health education; (3) the inability of the individual to pay for adequate dental care; and (4) the shortage of dental personnel. A comprehensive program to meet these problems—research, dental care, health education, and training of dental personnel—raises another problem, that of finance.

[6] L. G. Grace, "Frequency of Occurrence of Cleft Palates and Harelips," *Journal of Dental Research,* 22:495-497 (December, 1943).

[7] F. H. Daley, "Incidence of Vincent's Infection: Conclusions Based on a Study of Three Thousand Seven Hundred and Seventy-One Smears and Case Histories," *Journal of the American Dental Association,* 18:1025-1028 (June, 1931).

[8] Council on Dental Health, American Dental Association, "The Role of the Dentist in the Detection and Control of Tuberculosis," *Journal of the American Dental Association,* 36:218-220 (February, 1948).

[9] H. F. Dorn, "Illness from Cancer in the United States," *Public Health Reports,* 59:33-48, 65-77, 97-115 (January 14, 21, and 28, 1944).

Causes and Treatment of Dental Disease

Underlying the problem of dental care is the obvious fact of dental disease and its causes and treatment. No sound approach to the dental health problem can neglect an attack through research on the fundamental causes of diseases of the oral cavity. In consideration of a research program, it is well to bear in mind the fact that dental disease is the most universal of diseases. Its effects have far-reaching economic as well as physical consequences. In 1948, approximately a billion dollars was spent by the American people for the treatment of dental conditions, and this care represented only a small part of what was actually needed. In addition, wage losses and lost production caused by absenteeism resulting from dental defects amount to many millions of dollars yearly in this country. In view of the magnitude of the loss which the American public suffers annually from dental diseases, it could well afford to spend a greater part of the amount of its annual estimated losses due to dental diseases in an attempt to find the causes.

The most logical and effective means of ultimately bringing better dental health to the American people is by means of adequate dental services for children. Gerrie[10] has expressed the opinion that, if dental health programs are developed for the youngest age groups and continuity of care is provided thereafter, an accumulation of defects is impossible and the maintenance of an optimum condition of health, comfort, appearance, and function throughout the period of childhood will result. The broadest possible application of recognized preventive and control measures should be made early in life so that the later needs for dental services are reduced to a minimum. The solution obviously lies in improvement—through research—of methods for preventing dental diseases and in the development and maintenance of school and community dental health programs.

Beginning with the age of three years, the child should have proper and thorough prophylaxis at least twice a year, followed during the periods of eruption of teeth by a series of applications of a solution of sodium fluoride. From the evidence at present available on the basis of mass treatment of children with a fluoride solution, it appears that by this means a 40 per cent reduction in the caries attack rate of children less than sixteen years of age may be achieved. The benefits to accrue to adults from current incompletely tested research on this treatment, however, cannot be evaluated accurately at this time.

[10] N. F. Gerrie, "Standards of Dental Care in Public Health Programs for Children," *American Journal of Public Health*, 37:1317-1321 (October, 1947).

With regard to communal water, which naturally contains sodium fluoride, the evidence indicates that the DMF (decayed, missing, filled teeth) rate is approximately 60 per cent lower in children aged twelve to fourteen years who, throughout life, have ingested water containing about 1.0 part per million of fluorides. Studies designed to test the efficacy, safety, and practicability of adding sodium fluoride to community water are now under way in several communities.[11]

Early and periodic dental examination is an important measure for the prevention and control of dental caries. Another consideration is diet and nutrition, but, because of differences of opinion concerning the relation of nutrition to dental caries, further research in this field is necessary. It has been established, however, that the ingestion of carbohydrates plays a role in the predisposition to, and the development of, dental caries. Other measures to be considered in caries prevention and control are the inclusion of caries-inhibiting elements in the diet and the administration of antibiotics and other chemical agents. X-ray examinations and restorations also are important aids in the prevention and control of dental caries. The requirement for routine extractions should decrease as better measures for caries control are instituted. Since the proper placement of fillings prevents the extension of caries, the loss of teeth may be reduced by adequate care, even though the incidence of caries is high. The need for pulp management also should be decreased with better caries-control techniques.

Since it is becoming more and more evident that the genetic factor is the major etiologic determinant of occlusion, malocclusion probably will increase with further intermingling of racial characteristics. Although the better preservation of primary and young permanent teeth should have beneficial results, nevertheless an increase in orthodontic treatment should be planned for the future.

Impacted teeth and congenital anomalies involving the teeth probably will continue at their present rate if heredity is a determining factor. Likewise, oral clefts appear to be familial, about 50 per cent being explainable on this basis. In the prevention of harelip or cleft palate, prenatal care of the parent is a factor through the control of venereal disease. This may also be a factor in the prevention of malformations in the fetus. Accidents to the jaws probably will increase, as will the number of dental pulps exposed by trauma.

[11] Council on Dental Health, American Dental Association, "The Michigan Workshop on the Evaluation of Dental Caries Control Technics," *Journal of the American Dental Association,* 36:3-22 (January, 1948).

Preventive orthodontics should include maintenance of the primary teeth in a healthy condition, the use of space maintainers for missing teeth, maintenance of the normal contour of all teeth and proper contact between the teeth, and observation of the growth and development of the teeth and jaws. Control of habits which result in malocclusion and malformations of the teeth and jaws is important.

For the prevention and control of the various diseases of the gums and supporting structures, periodic and routine dental examinations and general physical examinations are indicated. Better preservation of the teeth may be expected to lead to somewhat better gingival health, but this gain may be offset by an aging population. Since more persons are now reaching the age of sixty to sixty-five years and more, there has been a proportionate increase in the need for the prevention and control of periodontal diseases. Consequently it may be anticipated that in the future a greater share of the time of the dentist and his auxiliary aides will have to be diverted to dental care such as scaling, polishing, occlusal adjustment, and education of the patient.

The necessary medical laboratory examinations should be undertaken to establish the diagnosis in cases of suspected systemic diseases. It is not uncommon for the mouth to present the first symptoms of some underlying systemic disease. Frequently consultation with a physician is indicated to differentiate lesions of systemic origin from those of local origin. The first signs of diseases such as syphilis, tuberculosis, diabetes, blood dyscrasias, hyperthyroidism, Addison's disease, metastatic malignant lesions, nutritional disturbances, and other conditions may be observed in the oral cavity. Although the treatment of oral lesions is secondary to general management of a systemic disease, the eradication of oral infection and restoration of an impaired masticatory apparatus is important.

Low Level of Dental Health Education

The problem of dental health cannot be solved on the basis of care of disease alone but must be attacked also from the standpoint of public health education and psychologic and economic factors. The low level of dental health education is closely related to the inability or unwillingness of the individual to pay for such services.

The development of a thoroughly functional program of dental health education should eliminate to a large extent such psychologic factors as procrastination, indifference, and fear. There seems to be general agreement that dental health education needs to be strengthened and adapted so that it will reach all groups and stimulate them to put dental knowledge into practice. The content and method of presentation of dental health education programs today should be examined critically and revised in the light of present-day knowledge and experience. Dental health education intelligently planned and skillfully applied would contribute a general knowledge of what constitutes good dental health and how it may be attained and maintained and would stimulate public interest in and appreciation of dental health.

Inability to Pay for Adequate Dental Care

Some of the economic factors involved in the problem of payment for and a more equitable distribution of dental services, regardless of the level of income and density of population, should be solved by an intensified program of dental health education and dental research. These two measures alone, however, cannot completely solve a problem which has a multitude of facets and is the responsibility of the individual, family, community, state, and nation. The participation of Federal, state, and local governments in the financing of studies on how best to provide dental care for low-income groups will do much to solve this economic problem.

Shortage of Dental Personnel

The fourth major problem is that of the shortage of dental personnel. The economic law of supply and demand is inexorable, and thus this problem also is closely related to dental health education. Because in the past the demand for service was limited, the number of students entering dentistry likewise was limited. The shortage of dental personnel, therefore, will pose one of the greatest problems in the field of the delivery of dental care if the demand continues to increase. The dentists are now seriously overworked and will continue to be so, at least as long as the present era of prosperity lasts.

It has become increasingly apparent to those working in the field of health-program planning that an immediate problem is how more dental personnel can be trained to provide service. From the appraisal of dental personnel, it is impossible to escape the conclusion that the physical facilities of the forty dental schools which are training dentists are appreciably less than optimum at the present time. The present limitations seem to consist of the inadequate physical plants, equipment, teaching aids, and materials; limitations of the teaching staffs; and inability of many students of proved ability to pay for a dental education.

Many school faculties fall below an effective teacher-student ratio because of the limited number of trained dental teachers and, perhaps to a greater extent, because of the low level of salaries paid to the teachers. There is need for training and opportunities which will attract men and women interested in research. The advantages to undergraduate education arising from intimate association with research programs and basic science teachers interested in research should not be overlooked.

The number of dentists in the United States in 1947 was roughly 78,500, and on the basis of an estimated population the number of persons served by each dentist averaged 1,817. It is estimated that this ratio in 1960 will remain approximately the same.

Estimates of the extent of accumulated dental disease for the entire population and its annual incremental increase reach astronomical proportions. It has been said that only approximately a fourth of the carious tooth surfaces that develop each year are treated and that the remainder are unfilled. Two-thirds of the untreated teeth must be extracted because of the extensiveness of the carious process. Klein[12] has said that the total yearly crop of dental need in the whole American population requires for its service at least double the present volume of dentistry man power. This estimate was based on the assumption that if complete dental service were available all people would apply for it. Such a demand for service is of course extremely unlikely.

The methods for enlarging the scope of services provided by auxiliary dental aids are still in the developmental stage. Currently the demand for dental hygienists appears to exceed the supply, but desirable ratios of dental hygienists to the population and to dentists have not yet been definitely established. The same may be said with regard to dental laboratory technicians.

Because of the difference between the ideal and the practical aspects of the problem, as represented by the needs of the American people compared with their demand for dental care and their ability and willingness to pay, a desirable ratio of dentist and of auxiliary dental personnel to the population cannot be determined categorically. The demand for dental care fluctuates from year to year, and no arbitrary desirable number of dentists or of auxiliary personnel can be determined academically.

[12] Henry Klein, "Dental Needs Versus Dental Manpower," *Journal of the American Dental Association,* 31:263-266 (February, 1944).

CONCLUSIONS

The Dental Health Section of the National Health Assembly, after considering the present status of dental health in the United States, the dental health goals to be attained, and the resources at the disposal of dentistry, concluded that a program for the achievement of such goals in the next decade should be based on the following principles:

Principles for Dental Health Programs

1. *Research.* Adequate provisions should be made for research which may lead to the prevention or control of dental diseases.

2. *Dental health education.* Dental health education should be included in all basic educational and treatment programs for children and adults.

3. *Dental care.* (a) Dental care should be available to all persons, regardless of income or geographic location, as rapidly as resources will permit. (b) Programs for dental care should be based on the prevention and control of dental diseases. All available resources first should be used to provide adequate dental treatment for children and to eliminate pain and infection for adults. (c) Dental health is the responsibility of the individual, the family, and the community, in that order. When this responsibility is not assumed by the community, however, it should be assumed by the state; or, failing that, by the Federal government. The community in all cases should determine its methods for providing service.

4. *Participation in program planning.* In all conferences that may lead to the formation of a plan for dental research, dental education, and dental care, there should be participation by authorized representatives of the dental profession.

Goals for Dental Health Programs

Goals to be reached during the next decade through these principles are:

(1) Prevention of dental diseases through the application of effective preventive techniques

(2) Control of dental diseases by making dental treatment and dental health education available to every child as rapidly as resources will permit

(3) Increased facilities for dental care in all hospitals and health centers

(4) Improved distribution of dentists between urban and rural areas and an increase in the number of qualified dental practitioners

(5) Training and utilization of additional auxiliary personnel—dental hygienists, dental assistants, and dental technicians

Specific recommendations for the achievement of these goals are:

Research. The Federal government should make provision immediately for expanded research in the field of dental health. The Federal government also should make funds available for administrative research in order to plan and conduct studies and experimental programs in selected communities for evaluation of various types of dental care programs for such groups as school children, the indigent, low-income groups, and residents of rural areas. Such programs should include various types of voluntary prepayment plans, part-payment programs, preventive care programs, and the development of various methods for providing dental care to children on different economic levels.

A commission should be created to define more explicitly the standards for dental health care.

Dental health education. Further experimentation on the part of all agencies in the techniques of dental health education is essential so that authoritative dental health facts can be selected and interpreted in understandable terms for all levels of society. Additional courses in dental health education should be provided in all institutions which train personnel for the fields of health and education.

Dental health services. The dental profession should utilize to the fullest extent the following measures of prevention and control, together with such extensions as advancing dental science may reveal:

(a) Routine dental prophylaxis and periodic examinations;
(b) Topical applications of sodium fluoride;
(c) Utilization of diagnostic aids, such as lactobacillus counts;
(d) Completion of all indicated dental treatment;
(e) Full utilization of preventive orthodontics; and
(f) Development of programs to combat the environmental hazards associated with certain occupations.

Financing dental health care. When indicated by needs established at the local level, the Federal and state governments should participate in the financing of dental health programs. In all cases the local communities should determine the policies governing such programs.

Federal compulsory health insurance should not be employed as a means of providing dental health care.

Dental personnel. To offset the current shortages of dental personnel in the United States, Federal aid should be granted to dental schools in the form of scholarships and fellowships, and dental schools should be operated at full capacity. Federal grants should be made available to all accredited dental schools for the construction and equipment of dental facilities and for assistance in maintenance, operation, and research. Federal aid should not supplant but should augment state, regional, and private support of dental schools. In all cases, Federal grants should not imply any form of intervention in the management or control of the recipient institution.

Encouragement should be given to the admission of qualified Negro students to dental schools, and an effort should be made to expand the opportunities for Negroes to secure dental education.

Additional courses should be established for the training of dental hygienists, assistants, and technicians under the auspices of accredited dental schools or other educational institutions operated on a non-profit basis.

In any program for the procurement of additional dental services for the population, the present high standards of dental practice should not be reduced.

RECOMMENDATIONS

The specific purposes of the Dental Health Section as suggested by Oscar R. Ewing, Federal Security Administrator, when he called the National Health Assembly, were:

To consider the need for dental health services and methods of closing the known gap between needs and dental care; the number of dentists and auxiliary personnel required, the existing provisions for recruitment and training of such personnel, how they may be augmented, and how better geographic distribution may be effected; and what measures are necessary to bring about an expansion in dental research and in the facilities for conducting such research.

To meet these objectives, subcommittees composed of six or seven persons each studied the following subjects:
(1) Dental health problems
(2) Prevention and control of dental diseases
(3) Dental health education
(4) Public dental health programs
(5) Financing dental health care
(6) Status of dental personnel

The following recommendations, submitted respectively by the sub-committees charged with the study of the subjects indicated, were adopted by a majority vote of the Dental Health Section:

Dental Health Problems

1. That a committee be developed from representatives of the American Dental Association, American Association of Dental Schools, American Association of Public Health Dentists, and the Federal health agencies concerned, to secure a well-supported statement of the standards for adequate dental care.

2. That legislation be initiated and promoted similar to S.178, a bill to supply funds for setting up administrative research programs in the application of defined standards of dental care to children and in the evaluation of the efficacy of dental health education techniques to promote the attainment of these standards.

3. That present information about the size and character of the dental health problem be increased and that, in order to reduce the size of this problem, bill H.R. 574 (S.176), the Dental Research Bill, be enacted into law without delay.[13]

4. That, since the continuous appraisal of available scientific information and the preparation of periodic statements of well-considered scientific recommendations for the extension of existing dental services require permanent machinery, an adequately financed commission be developed to function co-operatively for such study and appraisal and the periodic reporting of conclusions and recommendations. Such a commission should consist of representatives of the American Dental Association, American Association of Public Health Dentists, American Public Health Association, American Association of Dental Schools, International Association for Dental Research, and the Federal health agencies concerned.

Prevention and Control of Dental Diseases

1. That the best currently known methods of dental care be recommended for implementation as far as dental personnel will permit.

2. That dental facilities be made available to all persons and that the provision of such facilities be supported by Federal grants-in-aid or state funds wherever necessary. The administration of these facilities, however, should be placed on a community basis at the lowest feasible level.

[13] On June 14, Public Law 755 was passed by the 80th Congress. This act provides for a National Dental Research Institute, with an appropriation of $2,000,000 for a building and $750,000 annually for operations and grants-in-aid for research projects at dental schools and other institutions.

Dental Health Education

1. That provision be made for organized continuous planning for dental health education at national, state, and local levels in such a way that all agencies which have a vital interest in dental health education may participate as creative co-operators.

2. That the problem of dental health education be approached through study, experimentation, and demonstration; that provision be made for a study to determine the reasons for prevailing dental health attitudes, understandings, responses, and practices; that dental health education techniques be developed to bring about changes in the attitudes of individuals and communities to achieve dental health goals.

3. That authentic dental health facts be selected, clarified, and interpreted in understandable terms for all age levels.

4. That provision be made in dental, medical, and nursing schools for the development or expansion of courses designed to give a better understanding of health education in relation to the total development of the child and also of courses designed to give understanding of school, community, state, and national dental health programs.

5. That provision be made for the development or expansion of courses in teachers' education programs, both pre-service and in-service, which will prepare school administrators and teachers for effective participation in dental health programs.

6. That information and authentic data on dental health education be included in teachers' education programs, with the proper emphasis on standards, guides, and evaluation criteria developed by official agencies.

7. That provision be made for the development, distribution, and continuous evaluation of dental health teaching aids.

8. That ways and means be developed of financing dental health education on national, state, and local levels.

Public Dental Health Programs

1. That the following dental health goals be adopted:

(a) The prevention of dental diseases through the application of preventive techniques as soon as they are demonstrated to be scientifically valid; the support of intensified dental research with adequate funds, personnel, and facilities.

(b) The control of dental diseases by the initiation and expansion of community dental plans and, through private practice integrated with the general health program, the provision of dental care and dental health education to every child, regardless of income or location as far as possible. These programs should be maintenance programs centered on the control of the annual increment of new dental disease in children.

(c) The provision of additional facilities and uniform standards for dental care by making dental services available in hospitals and health centers for in-patients and out-patients.

(d) The recruitment of an annual enrollment of dental students equal to the capacity of all dental schools, in order to increase the number of qualified dentists.

(e) The adoption of measures to make dental practice in smaller cities and rural areas more attractive and rewarding, in order to procure a better distribution of dentists.

(f) The employment of hygienists and other auxiliary aids to the dentist; the provision of adequate training courses and facilities for the preparation of hygienists as auxiliary dental aids, within prescribed legal limitations, and of additional courses for those who desire to qualify for positions in public health departments and schools.

2. That the principles as previously outlined under CONCLUSIONS and the following objectives be adopted:

Objectives: Dental health is known to affect the general health, appearance, and social adjustment of a person throughout his lifetime. Since the control of dental caries and other diseases of the mouth can best be accomplished during childhood, the following objectives are recommended:

(a) Help every American to appreciate the importance of a healthy mouth.
(b) Help every American to appreciate the relationship of dental health to general health and appearance.
(c) Encourage the observance of dental health practices, including personal care, professional care, proper diet, and oral habits.
(d) Enlist the aid of all groups and agencies interested in the promotion of health.
(e) Correlate dental health activities with all generalized health programs.
(f) Stimulate the development of all resources for making dental care available to all children and youth.
(g) Stimulate all dentists to perform adequate dental health services for children.

3. That the following programs of activity be continued and further developed to completion:

(a) Program for elementary and secondary schools
(b) Dental care plan for low-income groups
(c) Experimental prepayment dental plan
(d) Legislation for the establishment of a Dental Research Institute
(e) Legislation for a program of grants-in-aid to assist states in developing dental health programs

(f) Caries control program

(g) Councils on dental health in dental societies at state and local levels and their co-operation with lay groups

(h) Standards for dental services in hospitals and health centers

(i) Co-operation between the Veterans Administration and the dental profession to provide dental services for veterans

(j) Research and experimentation with the use of fluorine in water supplies and applied topically for the prevention of caries

(k) Preparation and dissemination of authentic dental health education material and the promotion of educational programs on the national, state, and local levels

(l) Elevation of standards of dental education in order to supply highly qualified dental personnel

(m) Initiation of dental health programs for expectant mothers and pre-school children

4. That the responsibility for dental health programs be as follows:

(a) *Organized dentistry.* The responsibilities of organized dentistry are but a part of the pattern which includes the responsibilities of the individual, family, community, state, and nation. The dentist, both as a citizen and as a member of the profession, has obligations at all of these levels, but collective responsibility for individual health must be the basis of any sound public health program. Organized dentistry, representing a group of dentists bound together by common professional objectives and ideals, has definite responsibilities: to develop policies to guide society in the dental aspect of health service programs, to make those policies articulate for all its members and for the public, and to act as the connecting link between official and quasi-official bodies which have the authority and resources to make professional policies work in the interests of the whole society.

(b) *Community responsibilities.* Co-operative planning and a co-ordination of effort among the many independent local health agencies are fundamental in the development of an efficient and comprehensive community health service. When local health councils are provided with competent personnel, necessary funds, and able guidance, they have demonstrated an ability to obtain this co-ordination of activities. Health councils, which are made up of representatives of official health departments, voluntary agencies, hospitals, and medical and dental associations, are most common in cities of more than 250,000 population. Although many such councils are ineffective, their failure is generally traceable to an incompetent staff and lack of funds. Even under voluntary leadership in the smaller communities, health councils may make valuable contributions to improve health service.

(c) *Government responsibilities.* Programs for the promotion of dental health were from the very beginning originated by the dental profession, and dentistry's social obligation is still to guide the dental phases of social change into a sound basic pattern. A dental health program should be divided into two parts, national and local. The national aspects should be concerned with research, education, broad policies, and financial assistance. Efforts at the local level should consist of appraising the dental needs of the community and then requesting consultation and integration with the state and Federal health agencies.

Financing Dental Health Care

1. That the recommendations of the American Dental Association on the Dental Research Bill be adopted by the Dental Health Section of the National Health Assembly as a first step in a research program. It is further urged that this body recognize that the amount requested for this initial program of research would doubtless prove inadequate, and it is recommended that this amount be increased as rapidly as the results of research in this field indicate the feasibility of expanding the program.

2. That funds be made available, through the Federal and state governments to agencies working under or in conjunction with the American Dental Association, to plan and conduct a series of detailed studies to determine the content of several types of dental programs designed to meet several known problems—for example, school programs, programs for low-income groups, programs for the indigent, and programs for the rural population. It is further recommended that experimental programs be put into operation in selected communities to evaluate the various types of dental care programs—for example, voluntary insurance plans for children or programs for all age groups, programs for preventive care, programs for various methods of providing care to children on different income levels, and part-payment programs.

3. That the Section on Dental Health of the National Health Assembly go on record as approving and encouraging the participation of Federal, state, and local governments in the financing of health care programs. It is further recommended that, in any program financed by the Federal government, the state and local communities participating in the program have a voice in the determination of the policies governing the program.

4. That Federal, state, and local funds be made available, through public health agencies and educational agencies, to carry out a comprehensive program of dental health education.

Status of Dental Personnel

1. That the forty existing dental schools in the United States be administered at maximum capacity consistent with sound educational principles.

2. That additional dental schools be established in areas of demonstrated need and as integral parts of universities qualified educationally and financially to sustain them.

3. That encouragement be given to the establishment of additional courses for the training of dental hygienists, dental laboratory technicians, and dental assistants, under the direction of accredited dental schools or other accredited educational institutions organized and operated on a non-profit basis.

4. That Federal grants for scholarships for undergraduate students in accredited dental schools be awarded for merit through state educational authority on the basis of population.

5. That Federal and state grants be provided for the support of fellowships to graduate students in accredited dental schools, such fellowships to be awarded on merit and directly through the schools.

6. That Federal funds be provided to aid accredited dental schools and new schools established on equivalent levels in the construction of buildings and in the installation of equipment.

7. That Federal funds be provided to aid accredited dental schools in maintenance and operation costs.

8. That additional Federal grants be provided to accredited dental schools and other acceptable institutions for research.

9. That Federal grants be made for the purpose of providing greater opportunities in postgraduate education for dental practitioners in the United States.

10. That Federal support be made available for studies of dental needs and dental personnel on a state and regional basis throughout the United States, under the auspices of or in conjunction with the American Dental Association.

11. That Federal subventions as proposed above should not imply Federal intervention in the management and control of the recipient institutions.

12. That financial aid at the national level should not be considered as supplanting but rather as augmenting state and regional private support. This is equitable in view of the regional service rendered by the institutions and in the interest of preserving the responsibility for sponsorship and support by the private and state government agencies that have maintained them.

13. That encouragement be given to the admission of qualified Negro students to dental schools, and that an effort be made to expand the opportunity for Negroes to secure dental education.

14. That if dental care of the annual increment of dental disease of children is contemplated in the next decade, new methods and techniques be studied and investigated. Such methods and techniques must not lower the standards of dental service in this country, and the studies must be made by and in conjunction with the American Dental Association.

Federal Compulsory Health Insurance

The Dental Health Section voted to record its opposition to Federal compulsory health insurance as a means of providing dental health care. Since it is essential to complete co-operation that the possibility of governmental regimentation of the dental profession be ruled out, and since an extension of adequate dental health services to the entire population depends on such co-operation in all groups concerned, this Section also voted to recommend:

1. That the Federal health agencies indicate convincingly to American dentists that regimentation will not be attempted.

2. That Federal health agencies be consolidated into a separate autonomous division of government under the direction of an individual trained in the health sciences.

State Laws Governing Hygienists

The Dental Health Section voted that the American Dental Association be requested to undertake a study of the prevailing state laws governing the practice of dental hygiene, with the idea of making suggestions for the revision of those laws so as to increase the usefulness of hygienists to meet the increased needs for dental care.

APPENDIX

PLANNING COMMITTEE

Ernest G. Sloman, D.D.S., *Chairman*	Dean, School of Dentistry College of Physicians and Surgeons San Francisco, California
P. E. Blackerby, D.D.S.	Director, Division of Dentistry W. K. Kellogg Foundation
Mrs. Charles D. Center	National Congress of Parents and Teachers
Allen O. Gruebbel, D.D.S.	Secretary, Council on Dental Health American Dental Association
Harry Lyons, D.D.S.	Richmond, Virginia

STAFF ASSISTANT

John W. Knutson, D.D.S.   Chief, Dental Health Section
                                 States Relations Division
                                 Public Health Service, Federal Security
                                 Agency

SUBCOMMITTEE CHAIRMEN

The Dental Health Problem; Nature, Prevalence, and Relations of Dental
  Diseases:
Kenneth A. Easlick, D.D.S.   Professor of Public Health Dentistry
                                 School of Public Health
                                 University of Michigan

Status of Procedures for the Prevention and Control of Dental Diseases:
Theodore Kaletsky, D.D.S.   Editor
                                 New York State Dental Journal

Status of Dental Health Education:
Miss Annie Taylor   Educational Director
                                 Division of Dental Health
                                 Atlanta, Georgia

Public Dental Health Programs:
Walter A. Wilson, D.D.S.   Trenton, New Jersey

Financing Dental Health Care on an Individual and Public Basis:
Melvin Dollar   Executive Director
                                 Group Health Association
                                 Washington, D. C.

Status of Dental Personnel:
Harold J. Noyes, D.D.S.   Dean, Oregon Dental School
                                 University of Oregon

REGISTRANTS

George M. Anderson, D.D.S.   Baltimore, Maryland
Ira D. Beebe, D.D.S.   Chairman, Dental Health Council
                                 Connecticut State Dental Society

Otto Brandhorst, D.D.S.   Dean, School of Dentistry
                                 Washington University
D. W. Brock, D.D.S.   St. Louis, Missouri
M. D. Clawson, D.D.S.   President
                                 Meharry Medical College

Miss Hazel V. Dudley   Director, Division of Public Health Nursing
                                 Connecticut State Department of Health

Clifton O. Dummett, D.D.S.   Dean, School of Dentistry
                                 Meharry Medical College

L. A. Gerlach, D.D.S.	Director, City Dental Program Milwaukee, Wisconsin
Jasper A. Hennigar, D.D.S.	Greenwich, Connecticut
Miss Margaret H. Jeffreys	Director, Oral Hygiene Dover, Delaware
Leon R. Kramer, D.D.S.	Director, Division of Dental Hygiene Topeka, Kansas
R. C. Leonard, D.D.S.	Chief, Division of Oral Hygiene Maryland State Department of Health
Manley Michaels, D.D.S.	Washington, D. C.
Donald H. Miller, D.D.S.	Elmira, New York
John W. Ross, D.D.S.	Philadelphia, Pennsylvania
Leo J. Schoeny, D.D.S.	New Orleans, Louisiana
Alfred Seyler, D.D.S.	Director, Children's Clinic University of Detroit
R. M. Walls, D.D.S.	Bethlehem, Pennsylvania
Miss S. Virginia Wilson	Extension Nutritionist State College Station Raleigh, North Carolina
Carl Wilzbach, D.D.S.	City Health Commissioner Cincinnati, Ohio

⟨ XII ⟩

A National
Program for Mental Health

THE Mental Health Section of the National Health Assembly concentrated its attention on:

Assessing existing resources of facilities and personnel;
Determining the most urgent needs for developing a nation-wide mental
  health program;
Indicating lines of action leading toward the goal of adequate services and
  facilities to serve all our people.

Prepared papers and general discussion pointed up the problems in these areas.[1]

Discussion in the Mental Health Section stressed the inseparability of mental health and total health. The Section's chairman therefore requested that a representative of the Mental Health Section meet with the other sections of the Assembly—especially those concerned with areas in which emotional factors have been found to play an important role— such as the Sections on Hospital Facilities, Health Centers, and Diagnostic Clinics, on Chronic Disease and the Aging Process, and on a National Program for Maternal and Child Health. Statements of the psychiatric aspects of these various health problems will be found in the reports of the respective sections.

The Section on a National Program for Mental Health, in making its final recommendations, decided to consider the total question of mental health from two points of view:

The role of individuals—other than those in the mental health professions—
  in improving the mental health of large numbers of our population. These
  include pediatricians, nurses, teachers, and so on.
Problems in providing adequate facilities and services in psychiatry and
  closely allied professions.

[1] See Appendix A at the end of this chapter.

297

Separate subcommittees were established to consider these two areas. Their reports, together with their recommendations on the various needs to be fulfilled, as approved and adopted by the Section, are set forth below.

The salient facts considered by both subcommittees in making their reports were summarized and presented to the General Assembly by the Section's chairman, as follows:

SUMMARY OF FINDINGS AS PRESENTED
TO THE GENERAL ASSEMBLY

A. Incidence
1. Most individuals have minor emotional disturbances often not recognized but of *medical* significance.
2. Many productive persons continuously maintain a chronically neurotic adjustment.
3. From 30-60 per cent of all patients who consult doctors do so primarily for complaints due to emotional disorders. Many of these are expressed as symptoms of "physical" disorders.
4. Emotional factors are present in the majority of physical illnesses and may be of importance in treatment.
5. Psychological factors are of great importance in adjustment to physical handicaps and in convalescence and rehabilitation.
6. Statistical evidence indicates that one out of every 20 persons will need psychiatric services for severe emotional illness during his lifetime.
7. Over half the veterans now in veterans' hospitals are psychiatric patients.
8. One million or 6 per cent of all admissions to Army hospitals were psychiatric.
9. One out of every 8 men examined for the draft was turned down because of personality problems.
10. Thirty-seven per cent of all medical discharges in the Army were for psychiatric disorders; 51 per cent of all separations from the military service (718,286 men) were due to some form of personality disturbances.
11. On any one day, the mentally ill constitute about half of all patients in hospitals in the United States.

B. Personnel Problems
1. Currently there are 5,000 psychiatrists; the current pressing need is estimated at 15,000.
2. Most mental hospitals have one physician to about 300 patients; many have only one to 1,000 patients.
3. In 1948 there were 1,635 psychiatrists in state hospitals; six times as many physicians are needed for state mental hospitals as are now on duty.
4. Thirty-five per cent of all psychiatrists are in private practice; this means that there is one psychiatrist to 140,000 persons (compare this with the current ratio of one physician to 750 persons).
5. Several states have no psychiatrists except those located in state hospitals.

6. Of the total of 317,800 nurses in the nation about 5,500 work in psychiatric hospitals. This means that 1.1 per cent of all *practicing nurses* take care of about 50 per cent of all hospital beds.

7. There are now 1,000 qualified psychiatric social workers. Ideally there should be one psychiatric social worker per 10,000 population, indicating a total current need for 14,500.

8. At least 40 per cent of the billion-dollar Federal health budget and about one-fourth of the state budget for health is spent in the area of mental illness.

9. We need four times as many child guidance centers as we now have.

C. Psychiatric Facilities

1. The status of our approximately 200 state hospitals is one of America's most dire medical situations. The percentage of overcrowding in all state hospitals for the United States taken as a whole is 16.3. In some states it is as high as 50 per cent.

2. A minimum of 100,000 additional beds are immediately needed for severely ill mental patients.

3. Six hundred community psychiatric clinics exist. There is a current need for approximately three times this number. Twenty-five states have no type of psychiatric clinic.

4. Only nine adult criminal courts and an estimated twenty juvenile courts have psychiatric counsel.

5. Not more than fifteen of our universities and colleges have adequate psychiatric student counseling.

6. Psychiatric services in prisons and reformatories exist little more than in name.

D. Psychiatric Research

1. Total money spent for medical research, as estimated in the Steelman Report, is $110,000,000 annually; a liberal estimate of moneys spent in psychiatric research is between two and three million.

2. Sixty-five dollars is spent in medical research to every $2,500 in industrial research.

3. In 1942, only 37 out of 613 non-governmental medical institutions professed to do any research in psychiatry.

FINDINGS AND RECOMMENDATIONS

Non-Psychiatric Aspects of the National Mental Health Problem

The chief responsibility for the prevention of mental ill health lies primarily not with the psychiatrist but with the public at large. Clergymen, teachers, lawyers, social workers, nurses, recreation and group workers, law enforcement officers, public health personnel, representatives of management and labor, and many others are constantly presented with opportunities for recognizing emotional problems. They see emotionally disturbed people long before the specialists—or even the general physicians—do. They can become helpful by learning the principles of mental health while on the job and in the actual technical training for their specific fields, as well as by consultation with organized psychiatric groups.

In view of the shortage of personnel in the psychiatric professions, it is particularly important that the potential contributions which other groups can make to the mental health of the nation be fully explored and utilized. In discussing how to do this, your committee covered three broad areas:

Psychiatric orientation of individuals in professions other than the mental health disciplines to enable them to deal with the opportunities which come their way for promoting mental health in their daily activities.

The recognition that man's cultural environment affects his mental health; also the encouragement and development of community resources and leadership to improve and conserve the mental health of all people in the community.

The promotion of a program of public education designed: to remove major misconceptions regarding mental illness; to develop sound public understanding of the nature, treatment, and prevention of mental illness; to stimulate active public support of mental health programs.

Development of Mental Health Skills in Individuals in Professions Other than the Mental Health Disciplines

Persons who are not trained in the mental health professions but who can contribute much to mental health include: public health personnel; general physicians and specialists other than psychiatrists; nurses and other hospital personnel; social workers, including probation officers and staffs of institutions for delinquency and dependency; vocational placement counselors and rehabilitation staffs; management staffs in industry; shop stewards in labor unions; lawyers and judges; clergymen and religious educators; teachers and recreation and group workers; law enforcement officers and others in public services; volunteers in citizen participation groups.

In nearly all these fields there are leaders who have sound mental hygiene viewpoints and who can be depended upon, with proper backing, to continue the contribution to mental health which they have already made and to promote action. They are the case finders. They are also the most potent mental hygiene educators of the public.

Many persons in these fields, however, are not yet fully aware of their opportunities for furthering the mental health of people; nor, if they become aware, are they technically equipped to take advantage of such opportunities. Their formal training has not prepared them to apply mental health principles to their everyday work as a part of the service they normally render.

To help remedy this situation, your committee makes the following recommendations—first, as to methods for psychiatric orientation; and, second, as to organizations and agencies that are in a position to initiate and develop orientation activities:

A. Methods for Psychiatric Orientation

1. For persons in professions other than the mental health disciplines

(a) Conferences with mental hygiene specialists: to exchange information; to develop a better understanding between members of the psychiatric and non-psychiatric professions; and to plan next steps for action. Such conferences already have been held, for instance, for the Protestant clergy, for specialists in internal medicine and pediatrics, for recreation leaders, and for counselors in industry.

(b) Mental health institutes. These might be experimental, such as the one already conducted at the University of Minnesota for general practitioners; or they might be organized for regular application designed to serve a restricted area—perhaps employing a flying team of teachers.

(c) Mental hygiene consultation. Both the social work and public health nursing fields already are making wide use of specialized mental hygiene consultants. Other fields, including education and jurisprudence, could well increase such activity.

(d) Clinical training. This is now included in some of the schools for clergymen.

(e) Workshops—i.e., study groups working under experienced leadership with special projects in the field. Many universities have effectively used this device with teachers. It could also be effectively used in normal schools in the training of teachers.

(f) Postgraduate and extension courses.

2. For students in professions other than the mental health disciplines

(a) Courses dealing with the dynamics of human behavior, by psychiatrists in adjacent areas.

(b) Field work in the type of organization these students may later work in—supervised by a person in their own specialty who has a sound understanding of mental hygiene principles.

3. For schools offering training in non-psychiatric fields

(a) Review of pre-professional and professional curricula to see that mental hygiene concepts are woven into all aspects of the basic training and not just superimposed as new courses on the old structure.

(b) Selection of students who, because of their own high level of mental health, will maintain the best standards of their profession.

B. Organizations and Agencies to Conduct Orientation Activities

1. Federal Security Agency. Because it is one of the major Federal agencies concerned with health, welfare, and education, we recommend that the Federal Security Agency, in co-operation with the voluntary mental health organizations, be responsible for initiating, developing, and promoting the above orientation program.

2. Professional groups. Since the co-operation of the organized professional groups—physicians, teachers, and others—is essential to this undertaking, it is further recommended that steering committees for each of these professions be appointed to work with mental health personnel in activating the orientation program.

Role of the Environment and Mental Health

Man's cultural environment—his social reality—determines to a considerable degree his chances for the satisfaction or frustration of his individual needs. It has a great deal to do with the quality and extent of his self-fulfillment. It determines in large measure the balance between self-expression and the demands of social conformity and social responsibility. Recognizing this, psychiatrists are increasingly concerned not only with the nature of the individual's personality defenses but also with the social situation in which he operates.

Mental health is more than the absence of disease. Mental health clearly means that an individual has found a reasonable measure of peace within himself and with his environment—it means that an individual is able to pursue reasonable, purposeful goals; may use his capacities and talents fruitfully; experiences a sense of security, of belonging, of being respected; has a knowledge that he is liked, or loved, and wanted; has self-respect and self-reliance; has a sense of achievement; has an opportunity for new experiences and adventure. Mental health also means that an individual has learned to respect others, to accept others, and to live with others.

But man's health is very much at the mercy of what goes on about him. Unemployment, prejudice and discrimination, failure to share the civil liberties guaranteed to all citizens, inflation, inadequate medical care, delinquency, lack of housing, the threat of atomic war and world destruction—these are very real everyday problems, and they are the kind of social factors that can wear away the personality defenses and destroy mental health.

Your committee recommends the following steps that might be taken to reduce the severity of environmental factors that affect mental health:

1. Governmental and non-governmental agencies should concentrate efforts on combating the social ills which threaten mental health. To this end we urge full implementation of the recommendations contained in the President's Report on Civil Rights as well as vigorous programs to provide adequate housing and to fight inflation.

2. National, state, and local organizations should make their membership aware, through educational programs and other media of communication, that many aspects of a community's social, economic, and political life have a direct bearing upon the mental health of the community.

3. Communities should set up over-all voluntary community councils which are broadly representative of all major sections of interest (community officials; business, labor, and professional groups; religious groups; minority groups; women, youth, and veterans; civic agencies; and so forth). While an objective community survey probing into the relationship of mental health to all aspects of the social, economic, and political life of the community would be most desirable, it is recognized that for many communities such an undertaking is not immediately possible. However, the suggested community council can serve as a voluntary fact-gathering body and can publicize its findings. Such a council should inaugurate and maintain a continuous program of community education which, while it may employ all media of communication, will be primarily centered around small group discussions. For it is primarily through small group discussions that people in the community can best define the problems they face—consider their origins, implications, and connection with other problems; weigh carefully various proposals for solving them; select the solution which is most likely to succeed in that community; and map out a constructive civic action program.

4. We recommend that the Federal Security Agency undertake a study to establish a valid set of criteria for community surveys of the type recommended above. Such a study should be directed by appropriate personnel from the various social science disciplines.

5. We also recommend that the organized psychiatric bodies make available continuous consultation services to national, state, and local organizations whose program directors seek guidance in the preparation of educational materials and action programs dealing with community life and mental health.

6. We further recommend a joint-discipline approach (psychiatrists, psychologists, sociologists, anthropologists, social workers, and so on)

to study in greater detail the inter-relationship between the social, economic, and political aspects of our culture and our mental health.

General Public Education

A major stumbling block to progress toward better mental health lies in generally prevalent, popular misconceptions about mental ill health. There is a great need for developing sound public understanding of the nature, treatment, and prevention of psychiatric disorders and for stimulating active public support for, and use of, sound mental health programs. This is a responsibility which can be carried out by governmental, private, and commercial agencies at the national, state, and local levels. We recommend that:

A. On the National Level

1. All national agencies (governmental, volunteer, professional, and commercial) dealing with any aspect of mental health should co-operate with each other by exchanging information and plans and by arriving at mutual decisions as to which organizations can most effectively assume responsibility for different portions of the total effort. This voluntary association, or council of representatives of national agencies, should not be a policy-making body. Its decisions should not necessarily be binding upon the separate agencies. It should be a flexible, exchange, and planning group whose purposes would be determined by the needs and problems currently arising.

2. The Mental Health Act provisions for disseminating sound mental health principles and information should be fully utilized.

3. The Public Health Service, since it administers the Act, should be the clearing house for all public educational materials bearing on mental health produced by national groups.

4. There should be consultation with authorities in the field of mental health. Principles and problems should be made available to those directing the media of mass communication—radio, films, press, and others. Public and private agencies dealing with mental health—including the National Committee for Mental Hygiene, the American Psychiatric Association, and the Division of Mental Hygiene of the Public Health Service—should work together to develop a plan for reaching key people in these media and arrange to provide such services.

5. Agencies that are free to do so should stimulate public support for desirable mental health legislation. Such support should be based upon public understanding of the need for and the nature of sound mental health programs.

6. Techniques and principles practiced by the communications media should be carefully studied by both public and private agencies engaged in education for mental health. This will help the agencies produce in their educational programs the intended—and not some unforeseen—public reaction.

7. These same agencies should also study the mental hygiene aspects of material now commonly used in advertisements, comic strips, the movies, and other communications media. For example, does material which appeals to snobbery or which exploits fear, shame, ridicule, and the like affect emotional health?

B. On the State Level

1. There should be in every state a vigorously active citizens group specifically devoted to promoting mental health. Such an agency should be the spearhead in mobilizing public opinion behind sound mental health measures. It should help support the agencies providing national services.

2. Since the education of the child is an important part of public education, the school systems in each state should be assisted in integrating mental health principles into their educational methods and materials. Consultation services provided by mental health societies, psychiatric departments of medical schools, and mental health committees of medical societies could help achieve this.

3. State health education facilities should include mental health education.

4. Effective utilization of the media of mass communication should be sought by organized groups on the local and state levels as well as on the national level.

C. On the Local Level

1. Wherever possible, voluntary mental health organizations should be organized in local communities under the auspices of local mental hygiene societies and other interested citizen groups. They should undertake locally the same tasks that are undertaken by similar agencies on a state and national basis.

2. The local mental health organization should co-operate with other interested local groups in informing the community about existent and unmet needs for local mental health services.

3. Local agencies, as well as state agencies, should develop and maintain a wholesome public influence in mental hospitals, clinics, courts,

children's institutions, marriage counseling services, parent education services, schools, and other community services dealing with mental health problems. Assistance to state and local organizations can be obtained from national, governmental, volunteer, and professional organizations.

PSYCHIATRY AND ALLIED FIELDS

The treatment and care of psychiatric patients involves many different types of personnel, ranging from the highly trained psychiatrist to the attendant who is in charge of a patient's prescribed activities. The types of facilities also cover a tremendous range, since they must meet the needs of patients of varying ages and behavior patterns.

Your committee's discussion of the treatment of mental illness was focused on three major areas: need for personnel; need for facilities; and research.

Need for Personnel
A. Psychiatrists

At present 4,382 psychiatrists belong to the American Psychiatric Association. Including others who are not yet members, there are probably about 5,000 psychiatrists in the nation. Of these, 2,475 are certified by the American Board of Psychiatry and Neurology.

In 1948, 1,635 psychiatrists were engaged in state hospital work. This represents a ratio of about one psychiatrist to 275 patients and is less than one-sixth of the minimum standard recommended by the American Psychiatric Association.

Serious shortages of psychiatrists also exist in other areas of service. In fact, it is estimated that at least 15,000 psychiatrists are essential to meet the minimal requirements at the present time.

Present training facilities. As of August, 1947, there were 1,298 psychiatric internships and residencies in 193 hospitals; 79 of these were for one year only, and 97 were for three years. It is estimated that about 350 residents can complete their training each year. At this rate of training, in a thirty-year period (which is about the average duration of practice for psychiatrists) about 10,500 candidates will complete their training. The extent of the deficiency thus ranges from about 70 per cent in 1947 to more than 20 per cent in 1977, depending upon the increase in population by 1977. It is obvious that immediate plans must be made for expanding the training facilities, not only to eliminate the present deficit of psychiatrists but also to replace them at the rate at which they are withdrawing from practice.

The factors accounting for the present lag in training may be summarized as follows:

Lack of well-qualified training personnel and lack of adequate facilities in training centers.

The financial burden to the prospective trainee in view of the long period of training.

Lack of proper orientation in undergraduate medical training.

To meet the needs for training more psychiatrists, your committee recommends that:

1. Since there are not enough teachers to train an increased number of students, the training program should concentrate its immediate efforts on the selection and training of future psychiatric teachers.

2. It is imperative that Federal and state subsidies continue to be made available to strengthen existing training centers, to establish new training centers, and to provide individual stipends for prospective graduate trainees. Present appropriations under the National Mental Health Act are not sufficient to meet the needs. Research to ascertain sound estimates of actual need should be undertaken. This is of particular importance in view of the impending cessation of the G.I. Bill benefits, which are now enabling many to obtain training.

3. At the undergraduate level, greater emphasis should be placed on psychiatric principles and knowledge of the general and specialized practice of medicine. The American Psychiatric Association, through its Committee on Medical Education, and the American Medical Association should bring this forcibly to the attention of the Association of Deans of Medical Schools. Such action will serve two purposes:

(a) It will stimulate the undergraduate medical student's interest in psychiatry; and

(b) More importantly, it will give the non-psychiatric physician (pediatrician, public health officer, internist, surgeon, obstetrician, gynecologist, and so forth) a better understanding of the implications of mental health in medical practice. In this way, many referrals will be made to psychiatrists when needed, and a number of problems may be dealt with adequately without requiring the attention of a psychiatrist.

B. Psychiatric Social Workers

There are 1,001 members of the American Association of Psychiatric Social Workers, the body which sets standards for psychiatric training and is the accrediting body that determines what schools are qualified to provide training in this specialty. So far it has accredited twenty schools of social work, four of them during the past year.

These schools will graduate 464 psychiatric social workers in the academic year 1947-48. In 1948-49 the potential number of graduates will be 685.

If the need is measured by the standard of one psychiatric social worker to every 10,000 persons in the community, the current requirement is, roughly speaking, 14,594 psychiatric social workers.

At the current rate of training and with no loss of personnel from the field, it will require approximately ten years to reach a minimal goal of one psychiatric social worker to 20,000 people.

Present trends. Because of the scarcity of challenging clinical opportunities and because of low salaries, psychiatric social workers have been attracted into other kinds of case work.

In many clinical settings, well-trained and qualified supervisors of psychiatric social work are not available for postgraduate training. Although psychodynamic concepts should form the basis of training of all social workers, those who intend to specialize in the psychiatric field need more than this basic training.

The growing demand for psychiatric social workers in the armed forces adds to the seriousness of the shortage. The present Army plan calls for an assignment of one military psychiatric social worker to every 10,000 soldiers and for the orientation of general medical staff officers through two-week institutes which will be given in 1948 in the six Army areas. Your committee concludes and recommends that:

1. The most imperative need in the field at present is to train teachers and supervisors of psychiatric social work.

2. Next in importance is the expansion of clinical teaching centers capable of training a maximum number of psychiatric social workers in field work. The program conducted at St. Elizabeths Hospital in Washington, D. C., on a short-term basis during the war period and the long-term programs currently carried on at Winter General Hospital and the Menninger Foundation, both in Topeka, Kansas, might serve as patterns. There should be at least one training center in each Public Health Service district.

3. In intra-mural services the psychiatric social worker should be given specific responsibilities and functions in connection with intake, reception, treatment, and convalescence of the patient. In extra-mural services

the psychiatric social worker is an integral member of the psychiatric team. The psychiatric social worker may also be used as a consultant to non-psychiatric agencies which have opportunities to perform prophylactic functions.

4. Growth and development of psychiatric social work in a clinical setting requires that research be done in methods and techniques and that the results be evaluated. Some suggested areas are:

(a) Study of criteria for the selection of candidates for admission to professional training;
(b) Study and evaluation of supervisory methods and techniques;
(c) Study of techniques of interviewing;
(d) Examination of recording methods currently in use; and
(e) Evaluation of the progress of treatment directed toward determining methods of judging progress.

5. Psychiatric social work not only must be concerned with research in its own areas but should participate in general clinical research projects. Suggested studies in the total clinic operation are:

(a) Study of referral sources and their influence on subsequent treatment results;
(b) Study of factors related to interrupted or discontinued appointments;
(c) Comparative study of factors revealed in improved and in unimproved treatment cases;
(d) Study of factors determining accessibility to treatment;
(e) Study of criteria for determining the methods and type of treatment indicated for optimal results;
(f) Study of emotional patterns in family constellations; and
(g) Study of the interrelationship of social, environmental, and emotional factors.

C. Clinical Psychologists

Until recently the clinical psychologist has been a member of the treatment and diagnostic team only in out-patient services. At the present time, the use of such personnel in the hospitals as well as their extended use in out-patient care is expanding almost explosively. There are now about 1,100 members of the Division of Clinical and Abnormal Psychology of the American Psychological Association. This membership is roughly indicative of the number of clinical psychologists available. The number of students now training for doctorates in clinical psychology indicates that about 50 additional clinical psychologists will be produced during each of the next two years.

At this time there are approximately 1,000 positions waiting to be filled for which money is now available, and it is known that the dearth of personnel prevents the establishment of many additional positions. There is a demand for psychologists in the public schools, in mental hygiene clinics, in mental hospitals, and in other service agencies. In 1945, only twelve states had more than one psychologist in the state hospital system; thirty-one states had no psychological service whatever. Only 8 per cent of the need estimated for clinical psychologists in state hospital practice is now being met. With plans for the expansion of all psychiatric services, the need for psychologists will be even greater than at present. It is impossible, until more field experience has been accumulated, to give even the vaguest estimate of the need in the future. However, considering the present unfilled need and the relatively low rate of production of additional personnel, considerable expansion of training facilities in clinical psychology is obviously necessary. It is also desirable to improve and enrich the training programs now in operation and to improve the selection of students. To increase the supply of clinical psychologists, your committee recommends that:

1. Further study is needed to determine what constitutes adequate training for the field of clinical psychology.

2. There should be continuous research on the proper and most effective use of psychologists in the care of hospitalized and out-patient psychiatric patients. Only with this research can estimates of future needs be clearly formulated.

3. Training in clinical psychology has expanded rapidly but is still inadequate in amount. Programs which offer proper and complete training of carefully selected students should be supported.

4. Clinical psychologists should be trained with representatives of other professions on clinical teams. Mutual appreciation of the functions of the allied professions will thus be fostered.

5. Clinical psychologists in schools and in health departments (as well as in other types of agencies serving the healthy population) should be regarded as an important factor in the promotion of improved mental health and in early case finding.

D. Psychiatric Nurses

In 1946 there were 317,800 registered nurses in the United States. Of these 5,545, or less than 2 per cent of all registered nurses, were in psychiatric service. On any one day, the mentally ill constitute over half of all patients in hospitals in the United States. In view of these figures, the need to stimulate professional interest in psychiatric nursing and to prepare additional nurses for psychiatric services is obvious. In addition, general-duty and other nurses in non-psychiatric hospitals should receive training in the psychological care of all types of patients.

The most reliable projections of past experience for estimating future nursing needs are those made by the Veterans Administration. This agency estimates that it will need three times as many psychiatric nurses in ten years as it now has.

The annual increase in patients in all mental hospitals is 12,000. In addition to the present recognized needs, this annual increase in the load of patients must also be served.

The need for psychiatric nurses in public health cannot be estimated. In 1947 there were 21,499 public health nurses in the nation, all of whom have an important function in promoting mental health. Most of them have had no orientation in the psychiatric implications of growth and development. Less than fifty are trained to teach and supervise public health nurses in this essential area of their education.

Although some psychiatric training is now given to 67 per cent of all undergraduate student nurses (85 per cent in the New England States), few receive adequate training. We should be satisfied with nothing less than 100 per cent.

Less than a dozen schools of nursing offer postgraduate training in psychiatry. These schools will graduate only 25 students in 1948.

If the number of local health departments is increased, as the Assembly's Local Health Units Section recommends (see Chapter III), the shortage of psychiatrically trained public health nurses will be even more acute. Further experimentation is needed to determine the most effective nursing staff organization for these local health units, but it is quite possible that each unit will need a mental hygiene supervisor and instructor of staff nurses.

Altogether, it is variously estimated that between 15,000 and 47,000 psychiatric nurses are needed to meet current needs in hospitals and public health services. These figures do not take into account the loss of nurses resulting from marriage, maternity, and retirement. Your committee recommends that:

1. The enormous need for psychiatric nurses dictates that more effort be made to attract nurses into this field. Financial inducements are important and should be provided. The satisfaction of working with the personality problems of human beings should also be stressed in recruit-

ment. More fellowships should be offered as a means of increasing recruits.

2. The training of supervisors and teachers of nurses is of prime importance. It is recommended that a careful selection of persons for postgraduate training be made, with particular attention to proficiency in caring for patients.

3. Psychiatric nurse-training curricula, both undergraduate and postgraduate, should be the subject of continuous research. Psychiatric training should be included in all three years of the nurse-training course. The content of training programs should be strengthened, thus helping the nurse to achieve parity with the members of other professions and giving her more insight into the work of others on clinic teams. The Public Health Service should finance and encourage the recognized accrediting agencies to develop standards of training and should continue to provide stipends for the training of psychiatric nurses.

4. Sound nursing education and the increasing use of general hospitals to treat psychiatric cases demand that undergraduate schools connected with general hospitals have properly prepared psychiatric nurses on their teaching and service staffs.

5. Many psychiatric nurses now in service need further education but cannot be spared from their duties for full-time educational programs. It is recommended that part-time programs be provided by subsidy, if necessary, or as in-service efforts.

E. Attendants

The Committee on Standards and Policies of the American Psychiatric Association has set an immediate goal of an attendant-patient ratio of one attendant to 6 patients or of one to 8 patients (depending on the type of patient requiring attention and the service to be provided). In May, 1947, the Committee reported that the actual ratios they found were one attendant to between 12 and 30 patients. In other words, the attendant supply meets less than one-half of the need. At the present time there are 43,181 attendants in our state hospitals for the mentally ill to care for 650,000 patients. With an average annual increase of 12,000 psychiatric patients admitted to the hospitals each year, 1,500 additional attendants will be needed yearly to meet the lowest recommended ratio of one to 8 patients. To meet this ratio, 75,000 more attendants should be employed.

There is urgent need not only for more attendants but also for a higher level of training. This need stems from the complex nature of the personality problems with which the attendant must deal—both in the care of patients with somatic illnesses and behavior disabilities in general hospitals and in the care of patients in mental hospitals. Many of those now employed have had no training whatsoever in the care of either mentally or physically ill patients. Appropriate preparation tends to give attendants more satisfaction in their work and also assures greater stability in the care the patients receive. It is recommended that:

1. Studies should be made as to the type of training provided for attendants. Programs should be designed to give attendants satisfaction in their work and to provide the best care of patients.

2. Licensing programs should be developed by the states. If adequately trained attendants were licensed, employment of untrained attendants would be discouraged.

3. Attendants in training for care of physically ill patients should be given an opportunity to take training in the care of psychiatric patients.

4. A new status, "psychiatric aide," should be created for qualified personnel.

5. Better salaries should be paid to qualified persons performing the duties of psychiatric aides.

F. Occupational Therapists and Physical Therapists

Occupational therapy and physical therapy are of extreme importance in promoting the total health and rehabilitation of the mentally ill, when supervised by a physician whose training has given him an understanding of how to employ them effectively. Present training facilities for occupational and physical therapists are quite inadequate. Approved schools are having to turn away applicants because they do not have enough facilities or qualified instructors to train all who desire to enter. The shortage of adequately trained occupational and physical therapists is especially acute in local communities, because they offer neither a remuneration nor a professional status comparable to what these specialists can obtain in Federal positions.

Occupational therapists. Currently there are twenty-two approved schools of occupational therapy, with an annual enrollment of about 1,400 students and an annual graduation of about 500 students. There are 2,100 registered occupational therapists. Since the annual attrition rate is about 40 per cent, the new graduates just about balance the attrition rate.

The present need is far in excess of the available trained therapists. Over 6,000 are estimated to be needed at the present time.

These figures deal with the over-all problem. Exact figures for the problem as it pertains to the mentally ill are not available. The generally accepted ratio for trained occupational therapists is at the very least one to 75 patients in mental hospitals.

Physical therapists. There are twenty-five approved schools of physical therapy, with about 750 students in training and about 500 graduates annually. There are 1,800 registered physical therapists. Since the annual attrition rate is about 25 per cent, this means a very modest increase of 50 physical therapists per annum.

The immediate need is estimated to be in excess of 5,000.

Again, these figures apply to the over-all problem. Outlets other than mental institutions demand an even higher proportion of the total number of physical therapists than of occupational therapists.

Comments on Personnel Needs

The differential between the current need and current supply of these professional groups is so great that we are reluctant to hazard a long-range estimate of need.

It is very important as a first step that the current needs be met. We assume that it was the recognition of this principle which prompted the National Health Assembly.

Research is important at both the local and the Federal level. This research should embrace, among other things:

The actual needs at the patient-demand level; and
The establishment of more accurate ratios for trained professional therapists and subprofessional aides, attendants, or technicians.

While the basic training for these professional groups must include clinical orientation in problems of the mentally ill, it is extremely important that we also be prepared to offer specialized postgraduate training in this field. It is especially important to improve the professional status of those working in the mental health field at the local level. So long as local and state salaries are about one-half what is paid in the Veterans Administration and other Federal agencies, it will be virtually impossible to build up state hospitals and improve and expand state mental health services.

Underlying the whole problem of meeting current and future needs is a basic need for subsidies to supplement local support, which to date has been grossly inadequate. We urge that the Federal government interest itself in such subsidies.

Need for Psychiatric Facilities

A. Case-Finding Agencies

There are many types of agencies which, though they deal with people not recognized as mentally ill, nevertheless encounter a great many persons in the early stages of mental illness. The personnel of these agencies should therefore be trained to recognize early mental illness and should help to protect their clients from becoming chronically or more seriously ill. These cases, when recognized, can be referred to the appropriate facilities for treatment.[2]

B. Intra-Mural Facilities

At the end of 1946 there were 529,247 patients, or 382.4 per 100,000 population, in mental hospitals. The majority, 445,561, were in state hospitals. Veterans' hospitals cared for 48,235, county and city hospitals for 23,150, and private hospitals for 12,301.

Although standards of care vary widely, a majority of these patients now receive substandard care. A recent survey made by the Committee on Hospitals of the Group for the Advancement of Psychiatry showed that overcrowding in public psychiatric hospitals ranged from 20 per cent to 74 per cent. Personnel shortages were shown to be equally serious: one state hospital had no nurses; one area had a doctor-patient ratio of one to 500; one area had a nurse-patient ratio of one to 1,320. Per capita cost variations ranged from 43 cents to $1.94 per patient per day. Research activities were almost non-existent, and educational and training programs were infrequent. Almost no individual therapy was available. The existing situation in public mental hospitals as compared with standards established by the American Psychiatric Association is as follows:

Ratio of Staff to Patients

	APA Standards[3]	*Actual Situation*
Attendants	One per 6 or 8 patients	One per 12 to 30 patients
Nurses	One per 4 to 40 patients	One per 176 patients
Psychiatrists	One per 30 to 200 patients	One per 250 to 500 patients

To meet the need for additional facilities, your committee recommends that:

[2] For further discussion see the report of the Subcommittee on Non-Psychiatric Aspects . . . earlier in this chapter.

[3] Range takes into consideration varieties in types of patients and in services they require.

1. Mental hospital facilities should be expanded to a total bed capacity of five per 1,000 population.

2. More adequate support through local, state, and/or Federal sources should be secured to remedy the budget deficiencies under which most mental hospitals now operate.

3. American Psychiatric Association standards should be elaborated and clarified, and the rating of hospitals on the basis of these standards should be vigorously supported.

4. As a means of recruiting personnel for mental hospitals, salaries should be increased, more training opportunities should be established within the hospitals, and living quarters should be improved—or, preferably, arrangements should be made for personnel to live in the community.

5. There should be more integration with general hospitals, and a wider use of general practitioners and specialists should be made in the physical care of state-hospital patients—so that the psychiatrist's skills can be concentrated on functions which only he can perform. The use of part-time psychiatrists would also help to relieve the personnel shortage.

6. Psychiatric social service should follow through from the time the patient is admitted to the hospital until he attains his final readjustment in the community.

7. Teachers and research in state hospitals should be encouraged and financed, and affiliation of state hospitals with teaching schools should be encouraged.

8. Through educational and recruitment activities, efforts should be made to relieve, as promptly as possible, the acute shortage of all types of personnel—and particularly the shortages of psychiatrists, psychiatric nurses and social workers, clinical psychologists, occupational and physical therapists, and attendants.

C. Extra-Mural Facilities

Private practicing psychiatrists. At the present time there are 1,533 psychiatrists in private practice. If they were evenly distributed over the country there would be one psychiatric therapist for each 140,000 people, or one to each city the size of Canton, Ohio. Like other medical specialists, however, psychiatrists are largely concentrated in the large cities, and this leaves many areas of the country entirely unserved. There are states in which the only psychiatrists are those caring for patients in hospitals. Your committee recommends that:

1. There should be a better presentation of psychiatry in medical schools so that (a) more doctors will go into psychiatry and (b) all physicians will be better oriented in psychiatry.

2. Recruitment. Professional associations and government agencies should stimulate students to study psychiatry and similar closely allied professions. One way of stimulating students to enter these professions is to include more mental hygiene information in courses in the social sciences and in the undergraduate program of the medical schools.

3. Full utilization of present personnel. Present maldistribution of services would be partially corrected if psychiatrists in private practice who were willing to serve in unfavorable areas received government subsidies. We should also have extensive research programs to develop new, brief group methods of therapy so that each psychiatrist can serve more people.

Out-patient treatment clinics. There are about 638 out-patient psychiatric clinics of all types in the United States. Most of these are located in urban centers. Rural areas and small cities have little or no service. Clinics exclusively for children, which have a preventive as well as treatment function, are far too few. If it is accepted that one clinic for psychiatric treatment is necessary for each 100,000 of the population, the United States needs about 800 more clinics. These must be adequately staffed. In view of personnel shortages, however, it would be impossible to staff as many clinics as are needed. There is always a grave danger that inadequate personnel will be employed when such pressing unmet and unmeetable needs exist. It is recommended that:

1. Clinics for the out-patient treatment of psychiatric patients should be increased in number as rapidly as it is possible to do so without sacrificing quality of service.

2. All existing mental health clinics with qualified personnel should, if necessary, be subsidized so that they may be used for the training of personnel in psychiatry and the allied professions.

3. All out-patient departments should have psychiatric consultation and service.

4. The extent to which social workers and psychologists can do relatively independent therapy should be explored.

5. Grants-in-aid should be made to communities or hospitals for the establishment of psychiatric out-patient departments.

6. Traveling clinics should be supported and developed.

Psychiatrists in educational institutions. At present probably less than thirty psychiatrists devote full time to the mental health of school and college students. This number is ludicrously insufficient even as a pilot research in the prevention of mental illness. Practical techniques for giving children and young people some foreknowledge of the stresses and strains of adult life might prevent them from developing mental disease. It is quite impossible to estimate the number of psychiatric personnel or the particular categories needed to serve the nation's youth. Such service should include work with educators to keep them informed and interested in aspects of mental hygiene which are applicable to their profession. Our recommendations are that:

1. As they become available, psychiatrists, psychologists, psychiatric social workers, and nurses should be encouraged to engage in mental health services to children and to school and college students.

2. Research on the best methods of using personnel in this field should be encouraged.

3. The fullest possible use should be made of present facilities to train additional personnel for this field.

4. Psychiatric orientation should be an integral part of training in normal schools and other teacher-training institutes.

Psychiatric services to industry. The number of psychiatrists now working even part time in the industrial field is very small, perhaps under thirty. Less than ten are concerned full time with the enormously important socio-psychiatric treatment of persons whose illness affects productive efficiency in industrial plants, with the problems of the adjustment of the worker to his job, and with several interrelationships in plants. There is but one university with a special course of training in industrial psychiatry, and training plans in the field are as yet poorly formulated. Our comments are:

1. Industrial psychiatry as a field of preventive activity is of great importance and is as yet only beginning to be explored.

2. Research and service in the field should be expanded as rapidly as personnel become available.

3. Industry should be encouraged to finance research in this field, since it might result in the discovery of effective means to reduce absenteeism and employee turnover and to increase employee efficiency.

4. All facilities for furnishing psychiatric services to industrial em-

ployees should be developed in such a way that they can also be used for training additional personnel.

Research

Lack of knowledge concerning the causes, prevention, and treatment of mental illness cripples all our efforts to give mental health services. Such knowledge is meager not only because of the extreme complexity of the problem but also because of the relative lack of support being given to the study of mental illness. Totals spent in the United States for medical research are estimated at $120 million a year—for psychiatric research, $2 to $2.5 million. Of 709 institutions reporting research in 1948, only 159 had either money invested or actual research projects in mental fields. In almost every area of mental illness we need extensive research. In this field, your committee recommends that:

1. There should be an expansion of studies of the basic factors underlying normal brain activity and of the influence of heredity in nervous and mental illness and feeble-mindedness. Anatomic, physiological, and chemical research are greatly needed in such fields as brain metabolism, electrical potentials, and autonomic relationships with emotion and cerebration. Experience during the war emphasized the extreme importance of studying the relationship of fatigue to mental illness. Disturbances of the ability to rest and recuperate and disturbances of sleep are common symptoms in mental disease and call for thorough investigation.

2. Efforts to develop diagnostic techniques applicable to large groups of the population should be intensified. We must refine our diagnostic techniques for determining the degree of seriousness of mental illness in any individual. We need extensive work on the whole problem of diagnostic categories.

3. We should explore new methods of treatment for the millions of people with psychoneuroses as well as for the more severely ill patients who are in mental hospitals. Present methods are far too slow to cope with the vast numbers needing treatment. Particular avenues of study should include group psychotherapy, occupational therapy, recreation, and chemical, surgical, and mechanical methods.

4. Research in the preventive aspects of mental illness, especially in childhood, should be expanded. We need to know far more about the developmental factors that determine the personality, and how these factors contribute to the formation of character. We need very much to have organized information for parents to use in guiding their children.

We lack any well-accepted understanding or even classification of behavior disorders in children. The results of such research could be applied in child guidance clinics, schools, juvenile courts, and at home. We need to know more about the various factors of mental illness in relation to our aging population.

5. We should conduct surveys of communities (probably on a sample basis) to predetermine the extent of the problem, in order that a more systematic planning of mental health facilities can be achieved. We need research to relate the patient's clinical symptoms and the underlying dynamics of his disorder to the broad social, cultural, and community setting. This would encompass social class, family structure, ecology, and a host of other social factors, and it would require standardized analyses of mass clinical data now being collected. We should study the public's present mental health attitudes, knowledge, and behavior and the effectiveness of various types of educational programs concerned with mental health. We need investigation concerning the impact of a mental health clinic on a community. We also need research on the effectiveness of other types of community programs, such as the combination of education with counseling services, and also on that of the experimental programs being undertaken in schools and factories.

6. More effort should be made to determine what constitutes a normal individual. These investigations would include the structure and the physiology of the personality as well as the psychopathology of everyday life.

APPENDIX A

THREE MAJOR AREAS DISCUSSED IN THE MENTAL HEALTH SECTION

Specific Items Considered and Names of Discussion Leaders

The Child and the Family

"Personality Development of the Child"
John A. Rose, M.D.

"Interpersonal Relations within the Family"
William S. Langford, M.D.

"The Importance of Mental Hygiene in the School Situation, with Special Reference to the Role of the Teacher in Building the Mental Health of the Child"
Colonel H. Edmund Bullis

"The Need for Facilities for Care and Treatment of Special Problems Including Emotionally Disturbed Children Who Need Institutional Care"
Helen Ross

Community Planning for Mental Health Needs

"The Role of Mental Hygiene in Industrial Relations"
Leo Bartemeier, M.D.

"The Responsibility of Community Organizations in Building a Mental Health Program"
George S. Stevenson, M.D.

"The Contributions Which the Church Can Make Toward a Healthy Neighborhood"
Rev. Seward Hiltner

"A Sound Mental Hygiene Program as an Aid in Relieving Racial and Social Tensions"
Sol W. Ginsburg, M.D.

Public Education

"Building Public Demand for the Improvement of State Hospital Care"
Kenneth B. Appel, M.D.

"Stressing the Need for the Community General Hospital to Assume Its Responsibility in Care of the Mentally Ill"
Thomas A. C. Rennie, M.D.

"Building Recognition of the Need to Include Mental Health Emphasis in Our Entire Educational System, with Special Attention to the Need for Psychiatry in Medical Education"
William Malamud, M.D.

"Emphasizing the Importance of Improved Community Education in All Phases of the Problem of Mental Health"
Harold Barton

APPENDIX B

PLANNING COMMITTEE

William C. Menninger, M.D., *Chairman*	Medical Director The Menninger Clinic
Thomas A. C. Rennie, M.D., *Co-Chairman*	Attending Psychiatrist, New York Hospital; Associate Professor of Psychiatry Cornell University Medical College
Paul V. Lemkau, M.D.	Director, Mental Hygiene Study School of Hygiene and Public Health Johns Hopkins University
Miss Helen Ross	Administrative Director Institute for Psychoanalysis Chicago, Illinois

STAFF ASSISTANTS

James V. Lowry, M.D.

Chief, Community Services Section
Mental Hygiene Division
Public Health Service
Federal Security Agency

Mrs. Alberta Altman

Chief, Publications and Reports Section
Mental Hygiene Division
Public Health Service
Federal Security Agency

REGISTRANTS

Kenneth E. Appel, M.D.

Assistant Professor of Psychiatry
University of Pennsylvania

Grace Baker, M.D.

Instructor in Psychiatry
Johns Hopkins University

Leo Bartemeier, M.D.

Associate Professor of Psychiatry
Wayne University

Harold Barton

Executive Secretary
National Mental Health Foundation, Inc.

Rev. Thomas A. Bridges

St. Chrysostom Church
Quincy, Massachusetts

Rev. Ernest E. Bruder

Protestant Chaplain
St. Elizabeths Hospital
Washington, D.C.

Col. H. Edmund Bullis

Executive Director
Delaware State Society for Mental Hygiene

Albert Deutsch

The Star Daily
New York, New York

Dana L. Farnsworth, M.D.

Director, Massachusetts Institute of Technology

Lillian Gilbreth, M.D.

Montclair, New Jersey

Sol W. Ginsburg, M.D.

Instructor in Psychiatry
College of Physicians and Surgeons
Columbia University

Miss Margaret Hagen

American Red Cross

Samuel W. Hamilton, M.D.

Superintendent, Essex County Overbrook Hospital
New Jersey

Thomas A. Hendricks

Secretary, Council on Medical Service
American Medical Association

Morris Herman, M.D.

Assistant Director of Psychiatry
Bellevue Hospital

Rev. Seward Hiltner	Executive Secretary Commission on Religion and Health Federal Council of Churches of Christ in America
Miss Sarah Holbrook	Chairman, Mental Health Committee Parent Teachers Association
Joseph Hughes, M.D.	Laboratory Director Institute of the Pennsylvania Hospital Philadelphia, Pennsylvania
Marion E. Kenworthy, M.D.	Professor of Psychiatry New York School of Social Work
William S. Langford, M.D.	Director, Babies Hospital Columbia University
Miss Marian McBee	Executive Secretary State Charities Aid Association New York, New York
William Malamud, M.D.	Professor of Psychiatry School of Medicine Boston University
A. R. Mangus	Professor of Rural Sociology Ohio State University
Clifton T. Perkins, M.D.	Commissioner, Massachusetts Department of Mental Health
Raymond T. Rich	Chairman, Raymond Rich Associates New York, New York
Hector J. Ritey, M.D.	Vice-Chairman, Health Labor Council New York, New York
John A. Rose, M.D.	Philadelphia Child Guidance Clinic
Julius Schreiber, M.D.	Director, National Institute of Social Relations Washington, D.C.
Miss Mildred C. Scoville	Executive Director The Commonwealth Fund
Miss Ruth Slutzker	Director, Social Welfare Department National Council of Jewish Women
George S. Stevenson, M.D.	Medical Director National Committee for Mental Hygiene
Miss Frances Thompson	Chief Supervisor Psychiatric Nursing Massachusetts Department of Mental Health
A. L. Van Ameringen	Treasurer, National Committee for Mental Hygiene
Gerald Wendt, M.D.	New York, New York
John C. Whitehorn, M.D.	Henry Phipps Psychiatric Clinic Johns Hopkins Hospital

What Can Be Done
to Improve Nutrition?

DURING the last quarter of a century science has moved fast on many fronts, but nowhere faster than on the nutrition front. Indeed, so rapidly has knowledge of nutrition advanced that it has outmoded programs and methods of instruction in medical and public health schools and has revealed as pitifully inadequate the administrative machinery set up for its public application by Federal, state, and local governments.

Applied vigorously and wholeheartedly to certain population groups during the Second World War in the desperate attempt to survive, the new knowledge of nutrition revealed what it could do to maintain and improve public health under the most discouraging conditions. Particularly striking was the experience in Great Britain, where under the stress of war all ordinary environmental conditions steadily deteriorated and only the diet was improved. Various death rates, which in previous wars had always increased in Great Britain, showed surprising declines; new low levels were achieved, producing records never attained in peace time.

According to Sir Wilson Jameson, Chief Medical Officer of the Ministry of Health, maternal mortality in England and Wales declined by 45 per cent in 1945 as compared to 1938. During the same period, stillbirths declined by 28 per cent, the infant mortality rate by 13 per cent, and the neonatal mortality rate by 13 per cent. "In 1946 the fall continued in all these rates and each of the new figures was the lowest ever recorded. I have no doubt whatever that these results are due in the main to the priorities in essential foodstuffs granted to the mothers and children of Britain under a wise system of wartime rationing."[1]

Professional workers in nutrition believe that a wise use of the new

[1] Wilson Jameson: "The Place of Nutrition in a Public Health Program," *American Journal of Public Health*, Vol. 37, No. 11 (November, 1947), p. 1375.

knowledge of the relation between diet and health would bring about as great an improvement in public health as that which followed the work of Pasteur and his disciples. They know that only a small fraction of this new knowledge is being put to work, and they appreciate that the lag is preventing improvement in certain conditions, such as dental disease and neonatal mortality, which have proved most baffling to public health workers.

The delegates to the Nutrition Section of the National Health Assembly included representatives of organizations in the fields of government, education, industry, the professions, and voluntary agencies. Though approaching the problems of a national nutrition program from widely different points of view, they were all acutely aware of the wide gap—which exists even in the most highly developed countries—between the knowledge of what is needed to maintain sound health and the actual nutritional state and dietary habits of the majority of the people. They knew that resistance to disease, growth and development, and physical appearance and behavior are all affected by nutrition, and that the science of nutrition today not only seeks the prevention of disease but holds out the hope for more positive achievements—a state of complete physical well-being and optimum health for all people throughout their life span.

The delegates realized that the achievement of any considerable part of these possibilities would call for the closely co-ordinated effort of a large number of agencies, professions, and groups, but that the heavy responsibility for leadership would fall upon the national, state, and local official and voluntary health agencies. It was obvious to all that these agencies, as at present constituted, are not capable of carrying this load and that additional resources, revised programs, and new forms of organization will have to be provided.

It was in this spirit and with this knowledge of the needs and accomplishments of nutrition that this Section met to work out a program which would provide for a better use of the constantly increasing knowledge of the relation of diet to health.

Because of the complexity of the field of nutrition and the limited time at the disposal of this Section, the group was divided into six subcommittees, each of which concentrated on one of the major aspects of the nutrition problem and to one of which the delegates were assigned according to their special knowledge or preference. The subcommittees were created to deal with the following topics: (1) international aspects of nutrition; (2) food supplies; (3) research in nutrition; (4) organization and administration of official and voluntary nutrition programs; (5) professional education in nutrition; and (6) education of the public in nutrition. The reports of these subcommittees were presented to and adopted by the full Section, so that every recommendation which follows was approved by every delegate who attended the final session.

The participants in the Nutrition Section fully realize the impossibility of working out ideal programs in the limited time at their disposal. They believe, however, that the reports and recommendations represent a good beginning, which with perseverance and continued experimentation may lead to great improvement in public health. It is their hope—paraphrasing the words of Lord Woolton, Great Britain's Minister of Food during the war—that, as a result of the application of scientific knowledge to food, the next generation may be enabled to approach the formidable task of building a new age with the health and strength which come of good nutrition.

CONCLUSIONS AND RECOMMENDATIONS

International Aspects of Nutrition

A ten-year program to improve the physical, mental, and social health of the American people must of necessity take into account the international aspects of the problem. Particular attention should be paid to long-range as well as immediate measures that (a) offer opportunity for the improvement of the health of our neighbors in other countries and our own people and (b) provide a basis for the interchange of information and of persons with technical skills.

International relationships are particularly important in the field of human nutrition, since problems of food supplies, dietary standards, and the exchange of nutrition information can best be approached and dealt with on a world-wide basis. In our ever-shrinking world, the interdependence of nations for their vital food and dietary requirements sharply dramatizes the need for international co-operation in nutrition. The United States committed itself to a policy of improved health and nutrition throughout the world when it accepted the responsibility of membership in the United Nations and its specialized agencies.

With these factors in mind, the Nutrition Section adopted the following recommendations:

1. United Nations Conference on Food and Agriculture. The resolutions and recommendations adopted at the United Nations Conference

on Food and Agriculture in 1943 should be supported and implemented. The participation by the United States in this conference and the forward steps in nutrition taken there are recognized and appreciated. Important recommendations with respect to nutrition were that the governments of the United Nations should establish national nutrition organizations to determine the nutritional status of populations and to review existing agencies and legislation, that nutrition information and experience should be exchanged among the various nations, and that international dietary standards should be set up with the ultimate goal of promoting sound health and proper food consumption.[2]

2. National Nutrition Council. In recognition of the service that could be provided to this nation in a ten-year health plan, it is urged that a National Nutrition Council, of the type recommended in the Final Act of the United Nations Conference on Food and Agriculture, be organized. The Council should be authorized and directed to exchange information and experience with comparable organizations in other countries and to co-operate with and through the United Nations and its specialized agencies. Adequate funds should be provided by the government to support the Council. Its activities should include:

(1) Planning and supervising of periodic sample surveys of the nutritional status of the population of the United States.
(2) Promoting and supporting nutrition councils in the various states.
(3) Co-operating with the specialized agencies connected with the United Nations, such as the Food and Agriculture Organization, the World Health Organization, the U.N. Educational, Scientific, and Cultural Organization, and the U.N. International Children's Emergency Fund. Among the problems requiring co-operative study on an international basis are:

(a) Establishment of dietary standards;
(b) Methods of assessing the nutritional status of populations;
(c) Development of tables of food composition suitable for international use;
(d) Development of international standards for the appraisal of specific nutrients; and
(e) Determination of characteristic food patterns and habits on which to base plans for improving nutrition within various sections of this as well as other countries.

[2] The portions of the Final Act adopted at the 1943 United Nations Conference on Food and Agriculture which relate to nutrition are reproduced in Appendix A at the end of this chapter.

(4) Co-operating with the specialized agencies in promoting the international exchange of students and workers in the field of nutrition.

3. Interdepartmental Nutrition Co-ordinating Committee. The United States Government's Interdepartmental Nutrition Co-ordinating Committee began its work in 1936 and has made important contributions to the development of a nutrition program in this country by co-ordinating the nutritional activities of various departments of the Federal government dealing with human nutrition. The work of the Interdepartmental Committee should be strengthened by: (a) providing it with a permanent secretary, to assure continuity of effort; (b) including in its membership persons with top-level administrative responsibilities, thus enabling the Committee to take more effective action in the nutrition fields which are the concern of government departments; and (c) providing adequate financial support to maintain contact and liaison with technically skilled advisers, such as the Food and Nutrition Board of the National Research Council.

4. United Nations International Children's Emergency Fund. The United States is to be commended for its support of the United Nations International Children's Emergency Fund, which has as its purpose the improvement of the health and nutrition of children in war-devastated countries. Much of the relief work, of course, involves assistance of a dietary and nutritional nature. As long as the urgent need continues, it is recommended that intensified support of this activity be continued.

5. Food and nutrition problems of the Economic Co-operation Administration. In setting up the Economic Co-operation Administration to administer the European recovery program, the United States pledged its aid in the economic recovery of participating countries. The Economic Co-operation Administration is urged to seek the advice and guidance of food and nutrition experts who have special knowledge of food requirements and supply problems in this country and abroad.

Food Supplies

Nutrition depends on foods and the amount and type of foods available. Problems of population growth, conservation of soil and water, and food storage methods must all be considered for an understanding of nutrition. The processing and distribution of foods figure prominently in the well-being of the people of this country and of the world.

The Nutrition Section of the National Health Assembly reached the following conclusions and recommendations on the role of food supplies in nutrition:

1. Expansion of food production. The present food supply is fully adequate, on an average per capita basis, for meeting the nutritional needs of the present population of the United States. A program of health goals, however, must consider future needs in terms of our expanding population. By 1950 a population figure of 150 million seems highly probable. This population figure, at present levels and patterns of per capita consumption, would call for a total food supply nearly equal to the record output of 1947, with no food left for export. By 1960 it is possible that the population may approach 170 million people. Thus if we are to maintain our present levels of consumption, both quantitatively and qualitatively, an expanded production is called for. Allowances must also be made for export responsibilities, for stockpiling, and for other emergencies.

Health will best be served by basing production plans on actual nutritional needs, taking account of the probable age-sex distribution as well as of the total population number. In planning for nutrition needs, it is considered that milk production should be stepped up at a rapid rate, if the increase is consumed as whole milk or cheese. The recent general pattern of production for other animal products and for fruits and vegetables should be fully maintained, and the over-all amounts should be increased in accordance with population needs.

2. Conservation. In the interest of providing an adequate food supply, an over-all program of conservation must be instituted. The program must consider soil, water, and related biological resources.

Land resources constitute a special problem, since these are only slightly expansible in area beyond what is now being used. Research and education in conservation and in proper land use have already made a beginning in checking the wastage of soil resources. The problem is by no means solved, and our knowledge and practice of fertility maintenance and conservation must be expanded.

It should be recognized that the public interest lies not so much in the output of any individual acre of land as in the *total sustained food production from the total land base of the nation*. All land has its proper use, but not all can be used for farming. A vital need of land-use planning is the shaping of each acre that will continue to be farmed into its proper, long-term use. Soil-conservation work up till now has largely stressed the *quantitative* aspect of land. It is imperative for the future that land *quality* should be equally recognized.

Intensive crop farming should concentrate on the better crop land. Vast acres could make their maximum long-term contribution simply by remaining as grass land and being used for grazing. In this way an expansion of milk production can also be achieved.

American agriculture must continue to give high priority to livestock breeding and production. Conservation of soil resources, stability of farm operation and income, and the continuation of high quality and balanced diets demand such an emphasis.

3. Conservation education. Extension and improvement of education in nutrition are prerequisites for the maximum conservation of foods and their nutrients. Our present food supplies are used wastefully in marketing, in the kitchen, and at the table. This is a national problem of great importance if we are to derive maximum value and effectiveness from our food resources.

Conservation of food and their nutrients requires a knowledge of the effects of storage under varying conditions, of the effect of freezing and dehydration, and of the effect of processing in general on nutrient content and on acceptability. For the consumer, conservation requires a reasonable knowledge of food values and of nutrient losses in cooking.

4. Improvement of the nutritive quality of foods. Plant-breeding programs have successfully improved crop yields and resistance to disease and insects. New varieties have been developed which exhibit better shortage and shipping characteristics and have a higher consumer appeal. In addition to these important advances, there is a need for the development of varieties of plants and vegetables which will contain high nutritional values in an available form.

5. Research on the nutritive value of foods. Present studies of the effect of climate, water, and fertilization of the soil on the nutritional value of food crops should be continued and expanded.

6. Nutritional measures for low-income groups. Educational programs in nutrition should be developed and pointed particularly toward the needs of the malnourished and low-income groups, in terms of their food habits and income. An expanded school-lunch program is particularly needed for these groups.

7. Amendments to food and drug laws. The Food, Drug, and Cosmetic Act of 1938 and the Wheeler-Lea Amendment to the Federal Trade Commission Act, have been effectively and faithfully administered. Adulteration, misbranding, and misleading advertising of products covered by these laws have, to a great extent, been suppressed, to the immense advantage of consumers and honest businessmen. These laws, however, fail to provide authority or give doubtful power to control the nutritive

values of processed foods. Nutritional control of several kinds of processed foods is in the interest of the public health. It is recommended, therefore, that the Food, Drug, and Cosmetic Act be amended to provide the administrator of the Act with the authority, when establishing definitions and standards of identity for processed foods, to include standards of nutritional quality whenever he feels the scientific and medical grounds are adequate and compliance is feasible.

The amendment should provide authority to require, in interstate commerce, a designated content of vitamin A in margarine, a designated content of specified vitamins and minerals in cereal products, and a designated amount of iodine in salt for human consumption. The feasibility of these three procedures has been established and all three have been endorsed by the American Medical Association, the Food and Nutrition Board of the National Research Council, the American Public Health Association, and the Association of State and Territorial Health Officers. The amendment should also provide authority to require that other processed foods conform to standards of nutritive quality when such standards as are feasible and in the interest of the public health are established.

Organization and Administration of Nutrition Programs

If the new knowledge of nutrition is to be applied effectively to improve public health, as it was in Great Britain during the recent war, there must be adequate organization and administration of nutrition programs. Nutrition, as a health measure, must be planned for and co-ordinated with other health programs, in official as well as in voluntary agencies and groups.

Recommendations were framed for official agencies at the three governmental levels—national, state, and local—and for voluntary and nonofficial agencies.

1. National agencies. (1) A National Nutrition Council should be established. (2) There should be a *division* of nutrition instead of merely a section in the United States Public Health Service. (3) The Public Health Service should give special attention to nutrition programs among industrial workers. (4) The Federal government should appropriate additional funds for the development and expansion of its nutrition program. Increased emphasis and financial support under the grants-in-aid program should be given to nutrition programs developed by the Public Health Service and the Children's Bureau.

2. State agencies. (1) There should be a special administrative unit of nutrition set up in each state health department, comparable to the units responsible for the organization of such programs as venereal disease control, tuberculosis control, and maternal and child health. This unit should be directed by a full-time person with special training and experience in nutrition as it is related to public health. (2) Each state should have a nutrition council similar to the proposed National Nutrition Council; an advisory committee for the state health department should be set up from this body. The council should include in its membership representatives of official and non-official agencies in the field of nutrition, and full use should be made of the resources of any existing nutrition committees or councils. It is especially important for the state to make a full-time secretary available to the council in order to maintain and increase the effectiveness of its work. (3) Effective nutrition services and education should be provided for family groups, and particular attention should be given to the vulnerable groups in human society who are most likely to be inadequately nourished. These groups include pregnant and nursing women, infants and children, adolescents, the aged, industrial workers, and the economically vulnerable. Special services will also be necessary for American Indians on reservations, residents in institutions, those handicapped by injuries or chronic diseases, and individuals who are not members of family units. (4) Special nutrition services and education should be provided for all pregnant women in order to improve maternal and infant health through a reduction in the complications of pregnancy and in the number of stillbirths, premature births, and neonatal deaths.

3. Local agencies. (1) Health or nutrition councils should be established in local communities to arouse public interest in nutrition services and education and to act in an advisory capacity to the official agencies. (2) Among the basic functions of local health departments should be nutrition education and the provision of nutrition services. Local health department staffs should include, wherever possible, one or more nutritionists.

4. Voluntary agencies. Voluntary and non-official associations interested in nutrition should make every effort to establish programs of health education in nutrition at both state and local levels. Teamwork between state and local official and non-official agencies should be promoted vigorously, and the voluntary associations should take an active part in

arousing public interest, encouraging nutrition studies, and advocating and giving assistance in nutrition demonstration programs.

These organizations should stimulate official and non-official agencies to employ trained nutrition workers and should assist local voluntary and official agencies in the recruiting, training, and placement of nutrition personnel. They can encourage curriculum improvement and training programs for practitioners of medicine and dentistry, for nurses, and for health department personnel in the field of nutrition, with emphasis on nutrition in the areas of preventive medicine and on the dietary treatment of disease. They can develop nutrition programs for non-professional members of voluntary health associations, with special emphasis on the essential foods necessary for a well-balanced daily diet, on alternate low-cost foods, on proper food preparation, and on the use of the more abundant foods which are available in the market. They can also provide instruction in better buying and storage practices, in the importance of practicing food conservation, and in the elimination of waste.

It is the job of the voluntary associations to mobilize public sentiment in support of an expansion of the school-lunch program through additional Federal and state appropriations and in support of the training of teachers, social workers, and welfare workers in nutrition. State departments of education should be encouraged to develop continued and effective nutrition education for every school child.

Of particular importance are the services of the voluntary organizations in stimulating public interest in legislative action in matters concerning better nutrition. This would involve attention to restrictions on margarine, a more adequate school-lunch program, the enrichment of flour and other foodstuffs, more adequate pure food laws and regulations, the iodization of table salt, and the availability in convenient retail packages of adequately fortified dried milk.

On industrial nutrition programs, voluntary associations can encourage industries to provide well-balanced meals in plant cafeterias and to have milk available for sale. The food habits of employees should be studied to determine where supplementary nutrients are needed, and each employee should be informed of the results of such a survey so that he may work at his full productive capacity. Finally, voluntary associations should aid in developing improved techniques and media for the transmission of nutrition information to the various age, racial, and economic groups in the population.

Research in Nutrition

One of the major obstacles standing in the way of the development of adequate and far-reaching nutrition programs is a lack of sufficient knowledge about nutrition. It is true that more is known about nutrition than is put into practice; nevertheless much yet remains to be discovered. Without an effective and continuing research program, nutrition knowledge will remain incomplete and the benefits of the knowledge now available will be negligible.

Health may be expressed in many ways, but there can be no doubt that there is a strong relation between nutrition and health in terms of physical and mental growth and development, pregnancy, nursing, freedom from congenital defects, immunity and resistance to disease, aging, and longevity. Many studies on animals have indicated that relationships do exist between nutrition and these aspects of health. Investigations that merit urgent attention in planning a health program include studies of the development of nutrition appraisal methods, of the nutritional status of populations, of human nutritional requirements, of the effect of nutrition on degenerative diseases, of nutritional protection of the "vulnerable" groups, of the measurement of nutrients, and of methods of nutrition education.

1. Nutrition appraisal methods. Better methods of nutrition appraisal must be developed and perfected if substantial progress is to be made in arresting ill health due to faulty or improper diets. Any program to raise health levels through improvements in nutrition must begin with an analysis and evaluation of foods and diet. It is highly important that techniques be developed to identify the earliest signs of nutritional deficiency. These techniques should include tests based on physical examinations as well as on chemical analysis. Several promising tests have already been developed; the microchemical tests, by the use of only a few drops of blood, supplemented by physical examinations and dietary records, have become especially useful and have shown great promise in appraising school health programs. Such tests, as well as similar or related ones for other population groups, must be explored and perfected.

2. Nutritional status of populations. The nutritional status of various population groups, ages, and occupations must be accurately determined. From a public health point of view, there can be no doubt of the great need for carefully organized teams to survey representative segments of the population at frequent intervals. The knowledge gained as a result

of these surveys would be of great value in discovering trends in food practices as well as in gaining reliable information of the relationship between food practices, diet, and health. Every state and all large municipal health units should make provision for such surveys regularly and should participate in the related fields of nutrition research and education.

3. Human nutritional requirements. Research in the nutrition needs of animals has advanced nearly twice as far as in human studies. The study of human nutritional requirements is really in its infancy. It would be highly advantageous to develop public health research on the basis of controlled animal experimentation. Systematic efforts should be made to establish the qualitative and quantitative human requirements of each of the essential nutrients and the basic foods. In addition, careful investigations should be conducted to appraise the maximum contribution to body efficiency that can be made by non-essential nutrients.

4. Effect of nutrition on degenerative diseases. The health records of this country and of other parts of the world show unmistakably a broad trend of correlation between malnutrition and a high incidence of degenerative disease. Abundant evidence from animal experimentation shows such relationships even more strikingly. Yet the evidence at many points is not well enough established for adequate guidance in medical and public health practice. Scarcely more than a beginning has been made in research in the association of degenerative diseases with faulty food practices. Research to investigate this relationship and to explore new areas of nutritional requirements should be developed extensively.

Specialized research should also deal systematically with dental diseases and with the effects of malnutrition and poor diet on dental decay and ill health.

5. Nutritional protection of special groups. Studies must be pursued to determine adequate protection for special groups who are particularly exposed to poor nutrition or who require better-than-average nutrition because of special problems. Convincing evidence from several studies in the United States, Canada, and Western Europe has demonstrated that the health of mothers during the reproductive cycle and the health of their offspring can be benefited markedly by food practices better than those normally followed. In England, for example, significant improvements in maternal and child health followed as a result of special nutritional provisions for these groups. Maternal and infant death rates dropped to all-time low levels in the years from 1942 to 1948, largely as

a result of improved food practices. Gradually the incidence of tuberculosis and dental diseases also declined; this was to be expected from a comparison with careful nutrition studies on experimental animals. It should be borne in mind, however, that these and similar health gains in several parts of the world have been achieved in zones of nutrient intake well above the levels that show the classical signs of nutritional deficiency.

Still more constructive, in some respects, would be research to guide improved nutritional practices in infancy and early childhood to ward off early injuries which lead to impairment of health throughout the life span. It is clear that early injuries to the skeletal and glandular tissues, caused by marginal degrees of malnutrition, cannot be fully offset by later improvements in food intake. There is a great need, however, to explore more fully the long-time effects of faulty food practices and diet inadequacies in human beings.

6. Measurement of nutrients. Research in methods for the measurement of nutrients will be particularly valuable. More precise and more rapid methods of analysis are of major importance. The economies which will follow when expensive and non-specific animal experiments are replaced by rapid chemico-physical tests will be of great practical advantage.

Each basic enlargement of understanding in the functions of individual nutrients is of great significance. The functional role of nutrients in a bacterial cell may well lay the groundwork for rapid progress in animal and human physiology. Among all the areas of public health research, the basic job of exploring the nature of normal living processes will probably pay the highest dividends.

7. Methods of nutrition education. If the results of nutrition research are to be used to provide the people with better health, one last phase of research is essential—research in the methods of public and professional education. In every part of the world inadequate and insufficient education causes, at present, needless sacrifice of human health and the waste of economic resources. There is a very real need to develop channels of education so that the public will follow nutrition and diet practices which protect health. Since educational measures have been so woefully inadequate, highly specialized research is called for in order to find methods of promoting eating habits which will adhere more closely to known principles of nutrition.

Professional Education in Nutrition

Without an adequate number of well-trained and qualified professional personnel it would be extremely difficult to apply effectively what is now known about nutrition to a national health program. There must be more nutrition education for professional people and there must be an improvement in the quality and quantity of professional training in the science of nutrition and its related subjects. Such an improvement will also help to further the cause of research, which aims to clarify the relation of food and nutrition to health and disease.

There is an acute shortage of professional workers with special training in foods and nutrition. Few physicians, health officers, dentists, medical or health administrators, nurses, or social workers have received much training in nutrition. The number of dietitians has been decreasing since the war, and there are many more positions for nutritionists, both as consultants and as community workers, than there are persons trained to fill them. This situation indicates the need for an evaluation of the academic requirements for specialized nutrition personnel and for an analysis of the important economic and social problems of salaries, working conditions, and professional prestige.

Training of the following types of personnel must be considered: undergraduate and graduate students in the basic sciences; medical undergraduates and graduates; dental undergraduates and graduates; health officers, nurses, and health educators; nutritionists and dietitians; social workers; and teachers.

1. Nutrition programming in courses of instruction. A planned program of instruction in nutrition should be made an integral part of the training of all personnel in the field of health, especially for the physician, dentist, health officer, nurse, health educator, social worker, and teacher.

The infectious diseases, which were the leading causes of death in 1900, are no longer major public health problems. The professional school which concentrates on sanitation and the control of communicable diseases is simply resting on the laurels of the past. The health problems which confront this country today are the chronic and degenerative diseases; any progress in these health areas will be aided by an increased knowledge of nutrition. Professional education today, therefore, must include adequate provision for nutrition training at all levels.

(1) Undergraduate and graduate students in the biological sciences. Fundamental progress in the science of nutrition is most likely to come from the group of workers who have undergraduate and

graduate training in the biological sciences. A satisfactory pattern of training, including nutrition instruction, is well recognized in the requirements of most colleges.

All professional personnel in the field of nutrition should have some acquaintance with general chemistry, physiology, and biochemistry, the amount depending on what the professional worker's job will be. Since nutrition is an experimental science, it is important that professional people acquire an appreciation of the experimental method through experience in the laboratory. On the other hand, there are aspects of nutrition which are treated in the social sciences, and the worker who does not understand the interrelation between nutrition and social science will remain permanently handicapped in his efforts to adjust food practices to nutritional needs.

(2) Medical undergraduate and graduate students. In medicine, the applications of nutrition are so broad and varied that nutrition training can best be approached along two major lines: (a) Nutrition should be incorporated into many of the standard courses in the present medical curriculum. (b) There should be special courses for those who are particularly interested in nutrition. A special committee in the professional school should be made responsible for planning and integrating nutrition teaching with the regular teaching program.

Nutrition should be an essential component of the standard medical curriculum. It can be worked into a number of courses in each of the years of professional education. For instance, aspects of nutrition should be stressed in anatomy, biochemistry, physiology, bacteriology, pathology, physical diagnosis, laboratory diagnosis, pediatrics, medicine, surgery, obstetrics, and preventive medicine. Biochemistry, in particular, should emphasize the concept of nutrition, vitamins A and D, thiamine, riboflavin and niacin, folic acid, choline, ascorbic acid, other vitamins and growth factors, and the trace minerals. Bacteriology should present the fundamentals demonstrated by bacterial nutrition, and pathology should describe the nutritional deficiencies in detail. Second-year pediatrics should include the following nutrition material: nutrition and the physiology of the newborn, nutrition and the progress of growth, nutrition and the significance of retarded growth, and the nutritional requirements of infants and children. In third-year pediatrics, which deals with the principles of infant and child feeding, consideration should be given to the deficiency diseases and the relationship between deficiencies and infections.

In applied nutrition, students should learn to prescribe and interpret diets. Nutrition "rounds" in the hospital should be held weekly.

(3) Dental students. The dental curriculum should have the same type of emphasis on nutrition as the medical school. Operative dentistry and oral medicine for third- and fourth-year students can stress the relationship between nutrition and disease even more emphatically than can the medical curriculum, because of the great value of the oral cavity in the diagnosis of systemic conditions.

Nutrition should also be introduced into the refresher courses for dental and medical graduates, under the guidance of the graduate schools.

(4) Health officers, public health nurses, and health educators. Every health officer and, wherever possible, every public health nurse and health educator should have a course in public health nutrition in a graduate school of public health. The material necessary for such a course could be covered adequately in a series of 24 one-hour lectures. Nutrition education for nurses should follow the recommendations prepared by the American Dietetic Association and the National League of Nursing Education.

(5) Nutritionists and dietitians. The American Dietetic Association and the American Home Economics Association have established qualifications and educational standards for professional dietitians and nutritionists. These should be used as a guide for the education and training of professional workers in these fields.

(6) Social workers. Social workers must have adequate instruction in nutrition. This is necessary because social workers deal with family problems and because food is such an important item in the family budget.

(7) Teachers. Nutrition education should constitute a very important phase of the training of schoolteachers. From a public health point of view, nutrition instruction in teacher training is vital. If nutrition education is to be carried out effectively in the elementary and secondary schools, where it can have the greatest benefits

and most lasting effects on the food habits and growth of children, there must be adequate and effective nutrition instruction in teachers' colleges. The importance of nutrition in health must be appreciated by school administrators and school boards.

2. The need for additional funds. Because of the serious shortage of professional workers with nutrition training, there must be an increase in the number of personnel with specialized education in nutrition. Education in nutrition should be directed particularly toward physicians, public health workers, dietitians, and nutritionists. To accomplish this important purpose, increased funds should be made available for research, for scholarships, and for subsidy of special projects in community and public health nutrition for demonstration and field training.

Education of the Public in Nutrition

The importance of public education in nutrition has already been mentioned in connection with the necessity for research to discover the best methods of popular education. All nutrition research and organization is of little value if people cannot or will not change fixed habits of eating so that they may benefit from good nutrition.

Although the physician is responsible for the treatment of nutritional deficiency diseases and questions of nutrition as they relate to specific medical problems, the improvement of food habits and of the quality of the food eaten is part of lay education. Nutrition should be included in public education at all ages.

Information about food reaches the public from various sources. Many different types of motivation must be used to change food habits. It is essential that authentic nutrition education be given to all professional and lay workers who can influence individuals and family groups.

1. *Goal of nutrition education.* The general goal of nutrition education is to stimulate and establish good food habits in every individual by bringing him the knowledge necessary to select a good diet and helping him to understand the relationship between an adequate diet and good health. To attain this goal, a nutrition education program must be planned around the food needs and nutrition problems at different age levels and around those of special groups with common interests and similar problems.

2. *Nutrition education for specific groups.* Certain groups are particularly exposed to nutritional deficiencies or are subject to specific conditions which may affect their food consumption. Early and intensive

attention to the improvement of the nutritional health of the groups listed below will benefit a large portion of the population.

(1) Pregnant and nursing women. The importance of good nutrition to the health of pregnant and nursing women has been amply demonstrated. There is valid evidence available now to indicate that adequate diets during pregnancy will reduce the incidence of toxemia, premature births, stillbirths, and neonatal deaths.

(2) Infants. Proper feeding in infancy is recognized as essential to normal growth and development. The right to begin life with the health that comes from a well-nourished body should be the birthright of every American child.

(3) Pre-school children. Although the diet of pre-school children undergoes rapid change while food likes and dislikes are being established, there is often no provision for nutrition instruction in the period between infancy and attendance at school. This is a serious lack which should be remedied. Furthermore, the high rate of respiratory and infectious diseases of pre-school children imposes a special need for optimal nutrition during this period.

(4) School children. Since habits are formed most easily during childhood, the opportunity to establish good food habits is greatest at this period. Channels for instruction are available for school children. Methods must be developed, however, for making the instruction effective.

(5) Adolescents. Food requirements are at a maximum during the period of adolescent growth, yet few efforts have been made to reach children at this time. Nutrition problems also arise out of the emotional instability at this age, which produces specific problems in relation to food habits.

(6) Industrial workers. Workers share the need for better food practices which is common to the population as a whole. However, they frequently have additional food problems which arise from inadequate eating facilities in or near the place of work and sometimes from occupational stress or exposure.

(7) Older people and chronic invalids. Physiological food requirements change with advancing age, and many persons with chronic conditions require special diets. Also, studies have shown that members of the older generation generally consume especially poor diets. Proper nutrition at this age level could contribute to an extension of the period of active life.

(8) Homemakers. Housewives and homemakers have a position of special importance in relation to the food consumption of all members of family groups. They plan the meals, they buy and cook the food, and it is largely through their interest in and application of good food practices that the nutritional status of the family can be improved.

3. *Methods of public education in nutrition.* Education of the public in nutrition may be of three general types: (1) general education by the use of mass media; (2) group instruction; and (3) individual consultation and assistance. Nutritionists and educators should give careful consideration to the selection of information and teaching methods which may be used in any specific situation.

4. *Some nutrition education measures.* The education activities just mentioned may be promoted and extended by the effective application of the various measures which follow:

(1) Nutrition training for family health-and-welfare workers. There should be a program of pre-service and in-service training in nutrition for workers concerned with family health and welfare so that they may give nutritional guidance to individuals and families with whom they have professional contact.

(2) Nutrition training for teachers. Pre-service and in-service training in basic nutrition should be made available for teachers in elementary schools. Teachers and administrators should be assisted in making nutrition education an integral part of *all* curricula—health education, science, social studies, home economics, reading, and so forth.

(3) Supervision of special nutrition programs. Whenever possible, a trained dietitian or nutritionist should supervise the school-lunch program, the industrial cafeteria, and similar eating facilities. These facilities should play an important part in a broad nutrition education program. When a dietitian or a nutritionist is not available, appropriate in-service training should be provided for the personnel in charge of these programs.

(4) School-lunch program. The school-lunch program should be extended to include *all* children in *all* schools and should become the responsibility of school administrators as part of the regular school program.

(5) Local nutrition education material. Local groups should be encouraged, under adequate guidance, to prepare nutrition educa-

tion material that reflects regional, cultural, or local variations in food habits.

(6) Visual aids and printed material. Visual aids and printed material, including pamphlets, exhibits, and motion picture and radio material, should be widely used in the nutrition education program. Official and voluntary agencies can make their educational material more effective by seeking the advice of advertising experts, as well as that of educators and nutritionists.

(7) Local nutrition committees. Local nutrition committees, which should include representation from community nutritionists, physicians, and others active or interested in nutrition education, should be organized. These committees should act, wherever possible, as part of the local health councils. The committees can perform a valuable job by serving as clearing houses for local agencies, by filling in the gaps in the total community nutrition program, by stimulating interest in and awareness of proper food habits, and by sponsoring projects too extensive or controversial to be undertaken by any individual local group.

(8) Central office for nutrition education material. A vast amount of printed materials and audio-visual aids dealing with nutrition is prepared by individuals, by industry, and by educational, health, and welfare agencies, both official and voluntary. Some of this material is widely distributed and is used by a number of people with varying professional training. However, no standards have been set for the subject matter or the presentation; consequently much of this material does not measure up to high standards of accuracy, completeness, and effectiveness.

There is an urgent need for a *central office*, under national auspices, where materials from all sources may be assembled and appraised for their accuracy, truthfulness in emphasis, and effectiveness of presentation. Education material must also be classified according to its purpose, the groups it is intended to serve, and the people who can use it as an effective teaching aid.

(9) Research in nutrition education. The most effective methods of educating the public in nutrition must still be explored. The best approaches toward effecting permanent changes in food habits in various groups must be determined. It is also necessary to find out what methods and techniques will prove most beneficial in classroom instruction for specific groups, as well as to discover what

methods of mass education will produce the most desirable food habits. The Federal government should stimulate, conduct, and support research in the field of nutrition education to make these purposes possible.

The problems of nutrition are among the most important affecting this nation's health. Nutrition must take its place along with other preventive programs to raise the health of the people and to promote sounder bodies, greater happiness, and longer life. Much can be done in this country and throughout the world to improve nutrition. Much must be done if we are to set realistic and attainable ten-year health goals.

APPENDIX A

Sections of the Final Act of the 1943 United Nations Conference on Food and Agriculture in Hot Springs, Virginia, which pertain to nutrition:

VII. NATIONAL NUTRITION ORGANIZATION

WHEREAS:

1. A sound food and nutrition policy must be adopted by each government if national diets are to be progressively improved, specific deficiency diseases eliminated, and good health achieved;

2. Such a policy requires the guidance of a central authority with special competence and responsibility to interpret the science of nutrition in the light of national conditions and to propose to the appropriate authorities practical means for extending its benefits to all sections of society;

THE UNITED NATIONS CONFERENCE ON FOOD AND AGRICULTURE RECOMMENDS:

1. That the governments and authorities here represented:

(a) Undertake to establish national nutrition organizations, if such do not now exist, entrusted with the responsibility of ascertaining food-consumption habits and the nutritional status of different sections of the population; such organizations to be composed of authorities in health, nutrition, economics, and agriculture, together with administrators and consumers' representatives, etc.; to be provided with adequate funds and facilities for the efficient conduct of their work; and to have the authority to bring their recommendations to the attention of the public and to those agencies of government which deal with agriculture and the framing of economic and social policy;

(b) Re-examine and, if necessary, re-organize existing agencies and review legislation concerned with health, agriculture, and nutrition to the end that food and nutrition policies may be efficiently carried out.

VIII. EXCHANGE OF INFORMATION AND EXPERIENCE

WHEREAS:

1. Experience has shown that national nutrition organizations receive considerable benefit from periodic exchanges of views and information on methods employed, obstacles encountered, and progress achieved;

2. Governments participating in a common undertaking will wish to collaborate so that levels of food consumption may become more equitable not only among the different sections of the population in a given country but among the several nations of the world as well;

THE UNITED NATIONS CONFERENCE ON FOOD AND AGRICULTURE RECOMMENDS:

1. That the several national nutrition organizations exchange information and experience and provide mutual assistance, both directly, when desirable, and through the permanent organization recommended in Resolution II, to which they should submit periodic reports on the results of their investigations into national dietary habits and nutritional status, and on the progress achieved in raising the level of food consumption throughout the population;

2. That representatives of the several national nutrition organizations meet regularly under the auspices of the permanent organization to exchange views and to make proposals for any national and international action necessary to facilitate the progress of their work.

IX. DIETARY STANDARDS

WHEREAS:

1. It is essential that there be some measure of the extent to which food supplies should be increased, and of the character and extent of the dietary improvements which need to be carried out;

2. This measure is best provided by dietary standards or allowances based upon scientific evidence;

THE UNITED NATIONS CONFERENCE ON FOOD AND AGRICULTURE RECOMMENDS:

That the governments and authorities here represented adopt, as the ultimate goal of their food and nutrition policy, dietary standards or allowances based upon scientific assessment of the amount and quality of food, in terms of nutrients, which promote health, and distinguish clearly between these standards and the more immediate consumption goals which necessarily must be based upon the practical possibilities of improving the food supply of their populations.

APPENDIX B

PLANNING COMMITTEE

Frank G. Boudreau, M.D., Chairman
Executive Director
Milbank Memorial Fund

Mrs. Bertha S. Burke
Department of Child Hygiene
Harvard University School of Public Health

Rowland Burnstan
Executive Director
State Charities Aid Association
New York, New York

C. G. King
Scientific Director
The Nutrition Foundation, Inc.

L. A. Maynard
School of Nutrition
Cornell University

Frederick J. Stare, M.D.
Department of Nutrition
Harvard University School of Public Health

STAFF ASSISTANTS

Harold R. Sandstead, M.D.
Chief, Nutrition Section
States Relations Division
Public Health Service, Federal Security Agency

Fred W. Morse, Jr., M.D.
Assistant Chief, Nutrition Section
States Relations Division
Public Health Service, Federal Security Agency

SUBCOMMITTEE CHAIRMEN

International Aspects of Nutrition:
H. E. Longenecker
Dean, Graduate School
University of Pittsburgh

Food Supplies:
L. A. Maynard
School of Nutrition
Cornell University

Organization and Administration of Nutrition Programs:
Elmer L. Sevringhaus, M.D.
Medical Director
Hoffman-La Roche, Inc.

Research in Nutrition:
C. G. King
Scientific Director
The Nutrition Foundation, Inc.

Professional Education in Nutrition:

Frederick J. Stare, M.D.

Department of Nutrition
Harvard University
School of Public Health

Education of the Public in Nutrition:

Miss Pauline Murrah

Director, Nutrition Service of North Atlantic
Area
American Red Cross

Rowland Burnstan

Executive Director
State Charities Aid Association
New York, New York

REGISTRANTS

L. J. Babin

School Superintendent
Ascension Parish
Donaldsonville, Louisiana

F. C. Beelman, M.D.

Secretary and Executive Officer
Kansas State Board of Health

Mrs. Frank G. Boudreau

Country Women's Council
United Nations

Mrs. Anna dePlanter Bowes

Chief, Division of Nutrition
Pennsylvania State Department of Health

Mrs. Gertrude N. Bowie

American Home Economics Association

John H. Browe, M.D.

Research Associate
Department of Medicine
University of Vermont College of Medicine

A. Hughes Bryan, M.D.

Professor of Public Health Nutrition
University of North Carolina

Miss Louise G. Campbell

Committee on Tuberculosis and Public
Health
New York State Charities Aid Association

Herrell DeGraff

Department of Agricultural Economics
Cornell University

Max Shaw Dunn

Professor of Chemistry
University of California

Stanford F. Farnsworth, M.D.

City Health Officer
Oakland, California

Mrs. Martha Smith Fry

Chairman, Connecticut Nutrition Council

Grace A. Goldsmith, M.D.

Tulane University School of Medicine

Wendell H. Griffith

Professor of Biological Chemistry
St. Louis University School of Medicine

George M. Guest, M.D.	Children's Hospital Research Foundation Cincinnati, Ohio
Miss Violet B. Higbee	Extension Service Rhode Island State College
Herman E. Hilleboe, M.D.	New York State Commissioner of Health
Mrs. Icie Macy Hoobler	Director, Research Laboratory Children's Fund of Michigan
Miss Helen A. Hunscher	Head, Department of Home Economics Western Reserve University
Mrs. Alice M. Irmisch	Columbus, New Jersey
W. P. Jacocks, M.D.	Director, Nutrition Division North Carolina State Board of Health
Miss Flemmie P. Kittrell	Dean, School of Home Economics Howard University
H. D. Kruse, M.D.	Milbank Memorial Fund
Mrs. Paul H. Leonard	National Chairman, School Lunch Program National Congress of Parents and Teachers
Miss Elizabeth Lockwood	Department of Nutrition Harvard University School of Public Health
Miss Janie McDill	South Carolina Extension Service
Miss May McDonald	Senior Home Economist New York State Department of Social Welfare
Miss Florence S. MacLeod	Assistant Director, Agricultural Experiment Station; Professor of Nutrition University of Tennessee
Fairfield Osborn	President, New York Zoological Society
Herbert Pollack, M.D.	New York, New York
Miss Ruth Powell	State Supervisor, School Lunch Service Arkansas State Department of Education
Guy V. Rice, M.D.	Division of Maternal and Child Health Georgia State Department of Public Health
Miss Elda Robb	Professor of Nutrition Simmons College
Robert E. Shank, M.D.	Professor of Preventive Medicine Washington University St. Louis, Missouri
J. L. K. Snyder	Merck & Company
Winslow T. Tompkins, M.D.	Nutrition Research Clinic Lying-In Hospital Philadelphia, Pennsylvania

Miss Maxine Turner — Nutrition Consultant
Millers' National Federation

Miss Maude Wallace — State Extension Service
Virginia Polytechnic Institute

Miss Dorothy G. Wiehl — Milbank Memorial Fund

Russell M. Wilder, M.D. — Mayo Clinic
Rochester, Minnesota

Walter Wilkins, M.D. — Director, Nutrition Investigations
Florida State Board of Health

Miss G. Dorothy Williams — Chief of Nutrition Division
New York City Department of Health

James R. Wilson, M.D. — Secretary, Council on Foods and Nutrition
American Medical Association

John B. Youmans, M.D. — Dean, College of Medicine
University of Illinois

Miss Charlotte M. Young — Assistant Professor, Medical Nutrition
Cornell University

❰ XIV ❱

A National Program
of Environmental Sanitation

THE development of a national program of environmental sanitation
was a task that required the best efforts of the engineers, physicians,
scientists, and laymen responsible for considering that phase of the
National Health Assembly. Of all the Sections of the Assembly, it was
probably the least controversial. This was due primarily to the fact that
much of the knowledge required to provide a healthful environment is
well known and that the techniques by which it is applied have general
acceptance throughout the field.

The delegates accepted as a fundamental point in their deliberations
the view that "a safe and healthful environment is a prerequisite to all
activities aimed at preserving and improving the health of the people."
They also knew that the technical workers responsible for sanitation
activities could provide a disease-free drinking-water supply in sufficient
amounts for all domestic purposes; suitable means for the collection and
disposal of sewage and refuse; a food supply carefully guarded from the
producer to the consumer; a community and neighborhood environment
which would have healthful homes free of accidents, excessive noise, and
vermin; a clean atmosphere unpolluted by smoke and other noxious
gases; places of employment free of industrial hazards; and wholesome
recreational facilities.

All this and more the delegates knew could be provided. Though these
benefits may seem utopian in character, they are intensely practical and
potentially capable of achievement. Some of them, such as a wholesome
drinking-water supply, have already been provided to a majority of the
American public. Others have not progressed to the same degree; a few
have not even been initiated.

The clearly recognized need, apparent early in this Section's deliberations, was to seek ways through which existing knowledge and "know

how" could be made available to each citizen and each community. The subcommittee on administration reported that:

A fully effective program of environmental sanitation must have, as a basic essential, a widespread understanding on the part of the people of the need for and value of established procedures in environmental sanitation, together with a sufficiently strong desire on the part of the people for such full-time health services as are needed for the development of sanitation services.

The Section was emphatic in its approval of the need for public education concerning the importance of environmental sanitation. There was agreement that the demand for the services, utilities, or conditions which go to form a healthful environment would come only when the people themselves become concerned. It was emphasized that the public is not yet conscious of what environmental sanitation means and, lacking this knowledge, cannot effectively demand or undertake its share of responsibility for the necessary services.

Considerable discussion centered also on people's ability to afford such services. Again, the answer seemed to be that, if the people of the community concerned could be made to realize the menace to their health or welfare that was present, funds would be found.

With complete unanimity, the Section went on to make the following recommendation:

It should be the primary duty of every local and state public health department to carry out a program which will insure a safe and healthful living environment for the individual at all times. Further, inasmuch as any public health program is valuable only so far as it may improve the health and welfare of the individual, then it becomes the duty of the health department to acquaint the individual with the program in all details, even to the extent of providing community education, or special education within the schools, to make clear to the consumer or individual that he is the recipient of all programs in environmental sanitation and that he has his responsibility in making the program effective. It is not enough to establish programs to educate the health worker.

Equal agreement was reached on the necessity for expanding existing health agencies and forming new ones where none exist, in order to have the basic governmental structure from which sanitation services are initiated. In this connection, this Section emphasized its strong agreement with the recommendations of the Section on Local Health Units. It was believed equally important to supplement local sanitation programs with strong state and Federal programs to provide training, technical counsel, and general guidance in developing adequate state and national goals.

That the Environmental Sanitation Section took a responsible, broad-minded attitude in surveying the task is illustrated in its final general recommendation:

All sanitation programs should be administered with a deep sense of efficiency, bearing in mind that such a program is only one of the many necessary Federal, state, and local government activities aimed at improving the welfare of the country. Waste from unnecessary duplication of effort, duplication of personnel services, and duplication of paper work and records should be prevented.

Because of the many activities that are encompassed in the field of environmental sanitation, the Section members found it desirable to divide into seven subcommittees to consider the following broad topics: water supply, sewerage, and water pollution; milk and other foods; living environment; working environment; insect and rodent control; research; and administration. Each subcommittee briefly analyzed the problems existing in its particular field and suggested recommendations to the Section as a whole. The recommendations contained in each of the separate subcommittee reports as set forth below were subsequently approved by, and represent conclusions endorsed by, the full membership of the Section on a National Program of Environmental Sanitation.

CONCLUSIONS AND RECOMMENDATIONS
WATER SUPPLY, SEWERAGE, AND WATER POLLUTION

Water Supply

Human beings cannot live without water. The quality of water in any given location has a direct effect on health.

Public water supplies of proper quality are an essential requirement of our modern city existence. In 1900 there were only 3,200 public water supplies in the United States, and the quality of the water served was generally poor. In that year over 23,000 people in the nation died of typhoid fever, and more than 100,000 deaths were due to diarrhea-enteritis and dysenteries. Today over 14,000 systems provide water to about 85 million people, and the quality of the water furnished is generally excellent. In recent years the deaths from typhoid have dropped to less than 600 and deaths from other enteric diseases to about 15,000 per year.

There is need to continue service at the highest practicable standard and to be constantly alert to the danger of cross connections, uncovered purified water reservoirs, and other degrading influences. Water-safety programs, including more frequent bacteriological examination, supervision over construction and repairs, and elimination of sanitary defects, are essential to assure a water supply of the highest quality. Future needs include extension of the present systems as well as the construction of new systems in communities growing to the point where they can profit by such supplies.

Although much has been accomplished, a great deal has yet to be done. On the basis of a reasonable estimate of the needs, the United States Public Health Service survey of the nation's sanitation requirements[1] indicated that approximately 2,360,000 people in 5,710 communities with no public waterworks systems need such facilities; that almost 15,000 communities with over 79 million people have waterworks which need improvements or extensions; and that in rural areas, where community systems are impracticable, 27 million people need either new or improved water supplies. In terms of 1947 costs, it was estimated that to meet these needs would cost about $2¼ billion, of which roughly $400 million was allocated to work ready for construction, $600 million to work in various stages of planning, and about $1¼ billion to future projects.

Our expanding water requirements dictate that the health authorities should continually bear in mind the conservation of water resources, both surface and underground. Similarly, authoritative agencies should constantly evaluate the quantities of water available and, when necessary, should control such resources, giving preference to domestic water-supply needs.

At the present time there are many unknown effects from water impurities, in spite of the fact that drinking-water standards have been established. The immediate needs and those for the years just ahead include constant study and research to improve methods of treatment and of water-quality measurement.

In many areas of the nation, careful consideration is being given to water conservation and use. Many water uses conflict, with the result that water use and conservation agencies are being established to cor-

[1] *Nation-wide Inventory of Sanitation Needs,* Supplement No. 204 to the Public Health Reports (Washington: Public Health Service, Federal Security Agency, April, 1948).

relate the various interests and to arrive at an over-all plan for the greatest benefit of all concerned. Considerations affecting public health should have high priority in any plan for water development and control. Public health agencies, therefore, should be represented on bodies concerned with the development of water plans.

Sewerage

The importance of sewer systems is attested by the fact that over 70 million people are served by such systems today, as compared with only 25 million in 1900. Yet more than 9,100 communities, with nearly 6½ million people, need complete sewerage systems. Some 9,900 additional communities, with almost 80 million people, have systems which need improvements. In rural areas, more than 33 million people lack satisfactory sewage- or excreta-disposal facilities of even the simplest type.

The cost of these services in 1947 are outlined in the *Nation-wide Inventory of Sanitation Needs*[2] as follows: projects ready for construction, over $350 million; projects then planned, $1 billion; future projects, nearly $2½ billion; total cost requirements, $3¾ billion.

Suburban and Rural Water Supplies and Sewerage Systems

For nearly half a century the aim of health agencies has been to stimulate the construction of community water systems capable of producing safe drinking water. The ability of incorporated communities to care for their own problems through community action aided greatly in this effort. During the past fifteen years the tendency for substantial parts of municipal populations to move to low-tax, unincorporated suburban areas has created problems of sanitation which now must be faced by the residents themselves and by state and local government authorities not specifically geared to care for such problems. The hazard of individual sewerage systems and individual wells in heavily populated communities is an environmental health problem of the first magnitude. Areas lacking adequate basic sanitation facilities are likely to develop into the slums of the future.

The extent of the problem is illustrated by the housing authorized for construction in the incorporated areas and that authorized for the suburban areas in six locations:[3]

[2] See footnote 1.

[3] *Construction* (Washington: Bureau of Labor Statistics, U. S. Department of Labor, July, 1948).

Area	Percentage of Housing Authorized Within Corporate Limits	Percentage of Housing Authorized in Area Outside Corporate Limits
Philadelphia–Camden	38	62
Washington, D. C.	24	76
San Francisco	26	74
Atlanta	19	81
Los Angeles	36	64
New York–Newark–Jersey City	58	42

Further illustrating the problem is the percentage of housing units in Federal Housing Agency insured subdivisions requiring non-public water supply or sewerage facilities:[4]

Location	Total Number of Units	Percentage of Units Requiring Non-Public Water Supply or Sewerage Facilities
Birmingham, Alabama	11,889	21
Atlanta, Georgia	5,883	32
Charleston, South Carolina	2,250	30
Houston, Texas	21,547	23
Columbus, Georgia	10,404	16
Topeka, Kansas	3,669	22

The condition can be corrected by the extension of existing water and sewer mains into these areas or by the formation of government units able to build such utilities. In many states, enabling legislation will be required in order to allow counties or other local governmental units to engage in such activities.

Health services should be provided that would assure proper protection of water supplies and the disposal of human wastes in rural areas, where, of necessity, dependence on individual water supplies and sewage disposal must continue.

Water Pollution

Pollution of surface waters constitutes a serious problem and has a direct effect on the national public health as related to domestic water supplies, recreation, agricultural uses of water and, less directly, as related to industrial water supplies, wildlife, and other uses.

[4] Based on information from the Land Planning Section, Federal Housing Agency, for 1947 and part of 1948. (Location, or district insuring offices, selected at random from complete national files.)

The recent *Nation-wide Inventory of Sanitation Needs*[5] showed that, whereas in 1900 there were only 60 sewage-treatment plants serving 1 million people, today over 5,500 treatment plants serve 42 million people and over 90 million people are served by sewer systems. Sewage from approximately one-third of the population served by sewerage systems is discharged into streams without any treatment, and much of the sewage from two-thirds of the population with sewerage facilities is inadequately treated. The best data available indicate that even greater proportions of industrial wastes are either untreated or inadequately treated before being discharged into our waterways.

Since stream pollution can best be attacked in areas within stream basins rather than within existing political boundaries, an aggressive campaign to correct and abate surface-water pollution must be carried out co-operatively by Federal, state, and local agencies.

Water is the most valuable underground asset in many sections of the nation. Underground waters are being menaced on a large scale by overdraft and by pollution due to direct discharge of pollutional material into underground aquifers, as well as indirectly by the careless construction, abandonment, or uncontrolled operation of ground-water developments. It is imperative that consideration be given to the development and control of underground water resources to prevent further waste or pollution. This would seem to be primarily the concern of the state and local health authorities. It is recommended that:

1. Constant consideration by health authorities should be given to the conservation of water resources, both surface and underground. The qualified agency should evaluate the quantities of water available and, when necessary, should control resources so as to give preference to domestic water-supply needs.

2. There should be constant study and research to improve water-treatment methods and methods of water-quality measurement.

3. Wherever practicable, water and sewerage service should be provided by extensions to existing systems or by the construction of new systems to serve entire communities or extensive residential areas.

4. Aggressive campaigns by Federal, state, and local agencies must be conducted to abate water pollution.

5. Control of underground water resources should be developed to prevent further pollution and to conserve the quality and quantity of water available.

[5] See footnote 1.

MILK AND OTHER FOODS

Under certain adverse conditions of production, processing, and final distribution to the consumer, foods (including milk and milk products; meat and meat products; fish, shellfish, and other products; vegetables and fruits; baked goods; and bottled waters and beverages) may constitute an ideal medium for the dissemination of disease. United States Public Health Service compilations report 318 outbreaks—with 13,321 cases—of food-and-milk-borne disease during 1946.[6]

The general public has the right to expect that foods will be of such soundness and maintained freshness as will insure optimum nutritional value and that food values will be protected from destruction or spoilage by rodents, insects, or other causes.

These facts are recognized and accepted not only by public health officials but also by the majority of producers, processors, distributors, and other handlers of food—including public restaurants and industrial, school, and institutional food services.[7] It therefore appears in keeping with good public health policy to recommend the following program:

1. All the fluid milk consumed should be pasteurized by urban milk distributors, pasteurized milk sales to rural areas should be expanded, and home pasteurization should be promoted in areas not having commercially pasteurized milk.

2. Pasteurization or other adequate protection should be given to other dairy products.

3. Enforcement by health authorities and food handlers should include inspection of transportation, wholesale, and retail facilities; special attention in such enforcement should be given to the refrigeration of quick-cured and pre-cooked meat products, cream-filled bakery goods, and all foods capable of serving as a medium for disease-producing bacteria and to the protection of foods from insects, human (contact and droplet) infection, and rodents by all available means.

4. Food handlers should be educated with respect to the sanitation

[6] This represents no reduction in food-borne outbreaks but does indicate a reduction of 44 per cent in milk-borne outbreaks in comparison with the previous eight-year average. These figures are compiled from voluntary reports by state and local health departments; they are not complete for the nation.

[7] The United States Public Health Service reports that as of July 1, 1948, the Milk Ordinance recommended by USPHS was in effect in communities with a total population of 34 million, and that 60 million people resided in communities that have enacted the recommended Eating and Drinking Establishment Ordinance.

requirements in the handling of foods and the public health significance of such requirements.

5. Information should be disseminated to the consumer on the need for the adequate protection of perishable foods purchased for and prepared in the home.

6. Health authorities should adequately enforce the sanitation requirements for handlers of bottled waters—from source to consumer.

7. Studies should be made of the adequacy of state and city sanitary control of fresh meat, poultry, and fish.

8. In co-operation with official food-regulatory agencies, companies and associations concerned with producing, processing, distributing, and handling food should accept the responsibility for developing and promulgating acceptable sanitary codes, employee-training programs, and inspection service.

9. The proposal to have the National Research Council under the Research and Marketing Act study the effect of certain regulatory measures upon the quality, supply, and cost of milk should be highly commended and endorsed.

10. Research should be undertaken for the development of satisfactory field methods and laboratory methods for the evaluation of bactericidal materials and methods used in food industries; also for a chemical test for the identification of the enterotoxin of staphylococcus.

11. Adequate local public health laboratory service should be established. (See recommendations elsewhere in this report for the expansion of local health services.)

12. There should be long-term planning for the development and acceptance of sanitary food equipment similar to the development of sanitary dairy equipment.

13. A careful study should be made in each state toward elimination of any duplication of activities in this field by state and city inspectional authorities.

Living Environment

A primary duty of all public health departments is to assure a safe and healthful living environment. Since public health is primarily concerned with the well-being of groups of individuals, the public health departments must have the legal power of review and ultimate determination with regard to matters of environment in so far as they affect the health of the people. Not only has there been a lack of legal authority, but the program has been further delayed by the shortage of qualified professional personnel.

The very great shortage of engineering and other sanitation personnel in local environmental health work is evidenced by the 1942 data presented in the Report on Local Health Units for the Nation (1945)[8] which showed 306 engineers employed. More recent studies indicate that a sevenfold increase in the number of engineers must be added to local health units for environmental sanitation activities to furnish adequate coverage in health protection to the people and to make up existing deficiencies. These studies also show the need for a twofold increase in other sanitation personnel.

The health problems dealing with housing, community planning, and municipal housekeeping are complex, involving engineering, economics, sociology, and public health. Since the development of sound health programs requires well-qualified personnel basically equipped to deal with these problems, the public health personnel selected to do such work should meet the qualifications set up by the American Public Health Association.

Community Planning

The public health department has a primary responsibility in community planning because of its duty to promote and protect the health of the people. Other governmental agencies are generally charged with the legal responsibility for planning. It is therefore essential that public health departments be adequately represented at the policy-making level of the community planning agencies.

In addition to planning agencies as such, a number of other activities carried on primarily by other governmental agencies have as their basic justification the promotion and protection of the public health with respect to water supply, sewerage, solid-waste removal, housing, air-pollution control, recreational facilities, and so forth. To obtain proper recognition of the public health aspects of these problems, public health departments must participate in the formulation of policies and programs and must periodically review the effectiveness of such programs. This should be accomplished by the official inclusion of public health department personnel on directing boards and commissions or on an interde-

[8] American Public Health Association, *Report of the Committee on Administrative Practices* (New York: Commonwealth Fund, 1945).

partmental co-ordinating committee, as well as by developing effective liaison with other services. Your committee recommends that:

1. The United States Public Health Service and the state health departments should provide consulting service to the local public health departments in the health and safety aspects of community planning.

2. The necessary legal steps should be taken to include public health department participation at the policy-making levels in community agencies dealing with problems that impinge on the public health.

3. The United States Public Health Service should actively participate with funds and personnel in the development of standards for community planning and redevelopment.

Community Housekeeping

The health implications of community housekeeping form the basic foundation for community housekeeping functions. Health interests may be adequately served by the participation of public health departments in policy making and in periodic reviews of the effectiveness of programs. Public health departments need not have the responsibility for performing the actual collection and disposal of solid waste, but they should be represented at the policy-forming levels.

The techniques for the collection and disposal of solid wastes are generally well known and well developed, but they have not been fully utilized. New devices, such as the garbage grinder for the disposal of organic solids, need further study.

In metropolitan areas the final disposition of solid wastes is becoming increasingly difficult, particularly if long and expensive transportation problems are to be avoided. Area planning with the aid of state and Federal health agencies is needed to solve some of these perplexing problems.

Procedures for the control of atmospheric pollution are more closely related to the customary public health functions, and public health departments may well include such activities. Problems in this field include smoke abatement and the control of atmospheric contamination in the vicinity of industries, the plant pollens harmful to man, and other atmospheric contaminants. All of these problems can be advantageously attacked on the basis of their health significance.

Community housekeeping is a problem in which all citizens can and should participate. Education in the assumption of individual responsibilities and the development of community spirit must be a local, state, and national undertaking. It is recommended that:

1. The state health departments and the United States Public Health Service should actively participate in the development of standards of atmospheric purity, procedures for effective control, and techniques for evaluating accomplishments.

2. The United States Public Health Service should expand its research activities to include studies in the collection and disposal of solid wastes.

3. The United States Public Health Service and the state health departments should assist in solving the perplexing problems arising in metropolitan areas in the disposal of solid wastes.

Housing

Shelter is a basic human need. Adequate and healthful housing is therefore essential to the well-being of any community and to the development of any sound public health program. Housing is one of the most important problems—if not the most important—confronting local public health departments. Although the task is tremendous, the lack of qualified personnel, legal authority, and advisory services and the extreme complexity of the over-all problem have tended to discourage and prevent the development of effective programs. The Twentieth Century Fund, in its 1947 *Survey of America's Needs and Resources*,[9] reports that 8,391,000 of a total of 23,684,000 urban dwelling units were substandard and that 5,034,000 of a total of 7,360,000 rural dwellings were likewise substandard.

The health implications of housing go beyond the physical structure. Consideration must also be given to the socio-economic aspects of the problem; these include (1) the inability of large segments of the population to pay economic rents, (2) the factors which cause overcrowding, and (3) discriminatory and other practices.

The relationship between housing and health has been well documented. The American Public Health Association's Committee on the Hygiene of Housing has made tremendous strides in formulating standards and appraisal methods. Appraisal procedures for evaluating the quality of substandard housing on an objective and quantitative basis are now available and are actually in use in many cities. Regular routine inspection of problem areas—rather than haphazard response to complaints—should be the basis of housing control in local communities. The Committee on the Hygiene of Housing should be given full support

[9] J. Frederick Dewhurst and Associates, *America's Needs and Resources* (New York: Twentieth Century Fund, 1947).

and financial assistance in order to bring about widespread application of its findings.

Local public health departments in carrying out their functions must necessarily turn to outside sources for consultation, advice, and assistance in establishing sound programs. Such assistance logically must come from the state health departments and from the United States Public Health Service.

No report on housing is complete without mention of the household accident rate. Approximately 33,000 fatal accidents and an estimated 5,000,000 disabling injuries occur in homes annually. Many of these are preventable. It is logical that public health departments take the leadership in preventing this great human loss. In the field of housing, it is recommended that:

1. The state health department and the United States Public Health Service should provide consulting service to the local public health departments on the health problems related to housing.

2. The United States Public Health Service should provide funds and personnel for making studies and investigations of existing housing conditions.

3. The United States Public Health Service and state and local public health departments should formulate effective means for combating and correcting the inadequacies in housing and for providing an adequate amount of healthful housing for the low-income groups in both urban and rural areas.

4. Government should extend its financial participation in providing adequate and healthful housing for low-income groups as the only apparent means of meeting the present need.

5. The United States Public Health Service should actively engage in a program of research into the factors of housing which affect health and safety.

6. All types of living accommodations—whether individual homes, multiple dwellings, institutions, recreation facilities, or tourists' and migratory workers' camps of either a temporary or a permanent character—should be required to meet suitable standards in all the aspects of environmental sanitation, and local public health departments should assume responsibility for seeing that such standards are maintained.

Our general recommendations on living environment are:

1. Schools should incorporate in their curricula the teaching of basic

community sanitation and the individual's responsibility for sharing in the program.

2. The United States Public Health Service should assume national leadership to develop an educational program for public participation in environmental sanitation.

3. The environmental sanitation programs of local public health departments should be strengthened by the addition of qualified personnel and adequate funds for equipment, supplies, and transportation.

4. The United States Public Health Service and the state health departments should expand their present consulting facilities in all phases of environmental sanitation.

5. The environmental sanitation programs should be extended to meet the needs of all segments of the population by the expansion of existing activities and by their extension not only in urban communities but also in suburban and rural areas.

WORKING ENVIRONMENT

The health and well-being of the breadwinner is essential to the social and economic security of the nation. It affects the welfare of the worker's family and the prosperity of his community. It influences the productivity and profits of industry.

To secure and maintain this necessary condition, the worker must come to his job from a healthful home and community and must find within industry a safe working environment, free from specific health hazards, and one which does not impose upon him undue physiological and psychological stress. The older worker should have an opportunity to utilize his skills and experience in continued productive employment.

These are the objectives of industrial hygiene. For their accomplishment we must utilize all of the skills and techniques of public health. The needs for improving the working environment must not be considered independently of the medical aspects of industrial health. The problem is manifold, requiring teamwork from physicians, engineers, and other scientific specialists in industrial hygiene.

The accomplishments of the past quarter century in industrial hygiene are outstanding. The basic principles and procedures for the study and control of occupational diseases are firmly established. New health hazards will be created with the development of new industrial processes, but through the immediate application of the same basic procedures these too can be controlled. The essential requirement now is to provide the necessary trained personnel in industry and in the community to make certain that this knowledge and these special skills are made available to all industry.

With the continued progress that may confidently be expected in the control of occupational diseases, the attention of public health specialists must now be turned, as well, to the less obvious stresses of the industrial environment—those which do not cause specific disease but which nonetheless influence the total health, efficiency, and well-being of the industrial population. These are largely the consequences of our highly mechanized modern industry. Not only is it necessary to select the workers best fitted to the jobs available, but, more important still, it is essential that the job be fitted to the worker. Industrial machines and processes as well as the general working environment must be designed to meet not only the functional requirements of production but also the physiological and psychological limitations of the worker.

In order to effect the further extension and expansion of the activities and objectives of the industrial health program, agreement has been reached on the following recommendations:

1. Facilities should be provided both within and outside of industry to bring the benefits of industrial hygiene to our entire industrial plant and population, and management, labor, and the community at large should co-operate to attain this objective.

2. Training centers for industrial hygiene personnel should be established and financially supported by industry and by the Federal government, and engineering education should place greater emphasis on the responsibility of the engineer to consider the human as well as the functional requirements in the design of industrial machines and processes.

3. Special attention should be given to fitting industrial machines and processes to provide continued productive employment for the aging but more experienced worker.

4. Research facilities should be expanded to include investigations of industrial physiology as well as the so-called human engineering and also to accelerate the securing of information on occupational diseases and hazards resulting from use of new chemicals or industrial processes.

5. Funds for research, for the training of personnel, and for expansion of the industrial health services of the state should be provided by Federal and state appropriations.

INSECT AND RODENT CONTROL

Insect carriers of disease (such as mosquitoes, flies, and ticks) and the animal hosts which harbor disease-producing organisms transmissible to man have a very important and direct effect upon the health and well-being of the nation. Examples of such effects are the high endemic incidence of malaria, spotted fever, and murine typhus in some sections of the country and the epidemics of plague, encephalomyelitis in horses, and encephalitis in man.

The economic influence of insect and rodent prevalence, as well as the health hazards involved, must be given consideration. Mosquitoes affect not only the comfort and productive efficiency of individuals but also the desirability, and even the availability, of large areas for residential use. Species formerly considered merely as nuisance types are now known to be potential carriers of virus diseases. The high cost of quarantines and of curtailed commercial operations incident to the presence of plague in a community constitutes an important economic problem.

The malaria-control programs which developed following the First World War, the work during the recent war, and the co-operation that was developed between the various states and the United States Public Health Service have caused a decrease in malaria. Malaria is on the way out as a major health problem in the United States, although much remains to be done in a few areas. Continued effort will be required for some time to prevent a reversal of the trend.

Concurrently with the decrease in malaria there has been a considerable increase in the number of reported cases of murine typhus. This disease is now a major health problem in many sections of the country.

Although the occurrence of some diseases usually considered fly-borne has been lowered in many areas, wherever there are flies there is the problem of the spread of intestinal diseases. The relationship of the fly to certain other diseases needs further study.

Rocky Mountain spotted fever is spreading over larger areas. At the same time, the entire country is bearing a tremendous economic loss due to the consumption and spoilage of foods by rodents. Qualified investigators have estimated that rats alone are responsible for an annual loss of $3 billion, in addition to the losses due to suffering, illness, and death from rodent-borne diseases. Food losses are particularly important at present, when we not only must provide for our own needs but also are called upon to help feed the hungry peoples of the entire world. In general, rodent-control work has been intermittent and sporadic. The tendency has been to relax when the imminent danger of disease has passed. The discovery of highly efficient rodenticides and insecticides and the formulation of specific rodent-proof building designs have given effective means for the control of rodent-borne disease.

Rodent control is not merely a health agency problem. Effective control requires continued and joint effort on the part of Federal, state, and local government units having an interest in the problem. Such a co-operative program is in operation at present on a nation-wide basis. There is definite need for the continuation of this program on a more intensive scale.

Historically, in the United States, plague has been considered a disease carried by rats on ships. Major attention was therefore given to control at the seaports. For some years past, sporadic cases of plague have occurred at points distant from the sea coast, and recent surveys have shown the existence of plague foci in the wild-rodent populations scattered over a considerable area in the western half of the country. This is a serious situation which warrants far more consideration than it has heretofore received.

We have the knowledge, techniques, and materials to secure reasonably effective control of the present important insect and rodent vectors of disease. There is an urgent need for more adequate surveys and for prompt application of known knowledge in infected areas. It is recommended that:

1. The present mosquito-control program should be continued to further reduce and to prevent a reversal in the trend of morbidity and mortality rates for malaria.

2. Rodent-control work should be continued on a more intensive nation-wide scale to preserve health and to conserve food through the co-operative efforts of the several agencies concerned with the various phases of the program.

3. Extensive and intensive surveys should be made to determine the extent of plague-infected rodents, and plague-control measures should be instigated promptly in plague-infected areas.

4. Research should be conducted to determine what, if any, role the fly plays in the transmission of certain non-intestinal diseases and to discover better materials and more effective and economical methods of insect control.

RESEARCH IN ENVIRONMENTAL SANITATION

The development and operation of control programs should not be delayed pending further research. It should, however, be continued and supplemented by experimental field studies. Our civilization must progress or it will retrogress. Research enables us to go forward. From it we learn new ways and techniques: we discover relationship of importance never before realized.

Figures are not available for measuring the money or personnel engaged in research in environmental problems. Organizations involved in research include Federal agencies (such as the Environmental Health Center of the United States Public Health Service at Cincinnati, Ohio; the Department of Agriculture's station at Orlando, Florida; the National Bureau of Standards; the Army; and the Navy). Certain state official bodies are likewise carrying on research (at such institutions as the Lawrence Experiment Station, in Massachusetts, and the New Jersey Sewage Experiment Station) or have instigated co-operative research projects (such as that on cannery waste disposal and sanitation problems through the National Canners Association Research Laboratory and that on sulphite wastes at the Institute of Paper Chemistry in Wisconsin). Several of the larger water-treatment plants and sewage-treatment plants are conducting research at the municipal or district level. Schools of engineering in numerous universities carry on research, as do some of the departments of chemistry and biology in universities. In addition to these official or semi-official organizations, many commercial establishments contribute to the field of research.

During the four years of activity of the Office of Scientific Research and Development, $24 million were spent for "medical" research. Undoubtedly some of this sum was expended on subjects in the environmental sanitation field—water sterilization, insect and rodent control, the control of malaria, and so forth. The sum involved for environmental sanitation is not known. The President's Scientific Research Board[10] estimated that the total national expenditures for research in medical and allied fields amounted to $110 million in 1947—about 10 per cent of the total research bill. This item of $110 million was divided among the following groups:

---

[10] John R. Steelman, *Science and the Public Policy*, A Report to the President (Washington: Government Printing Office, 1947).

Industry	45%
Federal, state, and local government	28%
Foundations	13%
Voluntary associations	8%
All other sources	5%

An estimate of the number of personnel engaged in research in environmental sanitation could not be made from the information available. Obviously consideration of this important factor is mandatory for any complete picture of the research needs.

An effort has been made to determine the areas in which research is being carried on at present. A special committee of the Engineering Section of the American Public Health Association has commenced a survey of the United States to determine where research in this field is being carried on. An incomplete report as of October, 1947, showed the following number of research projects by subject:[11]

Atmospheric pollution	20
Food sanitation	58
Milk sanitation	17
Housing	34
Garbage and refuse	4
Industrial waste	68*
Sewerage and sewage treatment	51
Stream sanitation	13
Insects and rodents	36
Water	82
Total	383

* Includes two projects listed under two classifications.

Late in 1945 the Research Grants Division of the United States Public Health Service started administering a scientific research program made possible through appropriation of Federal funds. The purpose of the grants made through the Division is to stimulate research in medical and allied fields by making available funds for such research and by actively encouraging scientific investigation of specific problems on which scientists agree there is urgent need for information. The research provided

[11] This information is based upon replies to individual inquiries sent to universities, state departments of health, industrial organizations carrying on research, and other official and private agencies. The 1947 Directory of the Engineering College Research Council and the 1946 Engineering Experiment Station record were used also. Although most of the major subjects falling in the environmental sanitation category are listed above, it is interesting to note that not one project dealing with administrative techniques is listed.

by such Federal aid is performed in keeping with plans and methods developed by the sponsor.

Research Needs

Environmental sanitation is emerging from its pioneer age into a scientific age. The trial-and-error methods used in the past to develop environmental control measures will not suffice in the scientific age of today and tomorrow. A large amount of basic research is needed to make possible effective control of environmental hazards.

There are very few research centers in the United States where any significant amount of basic research in environmental sanitation is being done. Few individuals are engaged in such research. Many of them are engaged in "testing station" work which, though desirable, does not usually develop significant basic data of universal applicability. Inadequate remuneration for the research worker is a handicap. Individuals who might engage in basic research following the completion of their college training obtain employment instead in other work which offers greater financial returns. State and local control agencies, such as health departments, seldom have the time, facilities, or personnel for basic research.

Control measures must be devised for new environmental hazards. New industrial products and processes often create new hazards. Pollution of streams and of the atmosphere with radioactive wastes may become an important sanitation problem. It is within the realm of possibility that the environment may be a significant factor in the spread of such diseases as poliomyelitis, infectious hepatitis, and "Q" fever. Research is needed to determine the extent of the environmental hazard in such cases and to supply the basis for control measures.

Basic information is necessary as to the action of various poisons in the eradication of insects and rodents, and as to the effects of such poisons on operators, before full value can be realized on possible new chemicals.

The basic procedures in water treatment and in sewage disposal have not changed significantly in the past several decades. New principles may be discovered which would render many of our present methods extremely inefficient and expensive in comparison. There are strong indications that the long-honored test for the safety of drinking water, the coliform index, may furnish only part of the information that is necessary to enable us to determine whether or not a drinking-water supply is safe. There may be unrecognized contaminants of water which have an important bearing upon the incidence of disease, just as the role water may play in the spread of certain diseases may not be understood.

There is a growing need for the integration of research programs in all fields so that the results of one group may be carried over to serve the needs of another. Similarly, there is urgent need to provide some means by which research work under way can be tabulated for the information of other research workers to prevent duplication and to indicate areas where work is not being done that ought to be undertaken.

Research is suggested in administrative methods, for more efficient accounting and recording methods, for the developing of better report forms, and for sound means of measuring community needs for health services. Although this may fall outside the usual definition of research, it is a need that can be met only by a co-ordinated study supported by funds allotted in the same manner as are basic research funds.

There is need for a paid, full-time organization to be designated or established for the purpose of stimulating suitable agencies to undertake research, to study the areas of greatest need for research, to recommend action for most effective results, and to furnish financial aid.

The President's Scientific Research Board[12] recommended to the President that expenditures for basic research should be quadrupled and that those for health and medical research should be tripled in the next decade. It also recommended the establishment of a National Science Foundation to support basic research through financial grants. The Research Grants Division of the United States Public Health Service has estimated that during the fiscal year 1949 at least fifty sanitation research projects costing an average of $15,000 each could be efficiently carried out under its program. This would entail the expenditure of $750,000 for the year. Your committee recommends that:

1. Research in environmental sanitation should be encouraged and extended with adequate support from Federal, state, and other sources, with emphasis on the following items: the importance of radioactive waste materials; the production, storage, and distribution of foods and their by-products; milk production, processing, and distribution; requirements of good housing to provide the necessary physiological and psychological needs as well as protection against contagion and accidents; disposal of garbage and refuse; methods of measuring and procedures for the satisfactory disposal or utilization of industrial wastes; sewage treatment and sewerage systems and facilities, with special application to

[12] See footnote 10.

isolated and small installations; stream sanitation; the control of insects and rodents, including study of the role of insects not now recognized as vectors of disease; water supply, with special emphasis on methods applicable to rural and small systems; industrial environment, with particular attention to the hazards present in—and the control of—new chemicals, materials, and procedures; and the control, prevention, and measurement of atmospheric pollution.

2. In any over-all programs of research, provision should be made for the support and stimulation of applied and developmental research to facilitate the translation of basic information to practical use.

3. Grants to a research center or agency should be made for periods long enough to assure continuation of any proposed program and in sufficient amounts to make possible fellowships or salaries large enough to attract competent personnel.

4. A Federal organization, adequately supported by funds and competent personnel, should be established or designated for the purpose of maintaining records of all research being conducted, of all research centers with data as to their facilities and personnel, and of the number and qualifications of research workers, as well as to act as a clearing house for information on research. Attention of the Surgeon General, United States Public Health Service, is invited to this recommendation.

5. Research in administrative practices should be begun, with adequate support from Federal or other funds.

6. Encouragement should be provided for increased participation in all phases of research by industrial groups, private foundations, and all official bodies active in environmental sanitation.

ADMINISTRATION

In order to effect a healthful environment for all people, further emphasis must be placed on improving the administration of sanitation programs. To that end the following recommendations are made:

1. There should be a more generous provision of personnel having the skills and disciplines required for public health environment control, in addition to a better utilization of such personnel at the planning level.

2. Better educational programs should be provided for all the people with regard to the need for improved physical works and the established protective procedures which form an essential part of a total health program.

3. More sanitation programs should be developed to deal effectively with the design, construction, maintenance, and operation of the many necessary facilities and processes, with the production and distribution of food and other products, and with the disposal of any wastes which through failure to employ established or new sanitary controls may create an environment unfavorable to the health, welfare, or comfort of the people.

4. Health agency sanitation services predicated on the greatest possible use of the man power and facilities of official or unofficial agencies, groups, or individuals who are concerned directly or indirectly with the promotion, establishment, and maintenance of control facilities concerned with such environmental factors as water, milk, food, air, sewage, refuse, animal and insect carriers of disease, and other factors contributing to the health and comfort of those in living and working quarters under normal or disaster conditions should be developed.

5. Sufficient funds should be provided to establish and maintain much-needed sanitation services for all the people.

6. Adequate health agency facilities should be provided to service the established programs.

7. An appropriate scale of salaries for sanitation personnel should be established on the basis of position responsibility and qualification requirements.

8. Adequate provision for tenure of office and opportunities for the advancement of sanitation personnel who have demonstrated ability to meet their responsibilities should be made.

9. Research directed toward the formulation of uniform standards for all sanitation controls which can be employed by health agencies in carrying out sanitation programs should be developed.

10. There should be an increased emphasis on the advisory and consultative service offered by state sanitation staffs in order that local health agency sanitation programs may be more closely co-ordinated.

11. There should be an increased emphasis on the advisory and consultative service offered by the United States Public Health Service sanitation staff in connection with state health agency sanitation programs.

12. Serious consideration should be given to the need for the establishment of special political subdivisions or the combination of existing political subdivisions for administrative purposes—if better control of environmental factors can be so obtained.

13. A better appreciation of the fact that certain environmental con-

trol problems are of such a character that their solution depends on state-wide, multi-state, and/or Federal administration and policy and that such problems are resolved through the use of all necessary and available facilities and technical knowledge applied at the policy-making level should be developed.

14. There should be a reconsideration and modernization of the laws, codes, rules, and regulations affecting sanitation control, to the end that all matters of environmental control can be dealt with more effectively by health agencies.

15. A broader appreciation of the assistance that can be given to all other health programs by well-planned and organized sanitation services— and, conversely, a similar recognition of the concurrent health programs which support and assist the sanitation services—should be developed.

16. A comprehensive program of research on sanitation administration— such as will permit the development of factual data from which may be deduced the effectiveness of the use of professional personnel in sanitation programs, the delineation of specific position responsibilities and activities, the required number of personnel, the indicated qualifications of the required personnel, program procedures, salary scales, financial needs, the facilities required in both health department and community, and the extent of community co-operation and participation in environmental control—should be formulated and carried to completion.

APPENDIX

PLANNING COMMITTEE

Arthur D. Weston, *Chairman*   Director, Division of Sanitary Engineering
Massachusetts State Department of Public Health

Earnest Boyce   Professor, Department of Civil Engineering
University of Michigan

Mrs. S. J. Francisco   Chairman, Public Welfare Department
General Federation of Women's Clubs of America

W. L. Mallmann   Professor of Bacteriology and Public Health
Michigan State College

| Sol Pincus | Consulting Engineer
New York, New York |
| B. A. Poole | Director, Bureau of Sanitary Engineering
Indiana State Board of Health |

STAFF ASSISTANTS

| Leonard B. Dworsky | Sanitary Engineer
Environmental Health Services
Public Health Service, Federal Security Agency |
| Graham Walton | Sanitary Engineer
Environmental Health Services
Public Health Service, Federal Security Agency |

REGISTRANTS

William H. Cary, Jr.	Director, Bureau of Public Health Engineering District of Columbia Health Department
F. C. Dugan	Director, Division of Sanitary Engineering Kentucky State Department of Health
Mrs. Sarah V. Dugan	Director, Division of Foods, Drugs, and Hotels Kentucky State Department of Health
H. G. Dyktor	Commissioner, Division of Air Pollution Control Department of Health and Welfare Cleveland, Ohio
John Edelman	Textile Workers Union of America Congress of Industrial Organizations
Francis B. Elder	Engineering Associates American Public Health Association
Alfred Fletcher	Director, Bureau of Sanitary Engineering New York City Health Department
Ralph E. Fuhrman	Superintendent, District of Columbia Sewage Treatment Plant
Harry Gehm	Technical Adviser National Council for Stream Improvement, Inc.
Harold B. Gotaas	Professor, University of California Berkeley, California
N. O. Gunderson, M.D.	Commissioner of Health Health Department Rockford, Illinois

Theodore Hatch	Research Director Industrial Hygiene Foundation Mellon Institute
William T. Ingram	Engineering Field Associate American Public Health Association
E. B. Kellogg	Secretary, Milk Industry Foundation
George W. Marx	Director, Sanitary Engineering Division Arizona State Department of Health
Kenneth M. Morse	Chief, Division of Industrial Hygiene Illinois State Department of Public Health
John H. O'Neill	Director, Division of Public Health Engineering Louisiana State Department of Health
E. A. Piszczek, M.D.	Director, Department of Public Health Cook County, Illinois
E. A. Reinke	Chief, Bureau of Sanitary Engineering California State Department of Public Health
Joseph B. Robinson, M.D.	National Association for the Advancement of Colored People
Jerome H. Svore	Director, Division of Sanitary Engineering North Dakota State Department of Health
L. F. Warrick	State Sanitary Engineer Bureau of Sanitary Engineering Wisconsin State Board of Health
A. H. Wieters	Director, Division of Public Health Engineering Iowa State Department of Health
Frank E. Wilson, M.D.	Administrator of Medical Services American National Red Cross

《 XV 》

International
Co-operation in Health[1]

IT WAS inevitable that the National Health Assembly, in considering a long-range health program for the nation, would encounter problems of an international character. This was foreseen by the planners of the conference, and three leaders in the field of international health were asked to take part. Dr. Henri Laugier, Assistant Secretary General for Social Affairs, United Nations, spoke on "International Co-operation in the Field of Public Health"; Dr. Fred L. Soper, Director, Pan American Sanitary Bureau, on "International Health Work in the Americas"; and Dr. Morris Fishbein, Editor, *Journal of the American Medical Association* and *Hygeia*, on "Medicine as a World Problem." The discussion which follows is based upon the views which these leaders presented to the Assembly.

Broadly defined, international health embraces all health problems which require international action for their solution. Until recent years, however, international agreements in this field were restricted to those relating to the spread of infectious diseases across national frontiers. The quarantine measures which were applied were often ineffective and were entirely out of step with the rapidly increasing speed of transportation. As Dr. Laugier pointed out: "It soon became clear that such defensive action was not enough and that the common interests which the various nations obviously shared in this field made it necessary to give nations which asked for it international assistance in order to extinguish epidemics at their very source."

A concept of international health activities much larger than the control of epidemics is accepted today. This is based not only upon human-

[1] The Assembly did not have a section on international health, because it had been convened to develop feasible national health goals. Since, however, the relationship between national and international affairs is close, one evening meeting, open to all Assembly delegates, was devoted to international health problems.

itarian grounds but upon the realization that vast populations are depressed economically by malaria and other preventable diseases. In many instances these populations could be made self-supporting if adequate technical assistance were forthcoming. If proof be required, there are many highly productive agricultural regions which once were malarious swamps, and there are many rich industrial cities which not so long ago were notorious for yellow fever.

Dr. Laugier emphasized the intensive efforts being made by the United Nations and its subsidiary, the Economic and Social Council, "to improve economic conditions throughout the world, to protect the rights of man, to place within everyone's reach all the blessings of education, science, and culture, and to fight against disease and death."

SOME MAJOR PROBLEMS

Influenza remains a great threat to mankind. In 1918 a devastating epidemic destroyed millions of lives. *Smallpox*, preventable by vaccination, has been eliminated by many nations of the world but still takes a terrible toll, especially in Africa and the Orient. *Typhoid fever* has been almost wiped out in the United States but is still a common cause of sickness and death in many other parts of the world. *Tuberculosis* in our country has passed from first in the list of causes of death to seventh. Yet even in the United States this disease is still second as a cause of death among Negroes. In South America it remains first in many countries. In most tropical countries tuberculosis usually runs a shorter and more acute course and is a major cause of death. *Malaria* causes an enormous burden of sickness and kills hundreds of thousands annually. It is being rapidly eliminated from the United States, but not long ago it was a serious problem in the Southern States. The burden of malaria in many tropical and sub-tropical countries is so heavy as to be an effective barrier to social, economic, and cultural progress. The discovery of the effectiveness of DDT in mosquito control has made the eventual eradication of malaria a definite possibility. *Venereal diseases* are likewise a world problem. Recently great progress has been made in therapy, but to apply modern therapeutic methods on a world-wide scale will require men, materials, and facilities on a gigantic scale. *Cholera* causes tens of thousands of deaths annually, for the most part in the Orient. When introduced recently into Egypt it was confined to unsanitated areas and to the poorer classes. *Bubonic plague* is primarily a disease of rats and other rodents and is transferred from rat to man by fleas. As a disease of rodents it is endemic over a large part of the world. In the western part of the United States plague is an infection chiefly of ground squirrels, and human beings are rarely infected. Human plague is constantly occurring, however, at many foreign ports. The most promising preventive measure is the rat-proofing of dwellings and ships.

Infant Mortality

Mortality rates for the first year of life vary throughout the world from about 30 to above 500 per 1,000 live births. The principal causes of extremely high rates are the diarrheas and dysenteries. The balance of nature is often maintained by extremely high birth rates, but only *Homo stultissimus*, or idiot man, could conceive of such a wastage of life as salutary.[2]

Dietary Deficiency Diseases

Diseases resulting from inadequate diet are found in all parts of the world. Only two of the most important need be mentioned. Deficiency of thiamin (Vitamin B_1) results in *beri-beri*, a disease which affects chiefly the nervous system and which is particularly common among those whose staple diet is polished rice. Millions of Orientals suffer from beri-beri. Another important disease is *pellagra*, caused by a deficiency of nicotinic acid. Pellagra (rough skin) is manifested by a cutaneous eruption and by gastro-intestinal and nervous symptoms.

General malnutrition is more widespread and more important than any single deficiency disease. It results from forced deprivation of food or from voluntary deprivation based upon ignorance or misinformation as to the dietary requirements of the body. The results are serious according to the degree, and they vary from lowered capacity for work and decreased ability to withstand infection to death from starvation.

INTERNATIONAL ORGANIZATION
BEFORE WORLD WAR II

The menace of epidemics, especially of cholera, plague, smallpox, and yellow fever, was the prevailing stimulus which led to the acceptance of health activities as an essential function of governments. The spread of these diseases across national frontiers pointed to the necessity for international action. As Dr. Laugier expressed it: "Apparently the earliest attempts were made, for essentially national reasons, first and foremost by the great seafaring nations which had frequent connections

[2] This was Dr. Fishbein's observation.

and contacts with all parts of the world and wished to protect themselves against the risks of introduction of diseases which sea transport entailed." International action proved exceedingly difficult to attain. More than forty years elapsed between the first international sanitary conference in 1851 and entry into force of the first sanitary convention in 1892. Certain of the background is of interest.

Cholera was introduced into Europe from the Orient for the second time in 1847 and during the next three years struck nearly all European countries. In 1851 the government of France convened an international sanitary conference to consider means of combating the disease. A draft convention was prepared which failed to receive the necessary number of ratifications and consequently never came into force. A second conference, convened by France in 1859, failed because of political events, especially the Franco-Italian war. The reappearance of cholera in Europe in 1865 resulted in the Constantinople Conference in 1866. This meeting had some tangible results—certain of the principal maritime powers put the conclusions of the Conference into operation. In 1874, just as the cholera pandemic was dying out, a fourth conference was held at Vienna. Stringent quarantine measures were seriously hampering commerce. Doubts had arisen as to the value of such measures, and it was proposed to substitute for quarantine a system of inspection by a medical officer from shore. The Vienna Conference agreed to recognize both quarantine and medical inspection; in effect, attempts to adopt a uniform modification of quarantine failed. The Vienna Conference is noteworthy also for a proposal, probably the first, to establish a "Permanent International Sanitary Commission."

The United States exhibited its interest in international health in 1881 by convoking the Washington Sanitary Conference. Since for several decades the ports of the Americas had suffered periodically from epidemics of yellow fever, the primary topic of discussion was its control. A system was adopted by which each country would notify the others periodically of prevailing health conditions. The delegates, however, were working in the dark. Twenty years were to elapse before Walter Reed and his colleagues demonstrated the essential role of the *Aedes aegypti* mosquito in the transmission of yellow fever.

Other conferences took place during the 1890's. A Sanitary Convention designed to prevent spread of cholera by ships using the Suez Canal developed at a meeting in Venice in 1892. Venice was again the scene of a conference, this time on bubonic plague, in 1897. One other development from these early conferences should be mentioned. At Dresden in 1893 the practice of *surveillance* was adopted. This was a forward step, permitting observation of persons from infected ships at their homes rather than on ships or in detention quarters.

The first of a series of broader sanitary conventions resulted from an international conference held in Paris in 1903. To implement these conventions it was agreed that a permanent bureau was necessary. Four years later the International Office of Public Health at Paris was established. The Office regularly received and transmitted notifications of cholera, plague, smallpox, typhus, and yellow fever. Under its aegis, revisions of the 1903 convention were adopted in 1912 and in 1926. In 1933 a sanitary convention for aerial navigation came into force. During the Second World War the Office was unable to function effectively and its responsibilities were transferred to the United Nations Relief and Rehabilitation Administration. Modifications of both the maritime and aerial conventions were proposed by UNRRA and came into effect in 1944.

Pan American Sanitary Bureau

A Pan American Sanitary Conference held in Washington in 1902 resulted in the establishment of the Pan American Sanitary Bureau, the first permanent intergovernmental health body. The Pan American Sanitary Code, revised in 1924, was ratified by all the American republics.

The Bureau receives and disseminates epidemiological information, sponsors fellowship programs, and promotes co-operation in research by different countries. A new activity is the program of *Aedes* eradication. To quote Dr. Soper: "The resolution making the Pan American Sanitary Bureau responsible for co-ordinating the activities of the American nations in the eradication of *Aedes aegypti* on a continent-wide basis marks a step in public health philosophy and practice the importance of which cannot be overstated. Certain countries of the Americas have been free of yellow fever for so long that they have lost all fear of this disease, but after full discussion all recognized the right of Brazil and of Bolivia, which have been free of *aegypti* for a number of years now, to insist that they be protected from reinfestation by the eradication of this mosquito in neighboring countries. Initial steps have been taken to activate the program of eradication in all of the South American countries, and only lack of funds is now preventing extension of activities to the Caribbean and Central American area. Of course the United States, which is thought to present the most difficult problem of all, will be left to the last." In

1947, the 12th Pan American Sanitary Conference effected a complete reorganization. The Pan American Sanitary Organization is now comprised of the Conference—including representation of all the American republics—which meets every four years and is the supreme body; the Directing Council, on which all the republics are represented and which meets annually but is concerned chiefly with administrative matters; an Executive Committee, including representatives of seven republics; and the Bureau, which is the Secretariat.

The Health Section of the League of Nations

The Health Organization of the League was established in 1923. Its budget was supplemented generously by the Rockefeller Foundation. It established a reporting center for infectious diseases at Singapore and collaborated with the International Office of Public Health in the distribution of epidemiological data. But the Health Organization went far beyond epidemiological reporting. In its early days it assisted certain governments in stamping out epidemics which followed the First World War. It established international standards for biologics and hormones and sponsored international studies on cancer, leprosy, malaria, nutrition, and rural hygiene. It entered the fields of social insurance and housing, and on invitation of certain governments, notably China and Greece, the Health Organization assisted in the reorganization of national health departments.

DEVELOPMENT OF THE WORLD HEALTH ORGANIZATION

Early in the Second World War, leaders in public health in the United States and Great Britain began to think seriously of the post-war situation. They were unanimous in their desire that as soon as possible after the war a single international health organization be established.

Two events greatly stimulated these thoughts. The first was the Conference on Food and Agriculture held at Hot Springs, Virginia, in June, 1943. The Conference declared that "the first cause of hunger and malnutrition is poverty" and that "the primary responsibility lies with each nation for seeing that its own people have the food needed for life and health."

Out of this Conference came the Food and Agriculture Organization, the first of a series of new organizations which with their pre-war prototype, the International Labor Organization, constitute the specialized agencies of the United Nations.

The second event was the establishment of the United Nations Relief and Rehabilitation Administration in November, 1943. Among the functions of UNRRA was the provision of basic medical services for victims of war. The total expenditures for health over a period of about three years were close to $168 million. Approximately 1,100 international professional health workers were employed. As soon as the shipping lanes were cleared, UNRRA dispatched thousands of tons of DDT powder, hundreds of dust pumps, and a trained staff to assist local health workers. UNRRA also carried out extensive and highly successful operations against malaria in Greece and Italy.

At the United Nations Conference on International Organization at San Francisco in 1945, it was decided that health was a field in which a specialized agency should be established. A resolution jointly introduced by Brazil and China and calling for the establishment of a single international health organization was adopted. The interest of the United States was made evident in a number of ways. Our country supported this resolution; our Department of State called an Advisory Health Group in October, 1945, to examine a draft constitution which the Public Health Service and the State Department had prepared; and our Congress in December, 1945, passed a resolution requesting the President to take immediate steps toward convening a health conference and forming an international health agency.

In January, 1946, the Economic and Social Council of the United Nations acted. A technical preparatory committee was named; in Paris in April the committee met and adopted a draft constitution. Plans were made for the full-scale International Health Conference which was convened by the United Nations in New York on June 19, 1946. Representatives of the fifty-one members of the United Nations and observers from thirteen non-members were present. To quote Dr. Laugier: "I recall the warm discussions of the Health Conference at Hunter College, held in the sweltering heat, in premises that were ill adapted to the needs of the Conference, with a Secretariat that was often rightly but not always kindly criticized. Amid all these difficulties and amid very impassioned discussions, the Conference progressed slowly but surely toward the framing of a constitution for the Organization. Toward the end of the Conference a spirit of compromise and conciliation became apparent— a wish to come to an agreement—and the draft constitution was signed provisionally by all the United Nations, subject to future ratifications by their governments in accordance with their constitutional procedures.

Thus our most sanguine hopes were realized." It was agreed that the Organization would come into being when twenty-six Members of the United Nations ratified.

An Interim Commission of eighteen states was established to carry on essential international health functions until the required number of ratifications was obtained. This Commission was further instructed to make preparations for the first World Health Assembly, which was to be convened within six months after the date on which the Constitution came into force. Perhaps the most dramatic achievement of the Commission was the part it played in combating the cholera epidemic in Egypt in 1947. Thirty-seven tons of cholera vaccine and medical and sanitation supplies were dispatched to Egypt.

In order that the World Health Organization (WHO) might fulfil its functions as the single directing and co-ordinating authority in international health work, the Interim Commission laid the necessary groundwork for the Organization to proceed along the following lines:

(a) To establish and maintain effective relationships with various international bodies that deal with problems of concern to the WHO (the Economic and Social Council and its commissions, the specialized agencies, and the United Nation's International Children's Emergency Fund);

(b) To assume the duties and functions of the pre-existing international organizations in the field of health (the Office International d'Hygiène Publique, the United Nations Relief and Rehabilitation Administration, and the Health Organization of the League of Nations);

(c) To effect the integration of the pre-existing regional organizations (Pan American Sanitary Organization and Pan Arab Regional Health Bureau) with the WHO, in due course; and

(d) To make arrangements for effective relations with non-governmental professional and scientific groups which contribute to the advancement of health.

The functions of UNRRA under the Sanitary Conventions of 1944 were taken over by the Interim Commission in December, 1946. On December 9, 1946, an Agreement between the Interim Commission and UNRRA was signed providing that the Commission would take over UNRRA's health activities—from January 1, 1947, for Europe, and from April 1, 1947, for the Far East—with the exception of the medical care of displaced persons. For this purpose UNRRA transferred to the Commission $1,500,000 for 1947 and the same amount for 1948. Missions were sent to Austria, China, Ethiopia, Greece, Hungary, Italy, and Poland. The functions of these missions varied according to health needs, incom-

pleted obligations of UNRRA, and the wishes of the receiving governments. In China, for example, assistance was given in the training of
personnel and in the control of cholera, plague, and kala-azar. The chief
object of the Mission to Ethiopia was to provide training for nurses and
sanitary inspectors. The most popular method of assistance proved to be
the granting of fellowships for foreign study, 250 of which were awarded
between January 1, 1947, and April, 1948.

At the fifth session of the Interim Commission in Geneva in January
and February, 1948, the entry into force of the Constitution of the World
Health Organization appeared imminent. Accordingly, the Commission
decided that the first World Health Assembly would be held in Geneva
on June 24, 1948, and proceeded to complete its task of making recommendations to the Assembly for the program and budget of the Organization.

At the time of the National Health Assembly, only the recommendations
of the Commission were available for discussion. However, at the date of
this writing it is possible to review the actual accomplishments of the
first World Health Assembly. The functions of the Organization as outlined in the Constitution are broad and diverse. Manifestly it will be
impossible for the Organization to carry out a comprehensive public
health program in its initial year and perhaps it will be impossible for
many years. A selection was necessary and the Assembly approached the
matter in a practical manner. There are statutory duties, such as the
administration and revision of the sanitary conventions and the making
of recommendations for the international control of habit-forming drugs,
for revision of the international lists of causes of death, and for a unifica-
tion of the pharmacopoeia. Certain other technical activities were in-
herited from the League of Nations and have proved to be of great
usefulness, notably the establishment of international standards for prophylactic and therapeutic agents which can be determined only by
biological methods. Activities of this sort provide a basic core of responsibilities and duties which are to be carried on by sections in the Secretariat and by expert committees.

Many suggestions were received by the Interim Commission as to the
most profitable fields which the World Health Organization might enter
in 1949. The Commission was unanimous in recommending first priority
to malaria, tuberculosis, venereal diseases, and maternal and child health.
The World Health Assembly added nutrition and environmental sanitation. An expert committee and a section in the Secretariat were author-

ized for each of these fields. For tuberculosis a special expert panel on vaccination with BCG was directed to be established.

The program in each of these fields will provide assistance to governments in the form of expert advice, field teams to demonstrate practical programs, visiting lecturers, and fellowships. Attention will be given to those aspects of the problems needing action on the international plane.

Faced with budgetary and personnel limitations, other activities which were proposed and considered desirable were grouped and given priority in the following order: (1) *Public health administration*, including hospitals and clinics, medical care, rehabilitation and medical social work, nursing, health education, industrial hygiene, and the hygiene of seafarers; (2) *parasitic diseases*, including activities relating to hookworm, filariasis, leishmaniasis, schistosomiasis, and trypanosomiasis; (3) *virus diseases*, including poliomyelitis, influenza, rabies, and trachoma; and (4) *mental health*, including alcoholism and drug addiction. For each of these activities there will be a minimum staff within the Secretariat. Nuclear committees and panels of experts will be established to the extent the budget permits.

A budget of $5 million was approved to carry out the program of the Organization for the year 1949. Funds for the Organization will be provided by the members in accordance with the scale of contributions adopted by the World Health Assembly.

Geneva was selected as the permanent headquarters of the Organization. The Assembly also delineated six geographical areas in which regional organizations will be established as soon as the consent of a majority of the members in the area is obtained. These areas are: the Americas, the Eastern Mediterranean, Southeast Asia, the Western Pacific, the European, and the African.

The Assembly approved draft agreements with the United Nations, the Food and Agricultural Organization, and the International Labor Organization, all of which have special interests in the field of health. In addition the Assembly agreed to increase the scope of co-operation with the Economic and Social Council and its commissions initiated by the Interim Commission.

The Assembly also defined the relationship between the World Health Organization and the International Children's Emergency Fund, which has undertaken welfare and medical projects for the benefit of children and adolescents of countries which were victims of aggression and for child-health purposes generally. The most important co-operative program calls for the tuberculin testing of 50 million children and for the vaccination with BCG of an estimated 15 million in Europe alone.

The work of this World Health Assembly demonstrated that health workers of the world can co-operate effectively in planning a program to promote "the attainment by all peoples of the highest possible level of health."

NON-GOVERNMENTAL ORGANIZATIONS

A large number of international non-governmental organizations have interests closely related to those of the World Health Organization. It will be necessary, and mutually advantageous, for the World Health Organization to enter into co-operative relations with several of these, probably including the World Medical Association, the International Union against Tuberculosis, the International Union against Venereal Diseases, and the International Union against Cancer. It is too early to speak of a future "International Health Council" grouped around the World Health Organization, but, without attempting to influence their policies, the World Health Organization could make available many of its facilities to these organizations. Since the World Health Organization and these various organizations will doubtless be utilizing the services of the same experts, co-operative arrangements would ensure economy of effort.

Dr. Fishbein's remarks on the new World Medical Association may be quoted: "In September, 1947, in Paris, the World Medical Association was established, and its executive council has just completed a meeting in New York. Some of the difficult situations which naturally arise in the application of medical science and public health to great masses of people require medical judgments on which the medical profession of the world may well unite. The International Red Cross in the Geneva Convention established the principle of the protection of the doctor, the nurse, and medical personnel in time of war; yet, even now when World War II has ended, the right of the physician and his personnel to safety is being violated. Among the tenets of the World Medical Association is the recognition of the physician's deeds of mercy in time of war. In this field the World Medical Association may well deal directly with the organization of the United Nations in the necessary representation to any nation that would violate this convention."

The Rockefeller Foundation was created in 1913 for the purpose of "promoting the well-being of mankind throughout the world." Although it is a private philanthropic organization, it has accepted the invitations of a large number of countries in all parts of the world to assist in the solution of their health problems. It has constructed schools of public health, assisted institutions for medical research and education, and granted study fellowships to nationals of nearly every country. Among the diseases in which the Foundation has been especially active are hookworm, malaria, tuberculosis, and yellow fever.

PROMOTION OF EDUCATION
IN THE HEALTH FIELDS

One of the functions of the World Health Organization is to "promote improved standards of teaching and training in the health, medical, and related professions." The quality of medical education is of the first importance. To quote Dr. Fishbein: "Fundamental to progress in eliminating disease, as a hazard to life and health, are the quality of medical education and the availability of medical personnel. . . . The importance of a high standard of medical education cannot be too greatly emphasized."

Both the World Health Organization and World Medical Association will be faced with the problem of the provision of medical care for certain areas of the world in which the number of physicians is totally inadequate and hospitals are virtually non-existent. The basic difficulty is that present economic conditions in many of these countries do not permit provision of adequate services and facilities. General educational standards, furthermore, are below those regarded as essential for medical education. Even if these handicaps could be overcome, the capacity of existing medical schools would be far from adequate to meet the needs. A similar situation applies to other health personnel—dentists, nurses, and engineers. It is clear that there is no simple solution and that the situation presents a challenge to the World Health Organization, the World Medical Association, and also to the United Nations Educational, Scientific, and Cultural Organization.

MEDICAL RESEARCH

In the long run the success of all preventive and curative medicine depends upon active and productive medical research. In the medical field as in the sciences underlying medicine the basic discoveries have been truly international. Microscopic life was discovered by Leeuwenhoek, a Dutchman; the microbic origin of disease by Pasteur, a Frenchman and Robert Koch, a German; antiseptic technique by Lister, an Englishman. More recently there are many other examples: the discovery of insulin by a Canadian, of penicillin by an Englishman, of sulfa drugs and DDT by a Swiss, and of streptomycin by an American. To quote Dr. Fishbein: "Genius is not the exclusive property of any race or nation in all the world." The Constitution of the World Health Organization recognizes the fundamental role of research, charging the Organization broadly "to promote and conduct research in the field of health."

CONCLUSIONS

In assessing the health needs of the American people one cannot close one's eyes to the international scene. Just as an unequal development of health measures in the different states handicaps the nation, so unequal development in the promotion of health and in the control of disease stays the progress of the community of nations.

The United States has accepted its responsibilities in this community of nations by joining the World Health Organization.

As to the broader implications of international co-operation in health, the concluding remarks of Dr. Laugier may be quoted: "The wretched microbes have set us a great example. They take no notice of frontiers; they are indifferent to national sovereignties; they live and wage their terrible war in a world which to them is one world. Let us hope that men of wisdom, the representatives of *Homo sapiens*, will succeed in overcoming all obstacles that stand in the way of creating, despite all current difficulties, a world united in co-operation and international brotherhood."

INDEX

Academy of Medicine, New York, 194, 196
Accidents, 131
  prevention, 119, 132-3, 175
Adolescents, and nutrition, 341
Advisory Health Group, 382
Aedes aegypti, 379, 380
Aging population, 3, 15-16, 84-85, 90, 104-6
Agriculture, 33
Air Force, U. S., health-personnel needs, 5, 16, 20-21
Alcoholism, 385
Ambulation, early, 45
American Academy of Pediatrics, 14, 104, 116
American Association of Psychiatric Social Workers, 307-8
American Board of Obstetrics and Gynecology, 114
American Board of Psychiatry and Neurology, 306
American Dental Association, 16, 288, 292
American Dietetic Association, 339
American Home Economics Association, 339
American Hospital Association, 103-4
American Medical Association, 2, 3, 25, 33, 103, 114, 140, 149, 151, 177, 244, 307, 331
  and health insurance, 210-13, 216, 218
American Nurses' Association, 20, 206
American Psychiatric Association, 304, 306, 307, 312, 315
American Psychological Association, 309
American Public Health Association, 60-61, 103, 244, 288, 331, 359, 361, 368
American Public Welfare Association, 103
American Red Cross, 97
Animal experimentation, 176-7
Apprenticeship system, 21-22, 52
Arctic health, research in, 175
Army, U. S., health-personnel needs, 5, 16, 20-21
Arthritis, 87
Assistants, dental, 17
Association of American Medical Colleges, 2, 25, 33, 149, 177
Association of State and Territorial Health Officers, 331

Attendants, psychiatric, 312-13
Attitudes, parent, 130-31

Back of the Yards Council, Chicago, 243, 245, 246, 250
BCG, 386
Behavior, child, 130
Bellevue Hospital, 86-88
Bellevue School of Nursing, 21
Beri-beri, 378
Bingham Associates, 155
Biological sciences, 337-8
Birth certificates, 78
Birth rates, 113-14, 193, 224-5
Blue Cross plans, *see* Insurance
Blue Shield plans, *see* Insurance
Bubonic plague, 366, 377-8, 379-80
Buccal cancer, 279
Buncombe County, N. C., 239, 243ff.

Cadet Nurse Corps, 22
Canada, 46, 152, 154, 335
Cancer, buccal, 279
Caries, dental, 277-8, 281
Chicago, University of, 52
Child health, *see* Maternal and child health
Child labor, 116
Children's Bureau, U. S., 118, 244, 248, 265, 270, 331
China, 381, 384
Cholera, 377, 379, 383
Chronic disease, 46, 50-51
  and aging population, 84-85, 90, 104-6
  control programs, 83-84, 102-4, 107-9
  co-operation of patient, 95
  defined, 91
  diagnosis, 92-93
  emotional factors, 96
  extent, 82-83, 89-90
  financial needs, 92, 98
  government position, 89
  institutional care, 97-98
  and local health units, 76, 79
  mass screening programs, 93
  medical care, 91
  non-institutional care, 96-97, 106
  personnel training, 93-94